The Shop
Wisdom
of Rudy Kouhoupt

The Shop Wisdom
of Rudy Kouhoupt

Edited by Joe D. Rice

Village Press, Inc.
Traverse Ciy, Michigan

The Shop Wisdom of
Rudy Kouhoupt

Copyright© by Village Press, Inc.
All right reserved
First printing August, 1989

Village Press, Inc.
P.O. Box 1810
Traverse City, Michigan 49685-1810

International Standard Book Number 0-942653-01-4
Library of Congress Catalog Card Number 89-085024

Copy-editing by Clover McKinley
Design and Layout by Luana Dueweke

Typeset and printed at Village Press, Traverse City, Michigan, USA

INTRODUCTION

Since 1982, Rudy Kouhoupt has been a workhorse in the "stable" of contributing editors and authors for both *Live Steam* and *The Home Shop Machinist*. During the past seven years (this being 1989), Rudy has produced such a volume of work of the highest quality that we felt justified in producing a book of his efforts – that which you hold in your hands.

And what a volume of work! Those of you who read only *Live Steam* know well the magnificent model engines he has designed and built, but may never have been introduced to the amazing and thoughtful material he has produced for the machinist using a very small tabletop lathe or mill, giving him or her a remarkable array of accessories and other useful tools to make. His articles on techniques and other shop information have always been carefully thought through and proven in his own work.

Those of you who read only *The Home Shop Machinist* might never know of the marvelous and beautiful stationary steam engine projects that Rudy has brought to the hobby over the years. Not only are they aesthetically attractive, they function efficiently as well. Countless modelers have built his engines without anything but praise following their completion. Even more startling, perhaps, is the fact that he has produced these marvels on a tiny Unimat or a Perris lathe and equally tiny vertical mill. Rudy's shop happens to be housed in a room the size of a large closet – about 5 x 5 feet!

From an editor's standpoint, he is a dream come true; his text requires virtually no changes, his photos are always superb, and his drawings are impeccable. His type is rare among authors.

Therefore, I take great pleasure in introducing you to the multi-dimensional, multi-talented Rudy Kouhoupt. It is most appropriate that our first book in the new "Shop Wisdom" series would feature him. As you'll soon discover, his shop wisdom is far-reaching and profound. I hope you enjoy it as much as I do.

Joe Rice, Editor

The Shop Wisdom of Rudy Kouhoupt

TABLE OF CONTENTS

The Shop Wisdom of Rudy Kouhoupt

The Micro Machinist

Machine Shop in a Cabinet

It is probably safe to say that a majority of home shop machinists get their private shops going by purchasing one of the popular small size machine tools. For some, it is a matter of necessity, while others see the smaller machines as a relatively inexpensive means of getting their feet wet in machine shop skills. Whatever the specific reason may be, whether from a lack of experience in machining practices, limited funds, limited space availability for a shop, or the simple enjoyment that many of us derive from handling small projects on suitably proportioned tools, there are a lot of small machine tools around.

Perhaps a few words of definition are in order at this point. For our purposes here, the term small applies to any lathe having a maximum swing diameter of 4-1/2" or less. Also included in the small category are any milling machines or other types of machine tools built to similar proportions. It is obviously not possible to define the size of such tools so precisely as in the case of a lathe.

Some of the machine tools falling into this category are dedicated to a specific type of work, such as lathes like the Perris or Cowells. There are dedicated vertical milling machines, also, examples of which are the Sherline or Unimill. Then there is the well-known group of multifunctional machine tools in the category of Unimat SL or Unimat 3 which are called upon to perform several machine tool functions, working like the proverbial one-man band in accordance with the way they are set up. Like all things man-made, each tool has its strong points as well as its weak features. All of them are capable of turning out good, dependable work, provided that the operator recognizes their specific limitations and exercises judgment to stay within them.

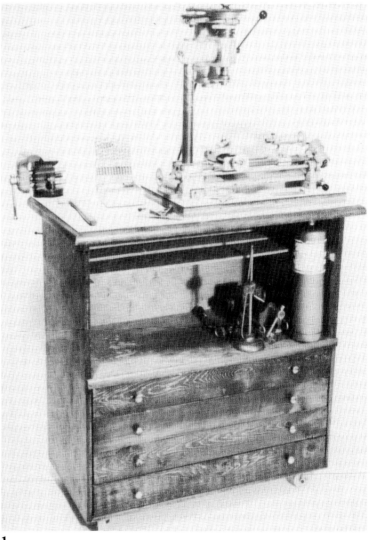

1

The major disadvantage of small machine tools in the minds of most users or potential users is undoubtedly their size limitation. In all fairness, it must be conceded that projects have to be selected in keeping with what the tools can reasonably be expected to do, head riser blocks and other tricks to extend their capacity notwithstanding. The fact remains that just so much torque is available at the spindle, and the machine bed is just so stiff. No more. There are limits.

Why bother with them, then? Because their small size, which is their limitation, also turns out to be their outstanding attribute. Look in your catalogs and compare the prices. Don't stop with a mere comparison of price tags of large vs. small machine tools, either. Compare the quantities and costs of metal and other materials that go into large vs. small projects. Metal prices vary roughly as the weight varies, but increase as the cube or third power of the linear dimensions. Therefore, the builder of smaller projects realizes a significant saving in the cost of raw materials, as well as in the cost of the machine tools he uses.

The small amount of space required to set up a small machine tool is a significant point in its favor, in many cases. Anyone who lives in an apartment or home where there is no basement or similar area to use for a shop may well be confined to arm chair status, if he is unwilling to own and use the smaller types of tools. It simply takes a lot less room to house and use a small lathe than a large one. Not only do the smaller tools take up less space, they are also much less demanding with regard to the strength and massiveness of the benches or other supporting structures upon which they are mounted.

Take the case shown in Photo 1 as an example. What we have here is a little multifunctional machine tool supported on or housed within a roll-around cabinet. During work sessions, the cabinet is strong enough to be used as a workbench for the machine tool and the hand tools. Between work sessions, the machine is stored away in the cabinet where it is safe and protected from the ravages of dust, moisture, and other local hazards. In essence, it is a complete machine shop that takes up just about 2-1/2 square feet of floor space. Note in Photo 2 that everything can be stored away very neatly and compactly.

The roll-around cabinet shown in the photos was home-built from half-inch plywood, the edges of which are finished with half-round molding strips. The box is 12-1/2" deep by 24-1/2" long. It stands 24" tall without the top surface or casters which bring the overall height to 27". This may seem a bit low for a work surface, but it proves quite comfortable when the height of the machine is added to it. When the cabinet was built, it seemed that an excessively high cabinet might be top-heavy, since

the cabinet is rather shallow. A deeper, more nearly square cabinet could safely stand taller.

The top half of the cabinet is an open compartment which provides plenty of room for storing the machine tool, which happens to be a Unimat SL. There is also ample space to store a small vise, a propane torch, the usual soldering equipment, a surface gage, and a few items that need headroom to stand upright. The front of the large compartment is closed by sliding a piece of hardboard in between the grooved moldings that are fastened along the top and bottom edges of the compartment.

The lower half of the cabinet is divided into four equally spaced drawers which are partitioned off on the inside. Lathe accessories, measuring devices, hand tools, and other things having low profiles are stored in the drawers.

There are grooves dadoed into the sides of the drawers to slip over the slide strips fastened to the insides of the walls of the cabinet. The idea of this cabinet is not so very much different from that of the roll-around toolboxes used by automotive and other mechanics. Indeed, one of the commercial steel toolboxes mounted on casters might prove to be a convenient and expedient way to set up shop for anyone interested in this sort of arrangement.

Having extolled the virtues of keeping a compact all-in-one machine shop in the living quarters, it seems important to make a few comments about the working conditions under which it is used. Since the normal living quarters receive top priority in the matter of summer and winter comfort, anyone who outfits himself to work in them winds up working in comfort. He will hot have to put up with a work area penetrated by winter chill or roasted in the summer sun. And his tools will not have to be subjected to excessive dampness or the potential damages that result from abrupt temperature changes. Bench space is at a premium, unless there is a convenient table or workbench in the area under consideration. Also, roll-around cabinets have a tendency to do just that – roll around! During work sessions, it is a good idea to slip a wooden wedge under each end of the cabinet to guard against any excursions it may try to take as a result of vibrations or under the thrust of hand tools.

Cleanliness is another consideration that definitely cannot be overlooked. Chips fly during lathe and other forms of shopwork.

Things can get messy in a hurry if you don't take precautions, such as putting up some small chip deflectors and collectors. These need not be elaborate. Bits of cardboard taped in place where they can't get into the works are usually sufficient to contain things and cause the chips to drop to a convenient container. A little extra time must be allocated to cleaning up at the end of each work period so everything can be put away and any stray chips or mess put to rights. But these are simple things to take care of, and it does not take long to become adept at being a neat and orderly worker. A routine soon develops for setting up quickly to begin work and for putting things away. The really messy or potentially hazardous jobs like boiler brazing are relegated to the garage. To my mind, the advantage of being able to work in comfortable surroundings cannot be overlooked and is one of the strong points in favor of small machine tools.

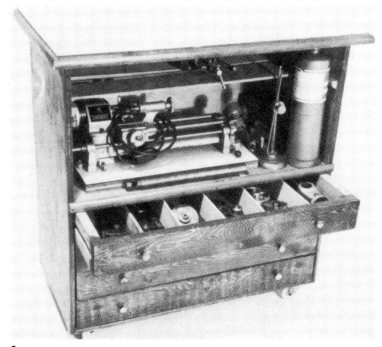

2

Test Indicator

A test indicator is an invaluable aid in checking runouts and for positioning workpieces accurately on the lathe or milling machine. When the workpiece is mounted on the face plate, gripped in the four-jaw chuck, or must be otherwise positioned accurately, the use of an indicator of some sort makes the work of setting up go much more quickly, and it improves the accuracy of the setups, as well.

Many home shops do without the services of an indicator, however. A look at the prices charged for them in most tool catalogs shows the reason. By spending a couple of hours in the shop, it is possible to make a relatively simple test indicator. No expenditure of money is involved, since all the parts of the tool are home built. The parts of the tool are so small that they can be made from scrap materials, in most cases.

The principle on which the indicator works is that a sensor is brought into contact with some reference surface of the work which is to be trued. By mechanical means, the indicator amplifies small deviations or eccentricities in the work surface in contact with the sensor to make them appear as much larger movements of a pointer. The amplification thus permits errors which are too small to be read easily by watching the deflections of the pointer.

The indicator being described here has an amplification factor of 15.6 to 1. Therefore, a variation of .001″ on any surface in contact with the sensor will produce a deflection of .0156″ or ¹⁄₆₄″ at the pointer tip. The markings on the scale behind the pointer tip are ¹⁄₆₄″ apart making it quite easy to detect an error of this small magnitude, even though the workpiece may appear to the unaided eye to be perfectly true.

Begin the construction of your indicator by marking out the outline and hole positions of the base, Part 1, on steel. The holes may be drilled before or after cutting out, as you prefer. Turn the mounting pin, Part 2, from a bit of steel rod held in the chuck. Shoulder down for the thread, and cut the thread with a die held in the tailstock dieholder. Reverse the part in the chuck to turn the shoulder that fits into the large drilled hole in the base. I used silver solder to secure the mounting pin in the hole.

The center of the scale at 0 reading coincides with the centerline of the base. The other graduations may be scribed in using an accurate square. Work from the reference edge of the base to mark each graduation with a distance of .016″ or ¹⁄₆₄″ between adjacent marks. In doing this, I made each fifth mark longer to aid in reading the scale. My indicator is marked with enough graduations to give a total range of 20 divisions with 10 divisions on either side of the 0 mark.

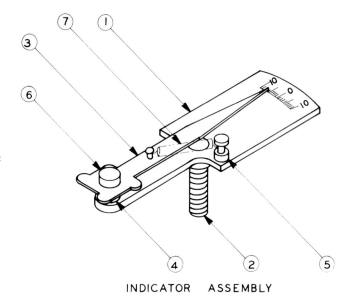

INDICATOR ASSEMBLY

If the pointer, Part 3, is made accurately to the dimensions shown in the drawing, each scale division marked on the base will be equivalent to .001″ at the sensors. Work accurately in marking the part on a piece of steel. Cut it out with a fine hacksaw, and file to the line carefully. Note that the pointer has three sensors which make it possible to use the indicator in a variety of positions against nearly any sort of surface. The sensors have been designated A, B, and C for easy reference later on. Some builders may feel that the sensors should be hardened. The contact made between the sensors and the workpiece is under very mild spring pressure and of short duration, at most. When you consider the cost and availability of spare parts for this home built indicator, hardening hardly seems worthwhile!

Drill the hole in the pointer for the bearing, Part 4, carefully. The location of the hole will

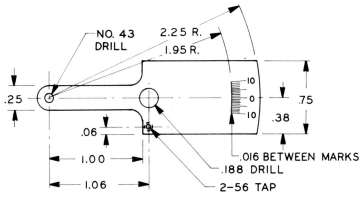

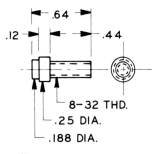

NO. 43 DRILL

2.25 R.
1.95 R.

.25

10
0
10

.75

.38

.06

1.00

1.06

.016 BETWEEN MARKS

.188 DRILL

2-56 TAP

① BASE: .075 THK. STEEL - I REQ.

.64

.12 .44

8-32 THD.
.25 DIA.
.188 DIA.

② MOUNTING PIN: STEEL
I REQ.

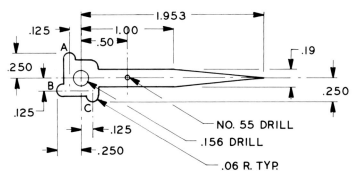

1.953

.125

1.00

.50

.19

A

.250

.250

B

C

.125

.125

.250

NO. 55 DRILL
.156 DRILL
.06 R. TYP.

③ POINTER: .036 THK. STEEL - I REQ.

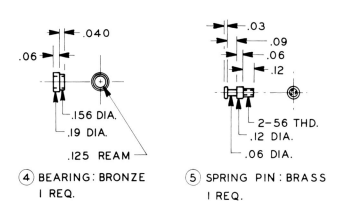

.040

.06

.156 DIA.
.19 DIA.
.125 REAM

④ BEARING: BRONZE
I REQ.

.03

.09
.06
.12

2-56 THD.
.12 DIA.
.06 DIA.

⑤ SPRING PIN: BRASS
I REQ.

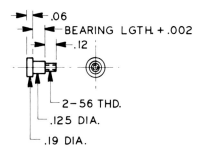

.06

BEARING LGTH. + .002
.12

2-56 THD.
.125 DIA.
.19 DIA.

⑥ PIVOT PIN: STEEL - I REQ.

have an effect on the accuracy of the scale readings. Drill the hole for the small spring pin. I cut the head end from a 16 gauge brass escutcheon pin and soldered it in the small hole to make the spring pin. The pin will hold the spring nicely when its head is about ⅛" above the surface of the pointer.

Turn the bearing, Part 4, from a piece of bronze or brass rod. Make the shoulder diameter a light press fit in the hole of the pointer. Drill a pilot hole while you have it in the lathe to be sure everything is concentric. Don't put the reamer through until after it is pressed into the pointer.

The spring pin, Part 5, and the pivot pin, Part 6, are both lathe jobs. Set them up about the same as you did to make the mounting pin. None of the dimensions are critical on the spring pin. However, the .125" diameter shoulder of the pivot pin is critical in both length and diameter. Turn the diameter and polish it with very fine emery to make it a smooth, free fit in the bearing. The best fit is when the bearing swings easily but has no slop or lost motion on the pin. Check the exact length of the bearing with a micrometer or accurate caliper. Make the shoulder of the pivot pin about .002" longer than the bearing to prevent any bind on the bearing between the head of the pin and the base.

The dimensions of the tension spring, Part 7, will have to be fitted on the job. The spring on mine was cut from a commercially wound spring. The wire in the spring is .010" diameter. It is close wound to give the spring an OD of .100". My spring consists of twenty turns and is just .625" long over the end loops. The least tension possible to return the pointer to its rest position against the spring pin is all that is required to guarantee a light motion to the pointer.

There is almost no limit to the ways an indicator can be used to assist in making and checking

1

2

3

4

5

6

the accuracy of machine tool setups. The two mountings and the link shown with this part are useful adjuncts to the little indicator shown last time. When secured to it by an 8-32 wing nut, the square mounting adapts the indicator to the lathe tool post, and the round mounting adapts it to the lathe or drill chuck. None of the mounting dimensions are critical to the accuracy attained in using the indicator. You may find it necessary to vary the dimensions a bit to fit your particular equipment, but the basic ideas for using them are what counts.

In using the indicator from the lathe toolpost, use the square mounting with the intermediate link to place the indicator as near as possible to the level of the lathe axis. Photo 1 shows a lathe mounting in which sensor A has been brought into contact with the outside surface of a large ring which has to be centered in the four-jaw chuck. In a similar lathe setup shown in Photo 2, sensor C has been brought into contact with an inside surface of a ring. In either case, as the spindle is rotated slowly by hand, the eccentricity of the work piece is obvious by the way that it causes the pointer of the indicator to be deflected back and forth. A reading of five or ten units to either side of the center of the indicator scale would be typical. By adjusting the jaws, the position of the workpiece is shifted until its centerline coincides with the lathe axis. When the ring is truly on center, the pointer does not move as the spindle is rotated. Since all readings on the indicator are relative, there could be a constant reading several marks off center of the scale. For example, if the indicator reading were a constant four scale divisions as the ring passed through a full revolution, you would be indicating perfect centering. The important point is that the reading be the same all the way around or across a true surface. Naturally, the sort of arrangement shown here using a four-jaw chuck could be duplicated in a face plate setup with clamps.

The flat surface of a workpiece can be indicated as well as circular surfaces. Note in Photo 3 that sensor B is in contact with a flat workpiece on a face plate. By slipping shims between the work and the face plate, the part can be adjusted until its surface is at exact right angles to the lathe axis. The lathe axis

itself can be checked by the indicator working from the toolpost. Photo 4 shows a boring bar of uniform diameter between lathe centers. By bringing sensor B into contact with the side of the bar and traversing the carriage longitudinally, it is possible to get a reading of how well the bar is aligned to the lathe ways. By adjusting the set over the tailstock, you can bring the lathe axis into a parallel position with the ways. This condition will be shown by a constant indicator reading as the carriage with the indicator moves from end to end of the bar. Or, this same arrangement could be used to indicate a suitable set-over for turning a slight taper on a mandrel or other part. In this case, the taper shows up as a deflection of a suitable number of units on the indicator scale when the carriage moves from end to end through the length of the taper portion.

Indicator readings may be taken from either lathe or drill chucks by using the round mounting. The setup shown in Photo 5 is useful for positioning a workpiece on the lathe saddle. With the indicator working from a chuck on the lathe nose, either sensor A or C is brought into contact with a flat surface of the work. As the carriage travels longitudinally, a constant indicator reading shows that the work is parallel to the ways of the lathe. By using sensor B against a face at right angles, it would be possible to get the work parallel to the cross slide.

Chuck mounting in a vertical arrangement is shown in Photo 6 where a piece is being aligned to the carriage travel for a milling cut. Either sensor A or C could be used against a side surface to get it aligned to either the X or Y axis. Sensor B could be used against a top surface to check that it is at right angles to the Z axis. By sweeping the indicator around in a chuck mounting with the sensor B against the top of a milling or drilling table, it is possible to check the perpendicularity of the vertical axis to the table's surface.

By considering what surfaces are important, it is possible to devise all sorts of ways to use an indicator to get things into line with one another, at known angles to one another, or to check how accurately the surfaces have been machined.

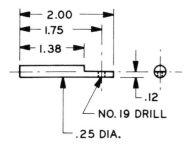

CHUCK MOUNTING: STEEL

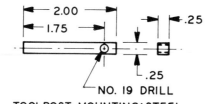

TOOLPOST MOUNTING: STEEL

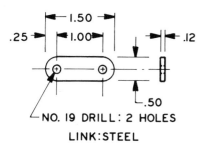

LINK: STEEL

Compressed Air Motor

The small compressed air motor shown in Photo 1 is a good project for a variety of reasons. In the first place, no castings are required in its construction, and it is not difficult to build. Even those individuals with little or no experience can tackle its construction as a first time engine project with every expectation of complete success. Its size makes it well suited to construction using very small machine tools. The amount of material required for the project is small; the metals used are not difficult to obtain.

As far as performance is concerned, the motor is capable of turning over at a dizzying rate of speed with only about five pounds of air pressure driving it. By virtue of its small size, it is obviously not a great powerhouse, but the prototype gives a very satisfying performance when connected to a tire pump. Because there is no compressor in my shop, it has never had a sustained period of running. However, the prototype motor has a snappy acceleration and a surprisingly sharp exhaust beat. When throttled down, it runs steadily at low speeds making the interesting action of the valve and crank assembly visible.

The pull-apart assembly drawing gives a clear indication of what parts must be and how they go together. My preference in working on any sort of engine project is to start at the bottom. As I finish each part, I fit it into the assembly to insure free motion with no binds or tight spots. By working in this way, all the parts are finished and assembled in a logical sequence with no waiting around to see that exciting first run. The part numbers assigned to the various parts shown in the assembly drawing coincide with the order in which I made the parts for the prototype.

As a matter of general interest, readers may wish to know that all machining operations involved in making the prototype compressed air motor were carried out on a Unimat SL. The old SL is now well into its *twentieth* year of continuous service in my shop. Perhaps this is a good point for me to add that the Unimat SL is no longer built. Furthermore, I have no connection with any manufacturer, distributor, or sales organization for Unimat or any other machine tools. References to tools in this volume are simply intended to give interested readers the benefit of my experiences with them and to help in the acquisition of machining skills as much as possible.

1 Begin fabricating the parts by marking out the Bed (Part 1) on a piece of metal. Aluminum was used in the prototype, but CRS or brass could be used if you prefer. Saw the part out, leaving a little metal all the way around the finishing. There is no reason that you could not finish to the mark with files. However, in the interest of doing accurate machine work, I set up the SL as a vertical milling machine with a Dremel No. 196 cutter in the chuck. By clamping the rough cut bed to a small milling table on the cross slide, the four edges of the part were machined to dimension. This produced a bed that was sharp-edged and square-cornered – an admirable condition for locating the six holes. Measure carefully to locate the positions of the holes, because the accuracy of their locations will have an influence upon how the rest of the motor goes together. Mark each location with a center punch, center drill, and drill through.

A similar procedure can be followed for Brass Bearings (Part 2). Saw the parts out, and finish as for the bed. Because of the greater thickness of the metal in this case, it may be preferable to use the side of an end mill as the cutter. Locate the positions of the tapped holes in the bottom surface of each bearing. Mark each location with the center punch, center drill, pilot drill, and tap to form the thread. Start the tap carefully to be sure the thread is straight. To accomplish this, I normally chuck the tap in the vertical setup and slowly pull it around by hand to start the first couple of turns. Then I transfer the tap to a tap holder to finish the thread to full depth manually. Clamp the two bearings together, using their bottom surfaces as the reference in order to drill and ream the crankshaft holes exactly in line through both bearings at once. The bearings may be attached to the bed by size 4-40 machine screws.

Drill rod is useful for the crankshaft because it is dependably accurate to diameter. Cut a piece to length for the Crankshaft (Part 3). Hold it in either an accurate chuck or a collet. Face off the end. Turn down the part which will be a press fit into the crank. Reverse the shaft in the chuck or collet, and face to the correct overall length. Turn down the part which will fit into the flywheel. Be careful to get the 1.500 length accurate, because this is a fit to the bearing spacing. Use a 10-32 die in the tailstock dieholder to cut about .19″ length of thread on the end. I do not like setscrews in flywheels and used a 10-32 nut to secure the flywheel on this motor. If you prefer to use a setscrew, eliminate the 10-32 thread. But, by all means, file a flat seat for the setscrew to bear against the crankshaft.

Cut off a slice of 1.50″ diameter brass rod for the flywheel. Chuck the slice in the three-jaw chuck. Form the rear surface of the flywheel by taking cuts. Don't overlook the .31″ projection at the center; it is a thrust surface. Use a center drill in the tailstock chuck to open the center. Drill through, and ream the central hole. Put the flywheel in place on the crankshaft which is held in either a collet or a true chuck. Using the crankshaft as a stub mandrel, face off the front of the flywheel to finish, and turn the rim true.

Continue construction of the small compressed air motor by making the Crank (Part 5). Chuck a short length of .75″ diameter steel rod. Take facing cuts to shape the rear surface of the crank. The purpose of the .31″ diameter projection at the center is to serve as a thrust surface, the same as the one on the rear of the flywheel. With the piece still gripped in the chuck, scribe a line across the machined face passing through the center mark left by the facing cut. Measure off .250″

ASSEMBLY

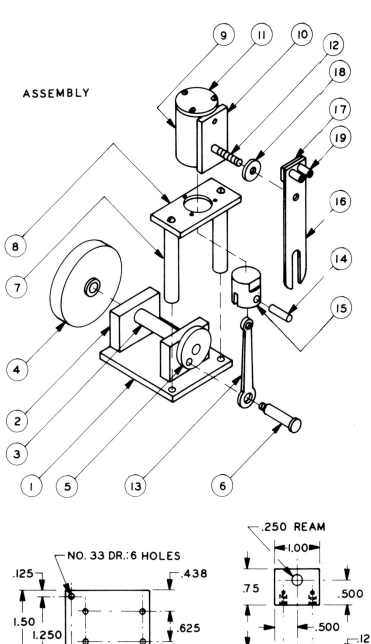

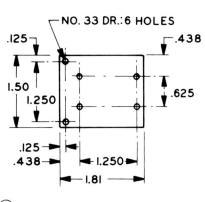

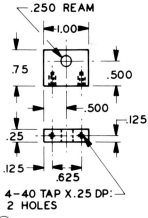

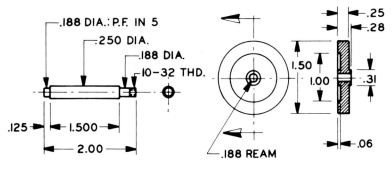

① BED: .12 THK. ALUM.–1 REQ.

② BEARING: BRASS– 2 REQ.

③ CRANKSHAFT: STEEL–1 REQ.

④ FLYWHEEL: BRASS–1 REQ.

from the center mark along the scribed line to center punch the position of the crankpin hole. Return the chuck to the lathe to center drill, pilot drill, and ream the central hole. Now you can center drill, pilot drill, and tap the other hole for the crankpin. If your lathe is stiff enough, part off, and the part is ready to be press fit or *Loctite*-assembled on the crankshaft.

If your lathe is not stiff enough for the parting off cut, saw the piece off with a little allowance for facing. Assemble it on the crankshaft.

2

Then crank the crankshaft, and take a facing cut to finish the outside of the crank.

Slip the crankshaft into place in the bearings, and be sure it is a good, free-running fit. Be sure it turns freely in the bearings but has no slop. End play between the rear thrust surfaces of the flywheel and crank and the bearing faces need not exceed .005".

The Crankpin (Part 6) is a simple lathe job. Chuck a length of steel rod. Face the end, then turn down the part to be threaded.

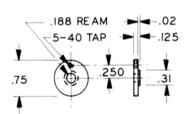

⑤ CRANK: STEEL—1 REQ.

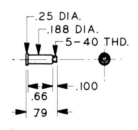

⑥ CRANKPIN: STEEL— 1 REQ.

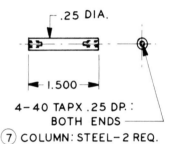

⑦ COLUMN: STEEL— 2 REQ.

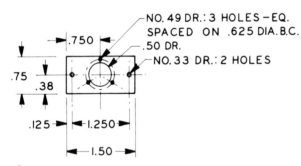

⑧ CYL. BASE: .12 THK. ALUM.— 1 REQ.

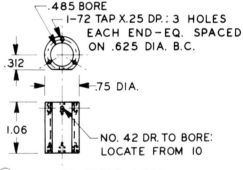

⑨ CYLINDER: BRASS—1 REQ.

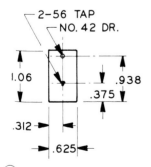

⑩ PORT FACE: .12 THK. BRASS—1 REQ.

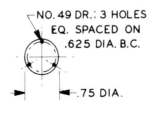

⑪ COVER: .06 THK. BRASS— 1 REQ.

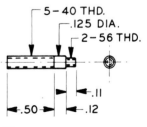

⑫ VALVE PIVOT: STEEL— 1 REQ.

Cut the thread with a 5-40 die held in the tailstock die-holder. Now you are ready to turn down the part that will be a running fit in the connecting rod and the slot in the valve. Finish this surface with fine emery cloth to give it a smooth polish. Part off to finish the crankpin.

When you make the pair of Columns (Part 7), which support the cylinder base, pay particular attention to getting them both the same length. This is important, of course, so the cylinder will be square to the rest of the engine. Take facing cuts across each end of each column to guarantee the squareness of the ends. After you face each end, center drill, pilot drill, and tap for the 4-40 bolts that go into them. Start the thread by chucking the tap in the tailstock chuck and feeding it slowly into the work as you turn the lathe spindle *by hand*. Do not attempt to cut this thread with the lathe motor driving it.

Machine the Cylinder Base (Part 8), using a setup like the one used for the bed. Measure carefully as you lay out the hole locations. Start each hole with a center drill to be sure the twist drills do not wander from the spots where you want the holes to be. Spend a few moments now to look at the assembly drawing and Photo 2. From these, you will be able to get an understanding of how the cylinder base is positioned and how the cylinder will be shaped.

I worked on the Cylinder (Part 9), and the Port Face (Part 10), at the same time, because they are so closely related and have to be soldered together. Make the port face from a piece of brass in the same way you made the other flat parts. Lay out the holes carefully, because their locations are important for the valve action.

Use a short length of brass rod for the cylinder. Cut it a little longer than needed to allow finishing the ends in the lathe. I set up the SL as a vertical milling machine and used an end mill to cut the flat surface on the side of the cylinder. Then I tinned the flat surface and the back of the port face and soldered the two parts together.

There are several ways the bore can be cut in the cylinder. None is more accurate than using a boring bar between lathe centers with the cylinder mounted on the cross slide. If you do it this way, clamp the soldered cylinder/port face assembly to the cross slide resting on the flat port face. Adjust, as necessary, to get the cylinder's axis to coincide

with the lathe's axis. Use a center drill to start the bore. Open out with twist drills to a diameter of 7/16". Then put the bar between centers and take a little at a time until you reach the desired bore. I used the .485" figure on the bore so the piston could be turned down from a piece of half-inch rod.

With the bore complete, transfer the cylinder assembly to a mandrel to face off both ends. Now you can drill through the No. 42 hole in the port face to finish the air passage to the bore. Clamp the cylinder in place on the cylinder base to spot through the three holes for the bolts that will hold them together.

Mark out the Cover (Part 11), on a piece of brass. Cut it out, and file to the mark. Locate the three holes. After drilling them through, clamp the cover in place on the cylinder to spot the holes for the bolts. Now you are ready to pilot drill and tap the three holes in each end of the cylinder. Work slowly and carefully so the tap will not distort the finished bore.

Face off and turn down the end of a .125" diameter steel rod for the 2-56 thread on the Valve Pivot (Part 12). Hold the die in the tailstock dieholder, as you did in making the crankpin. Cut it off to length. Reverse the part in the chuck to cut the 5-40 thread. Put a polish on the plain .125" diameter section where it will pass through the valve.

When you mark out the Connecting Rod (Part 13) on a strip of brass, pay particular attention to the spacing between the holes. Obtaining the correct distance between holes is an important point, since this determines where the piston travels inside the cylinder relative to the crankpin. Center drill, pilot drill, and ream the two holes first. It is easier to control these steps while the bulk of the metal is still there. After reaming the holes, saw the part out. Finish to the lines with files.

The Wrist Pin (Part 14) is nothing more than a short length of steel rod. After cutting it to length, chuck it in the lathe. Use a fine file to radius each end. If the wrist pin should drift in the piston, the end radii help to prevent scarring of the cylinder walls.

As I mentioned, I machined the Piston (Part 15) from a piece of half-inch diameter rod. There are a number of very interesting machining steps involved in making the piston. Careful work done on this part will be reflected in the motor's performance.

Chuck a piece of half-inch diameter rod with about .75″ length projecting from the jaws. Begin the machining by facing off. Use a very sharp tool to turn the diameter to fit your cylinder bore. "What is the proper fit?" you ask. I would think the diameter of the piston should be within .0005″ of the cylinder bore. As an example, the following description of the prototype motor's parts may be helpful. When I put the dry piston into the dry cylinder (no oil or any other lubricant or sealer) and cover the bottom of the cylinder with my finger, it takes thirty seconds for the piston to drop to the bottom against the air cushion. In other words, the fit of the piston to the cylinder in the prototype is more accurate than the measuring instruments with which I work. When you are satisfied that you have turned the piston to the correct diameter, remove it from the chuck with the unturned shank still attached. If you happen to have made a poor fit, it is not a tragedy. Simply turn another one.

At this point, I set the SL in position as a vertical milling machine once again. I mounted the workpiece in a V-block on the milling table, clamping by the unturned shank. This permitted the turned part to overhang the V-block where it was in the clear for the machining cuts. The first operation was to center drill, pilot drill, and ream the small hole for the wrist pin. Next, I put a slitting blade on the spindle and milled the clearance slot for the connecting rod. None of my blades happens to be the right width for the slot. Therefore, it was necessary to use a thinner blade and make successive cuts to open the slot to the required width. The final milling operation was to use an end mill to mill the flat surface on the side of the piston. The purpose of the flat is to give clearance to the port for admission and exhaust from the cylinder while maintaining minimal dead space and the end of the piston stroke.

When the milling is completed, return the workpiece to the chuck, once again gripping it by the unturned shank. With a pointed tool,

like a threading tool, cut two or three shallow oil grooves to a depth of .005″ or thereabouts around the side of the piston. Part off to free the machined piston from the unturned shank.

Mark out the Valve (Part 16) on a strip of brass. Measure carefully for the locations of the three holes. Their placement is important to the admission and exhaust events of the motor.

Use equal care in locating the edges of the slot that engages the crankpin. Start the slot by drilling through to form the radius at the end of the slot. Cut away the bulk of the metal from the slot with a fine saw, and finish the edges of the slot by filing. Work carefully in order to make the slot a close but free-moving fit on the crankpin throughout the full length of the slot.

Cut the Distribution Plate (Part 17) and the Spacer (Part 18) from the same piece of brass to guarantee that these parts are of the same thickness. Be very careful with the spacing of the holes in the distribution plate, because this is the part that actually controls the admission and exhaust of the air to and from the cylinder. Finally, cut the two Nipples (Part 19) from brass tubing. The length of the nipples is not critical, as they serve only as a connection point for a plastic tube that will connect the motor to a source of compressed air.

It is necessary to soft solder the distribution plate and the nipples to the valve. I tinned the surfaces of the valve and distribution plate first and made the nipples a light press fit into the holes in the valve. This permitted me to solder all the surfaces at one heating with a small propane torch. The metal is thin, so be careful not to overheat the parts. The spacer could be soldered to the valve, also, but it was left free on the prototype.

By now, you will most likely have assembled the cylinder on the cylinder base. Slip the piston with the connecting rod secured by the wrist pin into the cylinder with the flat on the piston facing the port. Screw the crankpin in

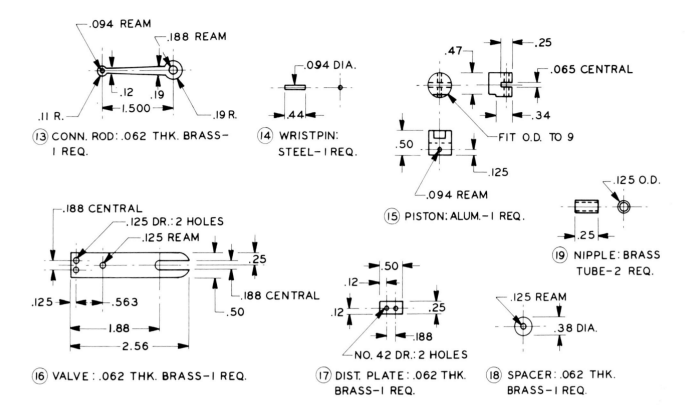

.094 REAM
.188 REAM
.12 .19
.11 R. 1.500 .19 R.

(13) CONN. ROD: .062 THK. BRASS—
1 REQ.

.094 DIA.
.44

(14) WRISTPIN:
STEEL—1 REQ.

.47 .25
.065 CENTRAL
.34
FIT O.D. TO 9
.50
.125
.094 REAM

(15) PISTON: ALUM.—1 REQ.

.125 O.D.
.25

(19) NIPPLE: BRASS
TUBE—2 REQ.

.188 CENTRAL
.125 DR.: 2 HOLES
.125 REAM
.25
.188 CENTRAL
.125 .563
.50
1.88
2.56

(16) VALVE: .062 THK. BRASS—1 REQ.

.50
.12
.25
.12
.188
NO. 42 DR.: 2 HOLES

(17) DIST. PLATE: .062 THK.
BRASS—1 REQ.

.125 REAM
.38 DIA.

(18) SPACER: .062 THK.
BRASS—1 REQ.

through the connecting rod. You should be able to swing the flywheel over now with no binds. Watch the piston travel up and down its stroke, paying particular attention that all motion is free throughout the full rotation of the crankshaft. If you are satisfied that everything is moving freely and properly, put on the cover and the valve. Pass the valve pivot through the valve and use the spacer between the valve and the port face. Refer to Photo 3 for a side view of the assembly with the valve pivot screwed into the port face. Slip a compression spring over the valve pivot, secure it with a 5-40 nut, and finally another nut as a lock nut. A quick check of Photo 2

will help you be sure that your assembled motor looks right. Check to be sure that the distribution plate is flat and contacts the port face uniformly across its surface. Once again, check to be sure that the motion is free at all points in the rotation. Lubricate all moving surfaces with light machine oil. Use a piece of plastic tubing, such as that sold for fish tank aeration, to connect one nipple to a compressed air source – a simple tire pump will do. The motor is single-action, so you will have to catch it on the proper side of the downward stroke. Then, be prepared for some snappy running!

Boring Bars

Mention of machining on the lathe normally brings to mind a picture of producing round or cylindrical objects, because this is the most obvious use for a lathe. However, a variety of other jobs can be handled on the lathe, also. One of these is the production of accurately machined hollow shapes, such as engine cylinders or main bearings. In the normal types of lathe work, the cutting tool is mounted on the lathe

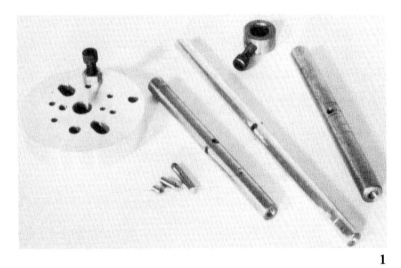

1

carriage as it cuts the workpiece which rotates between lathe centers. To generate hollow curves in parts such as engine cylinders, the procedure is reversed. That is, the workpiece is mounted on the lathe carriage and travels with the carriage while the cutting tool is mounted in a special bar which rotates between lathe centers. As the bar rotates, the tip of the cutting point sweeps through a circular arc, thus machining the inside surface of a cylindrical shape as the workpiece is moved along.

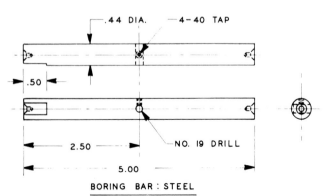

BORING BAR : STEEL

All the accessory parts that are needed to do successful boring in a lathe are shown in Photo 1. None of the parts is difficult to make. The necessary machining cuts can be carried out on the lathe in which the parts will be used. No special metals are needed for anything except the cutting points. Of course, the cutting points must be hardened tool steel, the same as any other tool bit intended to cut metals. I use the shanks of overworked or broken taps as the cutting points by regrinding them like miniature lathe tools. Three cutting points of varying lengths and shapes are grouped together in the photo.

The accompanying drawing shows the dimensions for a boring bar which I find extremely useful in building small engines. Because its diameter is .44", it may be started through a hole as small as 1/2" in diameter. By keeping the boring bar short, it is also kept rigid. Rigidity contributes to smooth, chatter-free boring. I routinely use this boring bar for boring cylinders up to 1" ID. Begin making the boring bar by cutting off a suitable length of steel rod. Mount this in a chuck in the lathe with the outer end supported in a steady rest set up like the one in Photo 2. Take a facing cut across the end of the bar. Then put a center drill in the tailstock drill chuck, and drill to form the hollow which will run on the lathe's center point. Reverse the bar in the lathe chuck. Repeat the facing and center drilling procedure on the opposite end. A size 3 center drill cuts a large enough hollow to hold a reasonable quantity of running lubricant while providing a solid bearing seat for the bar on the lathe's center point.

With both ends of the boring bar machined, locate the middle of the bar. Drill a hole all the way through to hold the cutting point. I specified No. 19 drill, because I make all my cutting points from the shanks of No. 8-32 taps. If you prefer to use a different size tap shank or tool steel from some other source, make an appropriate change in hole diameter. At right angles to the through hole, drill and tap a 4-40 hole for a short setscrew which will hold the cutting point in place in the bar. Refer to Photo 3 to see the single cutting point locked in position by a setscrew. Also, note the drive collar which is used to drive the boring bar around. Since the drive collar will be locked to the bar by a large socket head screw, it is advisable to mill or file a flat spot to serve as a seat for the screw.

Make the drive collar by cutting off a short piece of steel rod. Mount it in the three-jaw chuck to face off the first side. Then center drill to start the hole which can be finished with a 1/2″ diameter drill. Work from the tailstock drill chuck to accomplish the center drilling and drilling cuts. Reverse the part in the lathe chuck for facing the opposite side. Drill and tap for the socket head screw.

Photos 1 and 3 show the drive plate I put on the lathe nose to drive the boring bar. It is possible to use the lathe faceplate for this purpose. However, I feel it is worth making the special plate, since driving a boring bar has the potential to damage the edges of the slots in a faceplate. The drive plate shown can be machined from either 1/2″ thick flat stock or a slice of 2-1/2″ diameter round stock. Mount the piece in a lathe chuck to face off one side. Center drill and drill through with a suitable tapping size drill to match the thread of your lathe spindle. Tap a suitable thread, and finish the inside of the hole to be a close fit on your lathe's nose.

2

Screw the partially completed drive plate onto the nose of the lathe where it is to be used. With the part running in place, you can face it off and turn the outside diameter. Locate the position of the hole for the drive screw, then drill and tap for it. In running the boring bars, I select socket head screws of a length that allows them to meet head-to-head, as is shown in Photo 3. Since the screws of this type are hardened, they make excellent drivers that are rigid and not subject to bending or wear.

The cutting points that are used in the boring bar are rather small in size. This fact makes them a bit tricky to hold for grinding and sharpening. In order to get around this

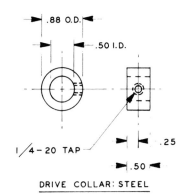

.88 O.D.
.50 I.D.
1/4 - 20 TAP
.25
.50

DRIVE COLLAR: STEEL

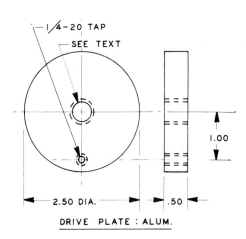

1/4 - 20 TAP
SEE TEXT
1.00
2.50 DIA.
.50

DRIVE PLATE : ALUM.

3

difficulty, I made a sharpening bar which is detailed in the drawing. It is apparent that the sharpening bar is intended to hold the cutting point in a position similar to what takes place in the boring bar. The sharpening bar is really a specialized handle. Its flat bottom and side surfaces simplify the job of grinding the cutting points, since the flat surfaces give reliable reference surfaces for gauging the clearance angles and other measurements.

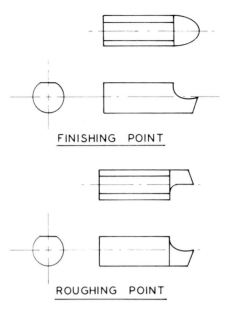

FINISHING POINT

ROUGHING POINT

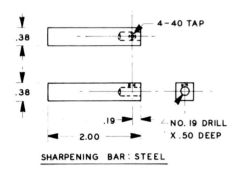

SHARPENING BAR: STEEL

Any short piece of steel square stock may be used for making the sharpening bar. I used keystock, but CRS would do as well. Cut a piece of the square stock to length. Chuck it centrally in the four-jaw chuck. Take a facing cut across the end. Open the end with a center drill held in the tailstock chuck. Then drill with a No. 19 drill to form the cavity that holds the cutting point for sharpening. Reverse the part in the chuck to face the opposite end. Drill and tap for the small setscrew, and you are ready to begin grinding and sharpening the cutting points.

For the most part, the grinding and sharpening of the cutting points is the same as what you do on your normal lathe tools. Two forms of cutting points I find very useful are detailed in the drawings. I have not indicated the angles on these drawings, because the clearance and relief angles will vary in accordance with the specific types of metal you intend to bore or cut with the boring bar. The roughing point cuts freely and can be used to machine internal shoulders. However, the finish that it leaves in the bore is a bit rough because of the narrow shape of the cutting surface. The finishing point, on the other hand, leaves a very smooth bore because of the broad radius of the cutting surface. The roughing point does an excellent job of opening the bore quickly, and a change to the finishing point will leave a cylinder or bearing bore that is glass smooth.

To begin grinding a cutting point, the first operation is to grind a flat on one side of the shank. This is the surface that will be in contact with the setscrew in either the sharpening bar or the boring bar. Mount the flat-sided shank in the sharpening bar with the broken end projecting. Grind away a half of the diameter so the cutting point's top surface coincides with the boring bar's center line. This corresponds to placing the lathe tool with its top surface on the lathe's axis. Now you can grind the point to shape finishing with the clearance and relief angles you will need for the intended use. Grind slowly so as not to overheat the cutting point, for overheating ruins the hardening of the tool steel. It is a good idea to grind several points right away in different lengths. Very short ones are needed for boring small cylinders and bearings, and longer ones are needed to reach out from the boring bar for machining larger cylinders or rings.

At this point, you are ready to begin using the boring bar. Refer to Photo 4 to see the setup I use in boring steam engine cylinders. The rough cylinder, which happens to be a casting in this case, is securely clamped on the lathe carriage. Notice the packing under the cylinder. Its purpose is to bring the cylinder vertically into the proper position for the desired center line of the cylinder to coincide with the lathe axis. This particular casting was not cored, so I put a center drill in the lathe chuck first to locate the bore. After starting the hole with the center drill, I drilled out with the largest twist drill possible to admit the boring bar, but stayed below the finished bore desired. With the lathe carriage backed off toward the tailstock, the boring bar was put through the cylinder and a cutting point slipped into the boring bar. The point was adjusted to take a light cut of only a few thousandths. For a smooth job, it is a good idea to use the power feed at the lowest possible rate to advance the workpiece toward the headstock. As each cut was completed, the carriage was run back and the cutting point repositioned for the next pass. The boring bar may be removed for checking the progress and quality of the cut. When the desired bore diameter is reached, the operation is finished.

Another use for boring bars is the machining of saddle shapes. Refer to Photo 5 for an example of a saddle shape being cut in the side of a block. While this particular cut was arranged for demonstration purposes, it is obvious that it is a useful method for shaping the undersides of locomotive domes or for fitting flat port faces to round cylinders.

Referring now to Photo 1, three boring bars are shown. The one on the left, next to the drive plate, is the one detailed in the accompanying drawings. The bar on the right is 1/2″ diameter x 5″ length. These are the most rigid bars I can use for heavy cylinder cuts or the discontinuous cuts in saddles. The slender bar in the center is 3/8″ diameter x 7-1/2″ long. Its greater length and smaller diameter are necessary when I am line boring main bearings. However, it is the least rigid of the set by virtue of its shape. Light cuts with it are mandatory to insure smooth, chatter-free bearing surfaces.

4

5

Milling Accessories

Anyone whose shop is not equipped with a true milling machine must find other ways of accomplishing such cuts as end milling slots or grooves, flycutting broad flat surfaces, forming keyways, and similar operations. The rotating spindle of either a lathe or multifunctional machine tool is capable of driving the cutter in an appropriate way. However, some means must be provided for securing the work in order to advance it to the cutter in a controlled and safe manner. The lathe or machine cross slide, with its longitudinal and cross-feed functions, provides control of the advance in both horizontal directions. This permits a somewhat limited amount of milling to be done on a lathe. In the case of multifunctional machine tools equipped with a vertical column, vertical advance becomes available, and the machine can be made to function as a vertical milling machine.

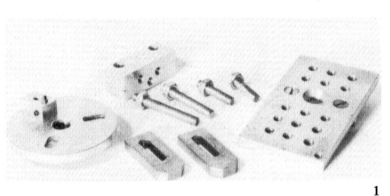

1

The question of how to clamp or otherwise mount the workpieces on the cross slide of the machine tool can prove to be a stumbling block. It is essential that the work be held securely against the forces of the cutting operation. However, there is seldom room for bulky clamps or other holding devices. Especially in using a vertical machine, it is highly desirable to maintain a low profile for clearance under the spindle housing and motor of the machine. A few simple accessories can be produced in the home shop on the machine tools with which they will be used in order to perform milling operations.

Photo 1 shows a group of accessories I have made and used over a period of about twenty years on my Unimat SL and Perris lathe. While neither of these machine tools is currently in production, there are many of

them still in use. The accessory parts described here will prove useful to anyone who owns later models of similar machines or different makes than mine, as well as to anyone who happens to own a machine identical to either of mine.

The basis for doing milling work on either type of machine is to have a milling table mounted on the cross slide. The milling-boring table shown in Photo 1 is detailed in the accompanying drawing. While different dimensions may be desirable for certain jobs or machines, I have found the table to be extremely useful in the form shown. The choice of metal for its construction is a matter of the builder's choice. Cold rolled steel is suitable for those who prefer a steel table. Mine is made of aluminum. In the years it has

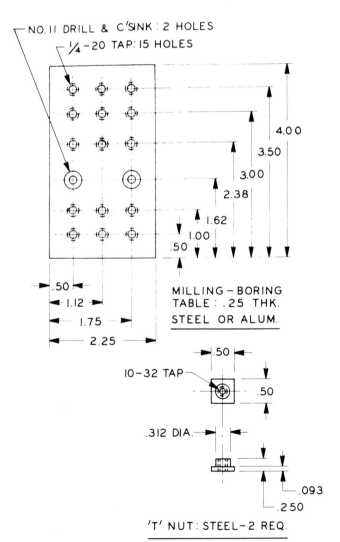

NO.11 DRILL & C'SINK : 2 HOLES

¼-20 TAP: 15 HOLES

4.00
3.50
3.00
2.38
1.62
1.00
.50

.50
1.12
1.75
2.25

MILLING – BORING TABLE : .25 THK. STEEL OR ALUM.

.50
10-32 TAP
.50
.312 DIA.
.093
.250

'T' NUT: STEEL-2 REQ.

been in use, no studs have ever pulled out, nor have any of the threaded holes worn to any degree that I can detect. Occasionally, I give the top and bottom surfaces a very light rub on 600 grit wet or dry abrasive paper on a plate glass surface to insure that the table has not developed any burrs or high spots. From the experience I have had with it, I do not think the use of aluminum in its construction detracts from it in any way.

Begin marking the table by marking out its outline on a suitable piece of .25″ thick stock. Edge dress with a file, as needed, to smooth the saw-cut edges. The chances are that the commercially rolled edge will be quite true. If it checks our fairly well against a plate glass surface plate, lay a sheet of wet or dry abrasive paper on the glass plate and rub the edge out until it checks true to the surface. Make the check for accuracy by standing the table on edge on the glass plate. Then use a feeler gage to check for rolled corners or bellies. As soon as the reference edge is true to the plate, use it to mark out the hole position. I made the left edge (nearest the headstock) the reference edge, because this is an aid in setting up the table for use. Drill and countersink the two holes indicated. These will be for the bolts used to mount the table on the machine.

Now you are ready to drill and tap the 15 holes that have the 1/4-20 thread. These are for placement of the clamping studs used on the table. When you have finished all the thread cutting, de-burr the holes on both sides of the table by twisting a 1/2″ drill between your fingers. At this point, the table should be quite flat. Lay a wet or dry abrasive paper on your glass plate, and rub the top and bottom surfaces flat to eliminate any distortion or stretching that may have occurred during the drilling and threading operations.

When the surfaces have been rubbed flat to the glass plate, the table is ready for mounting on the machine as shown in Photo 2. In order to use it this way, however, you will need two T-nuts to slide into the T-slot of the cross slide. The dimensions shown in the drawing of the T-nut are suitable for my Unimat SL. I suggest you check the slot of your machine before making the nuts to be certain they are suitable for your machine, also. To machine the nuts, chuck a piece of steel square stock centrally in the four-jaw chuck. Face off the end. Use the tailstock drill chuck to center drill. Then drill and tap the 10-32 hole for the flathead screw that will be used in it. Turn

2

down the cylindrical portion using a knife tool so it will be an easy fit in the T-slot. Square stock is not sweet to part off because of the discontinuity of the cut. If you have difficulty with the parting off, simply cut it off with a hacksaw. Then, grip the cylindrical portion in the three-jaw chuck and take a facing cut to finish it.

The table can now be set up on the cross slide. Check to be sure your T-nuts slide easily in the T-slot. I use slotted flathead screws of 10-32 size through the countersunk holes. Some builders may prefer to use hardened screws with socket heads for Allen wrenches. However, the socket heads accumulate chips, making insertion of the wrench difficult. This explains my preference for slotted screws. Notice in Photo 2 that the reference edge of the table is toward the left. The table is being indicated in to get its reference edge parallel to the cross-feed.

The clamps used for securing work on the milling-boring table may take a variety of sizes or shapes. I have shown a type and size of clamp in the photographs and drawings that has proven to be useful for general work. Many milling jobs require the security imparted by clamping from two positions simultaneously, so it is a good idea to make a pair of clamps right from the start. While a milling machine would be useful in making the clamps, the nature of their shape is such that they can be just as well made with hand tools.

Cut a suitable length of steel bar stock. Square off the ends by filing. Mark out the center line and position of the central slot. Form the slot by drilling away as much metal as possible followed by filing out with a narrow file of square cross section. Next, file away the two corners at a 45° angle to reduce the bulkiness and permit clamping in cramped quarters. Finally, rub the surfaces flat on wet or dry abrasive paper on a plate glass surface as with the milling table.

3

There is no need to make elaborate or fancy studs for clamping. Mine are simply lengths of 1/4-20 threaded rod. At this point, the box where I store the milling accessories contains studs in a variety of lengths. For starters, a pair each of 1″, 2″, and 3″ studs will accommodate many jobs. Whenever a particular job requires some special length, it is a simple matter to cut off threaded rod to suit the job.

Photos 3 and 4 show setups in which rather small workpieces are mounted on the milling-boring table by means of single clamps. Note

that one end of the clamp bears on the workpiece while the other rests on a supporting block that matches the height of the workpiece. For secure clamping, the supporting block must be the same height as the workpiece or very slightly higher. If the supporting block is lower, the clamp will fail to bear evenly on the workpiece, resulting in insecure mounting.

One thing leads to another, as they say. Toolmaking is a source of much delight, inasmuch as each newly finished tool or accessory can be put right to work to make some other useful item. Such is the case with the table, T-nuts, studs and clamps which can now be put to work to make a facing cutter.

The facing cutter, when mounted on a faceplate as in Photos 1 and 4, is an extremely useful item for producing broad flat surfaces on nearly any machined work or casting. In Photo 1 it is mounted on the Unimat faceplate, while Photo 4 shows it in place on the faceplate of my Perris lathe.

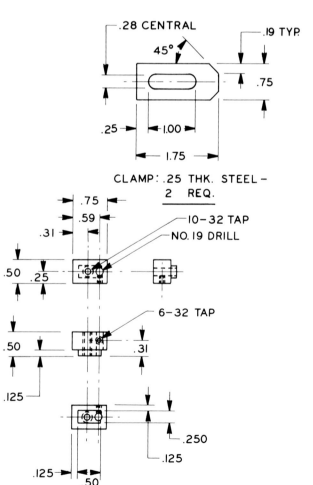

FACING CUTTER: STEEL

Cut a length of steel square stock to make the facing cutter. The saw cut ends may be file finished. Alternatively, the piece may be mounted in the four-jaw chuck and the ends faced off smooth. Notice that the facing cutter has a rectangular register or projection which fits into one slot of the faceplate. I make the setup shown in Photo 3 to form the register by cutting away metal with an end mill. In making the setup, I indicated the milling-boring table into position as was shown in Photo 2. This simplified the clamping operation, because all I had to do to guarantee a straight cut along the edge was to clamp the piece on the table with one side parallel to the reference edge of the table. Each side and end of the facing cutter was aligned in this way and end milled as shown. Pay particular attention to the depth of the milling cut so it will be constant all the way around the facing cutter. This is important for the cutter to have a firm and solid contact with the surface of the faceplate.

The slots in both of my faceplates are .25″ wide x .50″ long which corresponds with the dimensions of the rectangular projection on the facing cutter. The slots in most faceplates are unmachined surfaces in the faceplate casting. The projection on my facing cutter fit the slot in the Perris faceplate nicely. However, I had to use a thin file to remove slight irregularities from one slot of the Unimat faceplate to obtain a proper fit.

Drill and tap the 10-32 hole for a socket head machine screw which will be used to secure the facing cutter to the faceplate with a plain washer under the head. Next, drill the hole for the tool. The cutting tools I use in my facing cutter are the same ones I use in my boring bars. These were described in the previous chapter, along with a holder that facilitates grinding them. I have specified the use of a no. 19 drill, since I grind my tools from the shanks of no. 8 taps which have come to grief. Drill and tap from the side for a 6-32 setscrew to hold the tool in the facing cutter.

Refer once again to Photos 1 and 4 for the position of the facing block mounted on the faceplate. Note that in both cases I have mounted the facing cutter in a position such that the tool is near the center of the faceplate and the mounting bolt is toward the periphery. It would be possible to have the facing cutter turned the other way around to obtain a larger swept surface. However, this would also increase the loading on the spindle

4

of the machine and the stresses in the bearings and other parts of the machine. When mounted as shown, the tip of the tool sweeps through the circle of approximately 1.50" diameter which permits facing off quite a reasonable surface.

The lathe setup shown in Photo 4 is typical of the use to which I put the accessories described thus far. The operation in progress is that of milling a flat face on the side of a steam engine cylinder. In this case, the milling-boring table was indicated into position parallel to the cross-feed. Then the cylinder was clamped in place with its exact location in alignment with the reference edge of the table. While the motion of the table cannot be changed vertically, the tool held in the facing cutter sweeps through a sufficiently large arc to mill the entire face needed. The longitudinal feed is used to control the depth of the cut, and the cross-feed advances the workpiece into the tool. Rotational speeds are about the same as would be used for turning a shaft of 1.50" diameter.

The milling-boring table and clamps described thus far are well suited to handling workpieces that can be mounted directly in contact with the table in a more or less flat position. It is likely, however, that there will sometime be a need to perform a type of milling cut on an edge or surface that is best presented to the milling cutter in the vertical plane. When such a case comes along, the clamp block shown in Photo 1 and detailed in the drawing is invaluable.

Making the clamp block is an interesting exercise in accurate machining that makes use of the various milling accessories that have already been made. While none of the linear dimensions of the clamp block are critical, the squareness of its surfaces to one another is. Care lavished on getting them square to one another will be repaid many times over in accurate work done using the clamp block later on.

Cut off a length of aluminum square stock for the clamp block. Locate and drill the two clearance holes for studs to pass through when securing the clamp block on the milling-boring table. The reason for placing the stud holes off-center is to eliminate any chance that the nuts or washers used in mounting it might interfere with work clamped to the side of the block.

Probably the most accurate setup for machining the surfaces of the clamp block is a

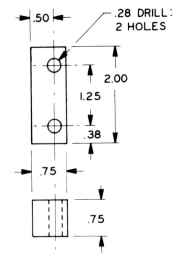

CLAMP BLOCK : ALUM.

horizontal one, which was shown in Photo 4. A word of caution is in order at this point. Don't automatically assume that the top surface of the cross slide on your lathe is parallel with the ways; it may or may not be so. One of mine is perfectly parallel, but the other one drops off evenly all the way across and winds up .004" low on the tailstock side of the saddle. Aware of this condition, I routinely slip in a .004" thick brass shim between the table and cross slide every time I

5

set it up. It is simple to locate a problem such as this. Mount your indicator in the lathe headstock on a suitable mounting. Bring the contact of the indicator against the top surface of the cross slide, and traverse the cross slide under the indicator by means of the longitudinal feed. Any deflection will indicate a lack of parallelism. Repeat this procedure with the milling-boring table in place as a further check.

When you have indicated the top surface and are satisfied with its parallelism to the ways of the lathe, proceed to indicate the reference edge of the table to get it parallel to the cross-feed. Mount the clamp block on the table with its bottom surface overhanging the reference edge by about .125". Use the facing block setup previously shown in Photo 4. In this case, the purpose is to machine a true flat surface on the bottom of the clamp block. The chances are that no more than .005" will have to be machined away. If the machined surface looks acceptable, rotate the block so it stands on the milling table on its machined surface. Now you can secure it by means of studs through the clearance holes. Proceed to take each side and each end in turn, and machine each one flat. If your machine is true and your setups have been made carefully, both sides and both ends of the clamp block will be at exact right angles to the bottom. Check this condition against a good square.

Assuming that your clamp block has proven to be truly square, it is now ready to go to work. When setting it up, it is a good idea to indicate its surface in parallel to one of the feed directions. Photo 5 shows the clamp block being indicated parallel to the cross-feed. In Photo 6, the clamp block is being used to mount a workpiece that is having an edge machined by the facing cutter. In this case, the vertical setup on the Unimat permits the facing cutter to be lowered a few thousandths at a time. Either the longitudinal feed or the cross-feed could be used to advance the work. Note that a parallel jaw clamp secures the workpiece to the clamp block. The low profile of such a clamp is desirable to avoid interference or contact with the facing cutter or the motor.

Multifunction machine tools that can be arranged vertically are undeniably a great convenience. However, some very helpful milling and boring setups can be made on a lathe. A cylinder boring operation was illustrated in the previous chapter on "Boring Bars." The same steam engine cylinder is

6

shown in Photo 7 here, ready for the end milling of the exhaust passage. Note that a piece of metal of appropriate thickness has been placed between the cylinder casting and the top of the milling-boring table. Its purpose is to raise the cylinder to the desired level so the end mill will cut the passage in the right place. Also note that a thin piece of metal has been placed between the cylinder casting and the clamp to prevent the clamp from scarring the already machined surface of the casting.

As experience is gained in using the milling accessories, other uses and setups will come to mind. The need to accomplish a particular end frequently indicates things to do or ways to do them. For example, when positioning the milling-boring table on a lathe cross slide, the process of indicating into parallelism with the cross-feed may not always be necessary. In setups where a slightly lower degree of accuracy is acceptable, the reference edge of the table may be aligned by bringing it into contact with the faceplate on the lathe spindle. This is a much more rapid method of alignment that produces satisfactory results for many operations. When aligning a work-piece or the clamp block parallel to the longitudinal feed of a lathe, another time-saver is to obtain accurate positioning by work-ing with an accurate square from the reference

7

edge of the table. By so doing, the only operation requiring the indicator is the alignment of the reference edge to the cross-feed.

The effort involved in making the milling accessories just described is not great. Anyone who takes the time to make them will be amply rewarded by their usefulness and the satisfaction derived from the good work done with them.

Stocking Stuffers

Is there a youngster in your life? Maybe a child, grandchild, niece, nephew – the kid next door? Whatever the relationship, the result will be the same if you take the small amount of time to make these little finger tops as stocking stuffers for them. They are sure to love you for it!

My growing up was all done in the pre-atomic, pre-television, pre-plastic whiz bang days. Things like these simple finger tops were the toys with which I grew up. Now, whenever I make such a toy for one of the second generation children in my life, it is a source of amusement to me to note how they gravitate toward them and obviously prefer them to their sophisticated, up-to-date toys.

Photo 1 shows the three finger tops which will be detailed in this article. They are all of the same dimensions, but I applied a different pattern to each disk so they would make a little set. The material requirements are minimal. A 5″ length of .125″ diameter steel rod will be adequate for the three top spindles. The three disk blanks may be made either from slices of a 1.25″ diameter aluminum rod or pieces of .25″ thick aluminum flatstock. Mine were made from slices of rod. The photos

and description will assume that you are working from slices of rod, also.

Begin by cutting off three lengths of the steel rod for the spindles (Part 1). Chuck each spindle in turn to take a facing cut across one

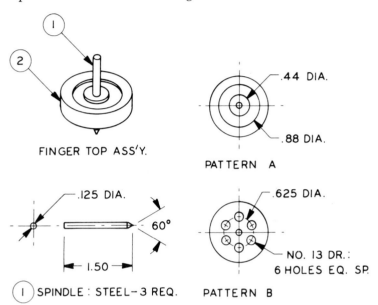

FINGER TOP ASS'Y.

PATTERN A
.44 DIA.
.88 DIA.

.125 DIA.
60°
1.50
① SPINDLE : STEEL–3 REQ.

PATTERN B
.625 DIA.
NO. 13 DR.:
6 HOLES EQ. SP.

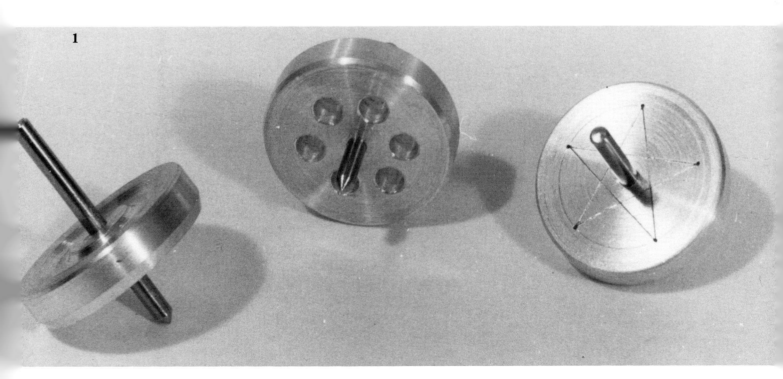

1

end. Reverse the spindle in the chuck to cut the taper on the opposite end. If your lathe has a compound slide, set it to machine the angle on the tip. Those using a lathe without a compound, such as my Unimat DB 200 shown in the photos, will have to slew the headstock for the angle cut. The included angle of 60° is not critical. After you have machined the angle on the tip of the spindle, give the tip a polish by rubbing it with fine emery paper while the lathe runs at high speed. The polishing operation will impart a slight radius to the tip, making for very sweet spinning.

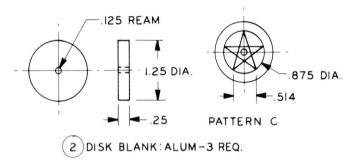

.125 REAM

1.25 DIA.

.25

PATTERN C

.875 DIA.

.514

(2) DISK BLANK: ALUM – 3 REQ.

To make the three disk blanks (Part 2), chuck each of the slices of aluminum rod in the three-jaw chuck and take a facing cut. The first side faced off on each disk will become the underside when the tops are assembled. Reverse the first one in the chuck to face off the upper surface. Refer to Photo 2 and Pattern

A. Use a tool with a radiussed tip to make the undercut in the disk surface. I had just finished the undercut when I shot Photo 2. Chuck a small center drill in the tailstock drill chuck to start the center hole in the disk. Drill through the center with drill No. 31. Now you are ready to put a .125″ diameter reamer in the tailstock drill chuck, as I had done in Photo 2 to ream the central hole to size.

Chuck the next disk blank in the three-jaw chuck to face off its upper surface. Drill and ream the central hole following the same procedure as you did on the first disk. Refer now to Pattern B. Put on a sharply pointed tool, like a thread cutting tool, to machine a slight groove forming the .625″ diameter circle shown on the pattern drawing. Set your divider for .312″, the exact radius of the circle. Step off the six equal divisions on the circle to locate the centers of the small holes. Punch each spot with a small, sharp center punch. Use a small center drill to start each hole. Then change to the No. 13 drill to drill each hole through.

Follow the same procedure on the third disk to face it off and make the central hole. Refer to Pattern C which shows the layout of the Christmas star. Use the sharply pointed tool, once again, to machine the circle of .875″ diameter. Set your divider for a distance of .514″ which is so close to $^{33}/_{64}$″ that the latter may be used. Step off the five equal divisions to locate the points of the star. Make a very light punch mark at each star point to help in locating the points. Place your straight edge across alternating punch marks, and scribe the lines heavily to outline the star. Anyone wishing to make a six-pointed Star of David should set their divider for a distance of .438″ which will locate the six points equidistant on the circle. Proceed from that point as described for the five-pointed star.

At this point, you are ready to press the spindles into the disks for the assembly work. Referring to Photo 3, note that I had chucked a disk in the three-jaw chuck with its upper surface turned out toward the tailstock. Chuck a spindle in the tailstock drill chuck with the pointed end toward the headstock. This setup places the spindle and disk in axial alignment

2

3

to start the spindle in the central hole in the disk. Advance the tailstock ram to start the pointed end of the spindle into the hole. Don't strain your lathe by trying to press the spindle all the way in. When you have pressed it in far enough to know it is started truly, transfer to the vise jaws with a ring supporting the disk from its underside. Press the spindle in the vise jaws until you have .75″ of the spindle above the disk and .50″ of the spindle below the disk.

Grip each assembled top in a collet or true running chuck, as I had done in Photo 4. Insert the upper end of the top spindle in the chuck. Use a slightly radiussed tool to take a light truing cut across the periphery of each top disk. Note in Photo 4 that I had just finished turning the edge of the Pattern B top, and that I had also applied a slight chamfer to each edge to eliminate any burrs or otherwise sharp corners. Any child who finds the set of tops in his or her stocking is sure to have fingers more tender than yours!

To spin the tops, grip the long end of the spindle between your thumb tip and the side of your index finger. As you roll the spindle back and forth a couple of times, you will be able to feel the flywheel effect of the disk. As you give the spindle a good roll between your fingers,

4

release the top near the table surface, and it will spin off on its merry trip.

They spin longest on a very hard surface, such as a porcelainized table top. As youngsters, we used to set up pins made from short pieces of wooden dowels to create games in which the spinning tops could bump against them to knock them over. Just watching them spin is fun.

Few other jobs that you will complete in the home shop will ever give you the reward offered by the joy and love brought to your youngster's face by these little Stocking Stuffers.

Use of Dimensions

A letter from an *HSM* reader crossed my desk a while back and raised a question. The thought behind that question and my reply to it are the basis for this installment. Perhaps it would be well for me to explain at this point that the person who wrote the letter is a long-standing friend of mine who has built every engine of my design for which the plans have been published. He is an excellent machinist and a careful worker. His friendship has been most welcome over the past 15 years.

Referring specifically to the small compressed air motor I detailed in the "Micro Machinist" column in the period from January through June of 1984 (and included earlier in this volume), he brought up the following point, "Why do you and other designers give measurements in thousandths and hundredths? Your cylinder and port face are 1.06, and a measurement on the base is .438. I'm sure that 1/2 thou. over 7/16" doesn't make that much difference as well as 2-1/2 thou. added to 1.06 making it 1.0625" or 1-1/16". Straighten me out!"

In reply, there is a standard practice followed by most machine designers in which fractional parts of an inch are specified as decimals. This is a convenient means of expression for most dimensions. However, some fractions of an inch convert to concise numbers in decimal form, while others do not. For example, .109375" is the full decimal equivalent of 7/64", while .5" is the full decimal equivalent of 1/2". Obviously, some rounding off is in order when using the decimal equivalents of dimensions such as 7/64". In rounding off, the decimal may be cut down to any desired number of places. Since we normally try to keep our machine tool work to the order of a thousandth of an inch, it is reasonable to round decimals off to three places. In this case, .109" would be the three-place equivalent of 7/64". going a step farther in the rounding off process, .11 would be its two-place equivalent.

The standard practice followed by most machine designers with regard to specifying dimensions goes a step beyond rounding off the decimal equivalents, however. It also assigns a tolerance or limit of accuracy to each dimension. The form in which the dimension is written carries an implied designation of the tolerance or limit of accuracy desired for the part in question. By using this convention in dimensioning, the designer is able to indicate his concept of the precision required in making the part without cluttering the drawing with tolerance marks, other designations, or written explanations concerning the relationships or fitting of the parts.

To cite a specific example, a designer wishing to indicate a dimension of one and one-sixteenth inch has the choice of writing it as 1-1/16", 1.06", 1.062", or 1.0625" as far as the dimension, itself, is concerned. Each of these four expressions means one and one-sixteenth inch. However, the implied meaning of tolerance, or limit of accuracy, is *different* in each case. The full meaning of each expression may be stated as follows:

1-1/16" means one and one-sixteenth inch ±1/64"
1.06" means one and one-sixteenth inch ±.01"
1.062" means one and one-sixteenth inch ±.005"
1.0625" means one and one-sixteenth inch ±.0005"

Following the same convention, two and one-half inches could be written 2-1/2", 2.50", or 2.500", despite the fact that the zeroes following the five cannot possibly change the dimension. In each form, the tolerance is implicit in the number of decimal places and is to the same limits as those indicated in the previous example.

The table shown here lists the commonly-used fractional parts of an inch. Their decimal equivalents, rounded off to two, three, and four decimal places, are grouped in columns to the right. The majority of projects undertaken in the home shop do not require the accuracy inherent in four-place decimal designations, but I have included them for general information value and in the event that such dimensions are encountered in some specific case.

In order to illustrate the use of two- and three-place decimal equivalents and the rationale behind their use, I have retraced the base of the compressed air motor referred to earlier and included it as an illustration here. The drawing indicates that the part is to be made from .12" thick aluminum. From the table, it is apparent that the thickness of the piece should be approximately 1/8″. Because it is shown as a two-place decimal, anyone looking at the drawing immediately knows that the thickness is not critical to the operation of the engine, and that any thickness in the range of .115″ to .135″ will be acceptable.

Likewise, the length and width of the piece are shown as 1.81 and 1.50, indicating to cut the piece 1-13/16″ long and 1-1/2″ wide. These dimensions are not critical, either, and will be acceptable if kept within ±.01″ of the specified value. When we got to the dimensions showing the locations of the drilled holes, the situation changes. All of these dimensions are shown as three-place decimals indicating that all of the holes are to be located quite accurately, within ±.005″ of the specified dimension, to be exact. Why locate the holes so accurately? Because they must line up with the corresponding holes in

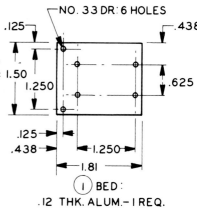

the bearings, columns, and cylinder base of the engine. Accurate positioning of the holes is obviously required so the other parts of the engine may be assembled properly. Proper relationship of the parts to one another is essential to smooth operation of the engine.

If you review each drawing of the parts of the engine, or any other drawing, with these principles of dimensioning and tolerance in mind, it becomes immediately obvious where the most precise work must be done on the parts. It also become obvious what result the designer was trying to achieve and what information he was passing on by his choice and use of dimensions.

Table of Decimal Equivalents of Fractions of an Inch

Fraction	Decimal Equivalents			Fraction	Decimal Equivalents		
	2 pl.	3 pl.	4 pl.		2 pl.	3 pl.	4 pl.
1/64	.02	.016	.0156	33/64	.52	.516	.5156
1/32	.03	.031	.0312	17/32	.53	.531	.5312
3/64	.05	.047	.0469	35/64	.55	.547	.5469
1/16	.06	.062	.0625	9/16	.56	.562	.5625
5/64	.08	.078	.0781	37/64	.58	.578	.5781
3/32	.09	.094	.0938	19/32	.59	.594	.5938
7/64	.11	.109	.1094	39/64	.61	.609	.6094
1/8	.12	.125	.1250	5/8	.62	.625	.6250
9/64	.14	.141	.1406	41/64	.64	.641	.6406
5/32	.16	.156	.1562	21/32	.66	.656	.6562
11/64	.17	.172	.1719	43/64	.67	.672	.6719
3/16	.19	.188	.1875	11/16	.69	.688	.6875
13/64	.20	.203	.2031	45/64	.70	.703	.7031
7/32	.22	.219	.2188	23/32	.72	.719	.7188
15/64	.23	.234	.2344	47/64	.73	.734	.7344
1/4	.25	.250	.2500	3/4	.75	.750	.7500
17/64	.27	.266	.2656	49/64	.77	.766	.7656
9/32	.28	.281	.2812	25/32	.78	.781	.7812
19/64	.30	.297	.2969	51/64	.80	.797	.7969
5/16	.31	.312	.3125	13/16	.81	.812	.8125
21/64	.33	.328	.3281	53/64	.83	.828	.8281
11/32	.34	.344	.3438	27/32	.84	.844	.8438
23/64	.36	.359	.3594	55/64	.86	.859	.8594
3/8	.38	.375	.3750	7/8	.88	.875	.8750
25/64	.39	.391	.3906	57/64	.89	.891	.8906
13/32	.41	.406	.4062	29/32	.91	.906	.9062
27/64	.42	.422	.4219	59/64	.92	.922	.9219
7/16	.44	.438	.4375	15/16	.94	.938	.9375
29/64	.45	.453	.4531	61/64	.95	.953	.9531
15/32	.47	.469	.4688	31/32	.97	.969	.9688
31/64	.48	.484	.4844	63/64	.98	.984	.9844
1/2	.50	.500	.5000	1	1.00	1.000	1.0000

Slitting Saws

When you buy a couple of plain slitting saws or jeweler's slotting saws, you greatly extend the range of your lathe. Of course, you will need an arbor on which to mount the saws in order to make use of them. But making the arbor is not difficult. One can be made directly on the lathe where it will be used, in fact.

What are slitting saws, and what sort of uses can be made of them in the home shop? Slitting or slotting saws are circular saw blades intended for cutting metal. They are made of high-speed steel, which makes them useful for cutting or slotting tubing, wire, or metal in a variety of forms. Jeweler's slotting saws have fine teeth, which makes them ideal for the thinnest materials and delicate work; plain slitting saws have larger teeth suited to metals of thicker sections. They are useful for cutting off metal parts, or for machining slots or grooves accurately in workpieces.

saw in a vertical setup to machine the slot in the end of a small clevis also intended for a steam engine. In this instance, the thickness of the saw blade was inadequate for cutting the slot full width in a single pass. By advancing the saw the necessary amount, the slot was opened a little at a time until the desired width had been reached.

Jeweler's slotting saws range in diameter from 1″ up to 2-1/2″, while plain slitting saws range from 2″ up to 8 or 10″. In thickness, jeweler's slotting saws range from .008″ to .057″. The thickness of plain slitting saws is customarily expressed in fractions of an inch in the range of 1/64″ up to 3/16″. For use on the small lathe shown, I buy saws in the 2″ to 2-1/2″ diameter range. The 2-1/2″ slitting saw in Photo 1 is 1/32″ thick, while the 2″ jeweler's slotting saw in Photo 2 is .053″ thick. For slitting cuts, the thinner saws naturally waste less metal. However, they are also more delicate and susceptible to breakage because they are thinner. I have the greatest amount of use for saws in the thickness range of .025″ up to 1/16″.

1

2

Photo 1 indicates a typical slitting saw job. In this case I used a 2-1/2″ diameter slitting saw on the nose of the lathe to cut through .25″ thick brass to form an accurate center joint in an eccentric intended for a model steam engine. A somewhat different use is shown in Photo 2, where I used a 2″ diameter slotting

The slitting saw arbor shown in Photo 1 and detailed in the accompanying drawings is home-built. While the exact dimensions indicated may not suit your lathe directly, the principle can be adapted to your specific needs by altering a few dimensions. The mounting

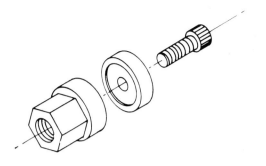

SLITTING SAW ARBOR

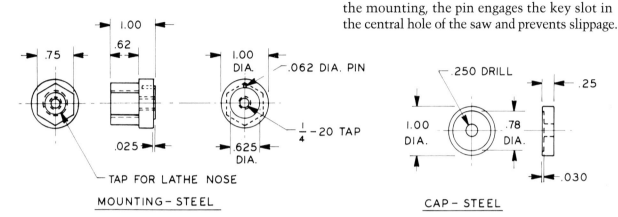

MOUNTING – STEEL

CAP – STEEL

upon your uses and the specific saws you want.

Whatever diameter you use for the shoulder, make it an accurate fit in the hole of your saws so they will cut evenly with all their teeth. Center drill, drill, and tap the central hole for the 1/4-20 socket head cap screw that clamps it together. Next, drill a hole 1/16" diameter x .19" deep into the round part just off the shoulder. Press in a .062" diameter steel pin. File off the end of the pin flush with the face of the shoulder. When saws are put on the mounting, the pin engages the key slot in the central hole of the saw and prevents slippage.

of my arbor was made from two piece of metal that I silver soldered together. You may machine it all in one piece or follow the two-piece procedure, as you prefer. To make it from two pieces, cut off a length of .75" hexagonal stock to begin the mounting. This is a natural choice, since it provides built-in wrench flats. First, face off both ends of the hex stock. Then, using the tailstock chuck, center drill, drill through with a pilot drill, and tap the hole to fit the lathe nose. In my case, the thread is 1/2-20. If your lathe has a larger thread, you will probably have to use larger hex stock.

The circular part of the mounting is made from a slice of steel round stock of 1" diameter. After cutting it off, chuck it in the three-jaw chuck to take a facing cut across one side. The faced off side is the one that is silver soldered centrally to the end of the hexagonal part. After you silver solder and clean up, screw the mounting right onto the nose of the lathe and finish the machining in place. First, turn the round part to get it running true. Then take a facing cut across it. Finally, turn down to form the shallow shoulder that goes in the central hole of the saw to position it on the mounting. I buy saws with a .625" hole diameter and have indicated this size in the drawing. Check your supplier's catalog for dimensions; you may prefer some other size, such as .750" or .500", depending

Make the cap from another slice of steel rod. Face off in the three-jaw chuck. Reverse in the chuck to face the second side. Center drill and drill the .250" hole to clear the cap screw. Use a knife tool to machine the undercut. The dimensions of the undercut are not critical. Its diameter must clear over the outside of the pin pressed into the mounting, and it should be deep enough to stand just clear of the shoulder when no saw is in place.

Photo 1 and the isometric drawing indicate the assembly of the parts. With a saw blade in place, as in Photo 1, you are ready to put it to use. Note in Photo 1 that I had used a very secure clamping arrangement to mount the workpiece on the lathe carriage. This is an important consideration; if any slippage of the work occurs as a result of the force of the cut, it virtually guarantees breakage of the saw, because there is so little clearance. Notice, also, the direction of the cut. As in any milling type of cut, the best results are obtained when the work is moved *against* the cutting direction of the cutter. You can see that I used the cross-feed to move the work *toward* the operator's position in order to move against the cut of the saw. The same statements are true about the work in Photo 2 with regard to secure clamping and moving against the cutting direction of the slotting saw.

Fixed Steady Rest

Whenever a long, relatively slender workpiece of cylindrical shape must be supported in the lathe for turning, facing, or boring cuts, there is likely to be a need for a fixed steady rest. One which I have built for my Unimat DB 200 is illustrated in Photos 1 and 2. Over the years, it has proven to be a very useful accessory in my hands and was well worth the small amount of time and effort that went into its construction. It is presented here as a handy addition to the lathe which others may wish to duplicate.

Refer to the assembly drawing for a complete view of the parts that must be made and their relationship to one another. From the assembly drawing and Photos 1 and 2, you will be able to see the way it mounts on the lathe ways. The details and dimensions shown are specifically for use with the Unimats having cylindrical ways. The same principles of construction and use apply to any lathe, regardless of the specific shape of its bed and ways. Any prospective builder wishing to construct a similar fixed steady rest for a different type of lathe should have no particular difficulty changing the necessary dimensions of clamping arrangement, provided that he or she has a clear understanding of the function and applicability of the tool.

There are a number of ways that you can proceed with making the various parts. I did all of the machining operations right on the Unimat for which the steady rest was being built. This entailed extensive use of the vertical column for working the Unimat as a vertical milling machine besides working it as a lathe in the horizontal configuration. It will be noted in the accompanying photos that the milling table, facing cutter, clamps, and other home built tools described in previous installments of this column played vital roles in the construction of my steady rest. As I have commented at other times, one thing leads to another!

Mark out the outline of the Clamp (Part 1) on a suitable piece of stock. Cut it out, then finish to dimension by either filing or milling. In a

1

2

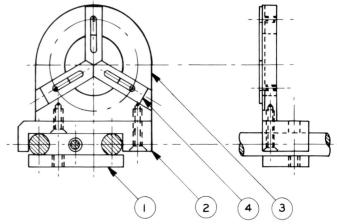

FIXED STEADY REST ASS'Y.

case like this, I like to use the facing cutter referred to earlier to machine all the edges. Locate the tapped hole after truing the edges. Center drill, drill no. 3, and tap the ¼-28 hole for the clamping screw which will be used to secure the steady rest on the lathe ways.

Accurate work is called for in making the Base (Part 2), since it is instrumental in aligning the parts of the steady rest as well as placing it accurately on the lathe ways. Mark the outline and saw it out with a little allowance for machining. This part could be cut from a length of bar stock or it could be cut from a plate. Mine was cut from a piece of 1" jig plate. Jig plate is an especially good material for this type of work, because the surfaces are flat and parallel to a high degree of accuracy. Once again, I used the facing cutter to machine all saw cut surfaces to dimension. Then I used the same cutter to machine off the 45° chamfer on

3

The recess in the bottom surface of the base fits over the lathe ways. The fit can be seen in the assembly drawing and in Photos 1 and 2. A vertical setup, such as I was using in Photo 3, is very convenient for end milling the recess. In making the setup, I had aligned the edge of the milling table parallel to the cross slide travel to simplify positioning the part on the milling table. In Photo 3, I was nearing the end of the milling operation and had shifted one clamp to clear the end mill. Initially, the part was clamped at each end, but the offset position of the recess made the shift of the clamp necessary. Check the 2.045" dimension against the outer width of the ways of your lathe. It is desirable for the recess to fit the ways closely with accurate surfaces which hold the steady rest truly vertical and at right angles to the axis of the lathe.

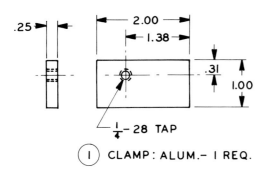

① CLAMP: ALUM.– 1 REQ.

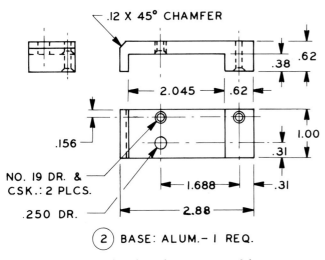

② BASE: ALUM.– 1 REQ.

one corner. The chamfer is required for clearing the front jaw when a workpiece of large diameter is being supported in the steady rest.

Mark out the locations of the three bolt holes. These are clearance holes which can be drilled through immediately. Start each hole with a small center drill before drilling through with twist drills. Do not countersink the no. 19 holes at this point.

After milling the recess, you can countersink the no. 19 holes from the underside for the flathead screws which will secure it to the Frame (Part 3). When we resume next time, we will finish detailing the parts of the fixed steady rest and get into some further information about setting it up on the lathe and using it.

Begin work on the Frame (Part 3) of the fixed steady rest by cutting out a 2.50" square from a piece of .31" thick aluminum. Machine three edges to form the sides and bottom, as you did on previous parts. Pay particular attention to the bottom surface; it must be straight and square to the faces so it will be vertical when erected on the base.

Mark out the locations of the two tapped holes on the bottom surface. Position the holes carefully to be sure they will line up with the no. 19 clearance holes in the base. Start each

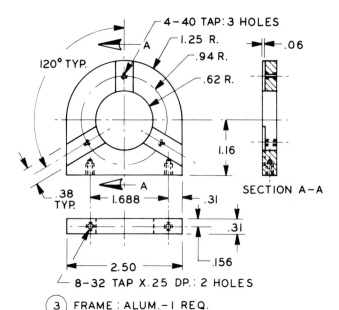

4-40 TAP: 3 HOLES
120° TYP.
A
1.25 R.
.94 R.
.62 R.
.06
1.16
A
SECTION A-A
.38 TYP.
1.688
.31
.31
.156
2.50
8-32 TAP X .25 DP.: 2 HOLES
③ FRAME : ALUM.-1 REQ.

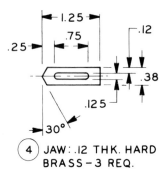

1.25
.25
.75
.12
.38
.125
30°
④ JAW: .12 THK. HARD BRASS – 3 REQ.

hole with a center drill. Follow with a no. 29 drill and, finally, tap an 8-32 thread to a depth of .25".

The nominal dimension of 1.16″ from the bottom of the frame to the horizontal center

4

line is only an approximation. My reason for specifying the approximate dimension is to allow for some variation in the thickness of the base where it rests on top of the ways. It is obvious that the center line of the frame must coincide with the lathe axis both vertically and horizontally. Rather than impose very tight limits of tolerance on the dimensions, it seems more reasonable to proceed as I was doing in Photo 4.

After erecting the frame on the base, clamp the assembly to the lathe ways near the tailstock, as indicated in Photo 4. Check to be sure that the assembly is square to the ways and that the frame is vertical. Put a dead center in the tailstock, and tighten the tailstock to the ways. Run the tailstock ram forward until the tip of the dead center is just touching the surface of the steady rest frame. If everything looks right, give the frame a very light hammer tap from the back to drive it against the dead center. The resulting mark on the surface of the frame will be the *exact* location of the lathe's axis of rotation. Working from the mark left by the dead center, use your dividers, square, and protractor to finish marking out the frame. Refer to Photo 5, which illustrates my marked out frame, at this point.

Start the remaining machining operations by center drilling the three locations for the tapped holes. Follow with the no. 43 drill, and tap a 4-40 thread in each hole. Now you are ready to end mill the slots into which the jaws fit. Refer once again to Photo 5 where I was doing this end milling cut. Note that I had already milled the vertical slot and was a little more than halfway done with the second slot. While the exact depth of the slots is not critical, they must all be milled to the *same* depth in order that the jaws will hold the work evenly. Of course, it is necessary to turn the frame for milling each slot. By aligning the edge of the milling table exactly with the cross slide, I was able to position the frame on the milling table by using a machinist's protractor with reference to the edge of the milling table as a base line.

When the slots are all machined, mount the part on the lathe faceplate, using the three 4-40 tapped holes for the mounting bolts. This is the setup for boring out the central hole. On the Unimat, it was necessary to use the elevator block to obtain clearance for the corners of the part. Refer to the mark left by the dead center to get it running true. Use the tailstock chuck to center drill and drill as large as possible. Then finish the hole to diameter with a boring bar mounted on the tool post. Now you can saw away the bulk of the top corners and finish the radius to the mark with files.

Hard brass is an excellent material for the Jaws (Part 4). Cut the three jaws from either flat or bar stock. Mine were cut from a piece of flat stock. Therefore, it was necessary to mill the edges along the sides and across the square end. When you have them the right width to fit the slots in the frame, mark out the central slots which clear the mounting bolts. Use a .125″ end mill to mill the clearance slots. I used a .125″ drill to make a pilot hole through which the end mill could be started. This permitted milling the full slot on a single pass.

The 30° taper at the tip of the jaws will have to be cut fairly accurately so that the jaws will center up nicely to hold the workpiece. My setup for doing this cut is shown in Photo 6. Note that I had clamped a block to the milling table to form the required 60° angle to the lathe faceplate. With the three jaws stacked against the block, I was able to clamp them to the milling table in exactly the right position. Using the facing cutter on the faceplate, I faced off all three jaws simultaneously. By flipping the whole stack over, the operation could be repeated for the second side with certainty that the tips would be symmetrical and all at the same angle. This completes the fabrication of parts and allows the fixed steady rest to be fully assembled.

The setups shown in Photos 1 and 2 are typical of the sort of work that can be mounted in the lathe using a fixed steady rest. Either tubular stock (Photo 1) or solid stock (Photo 2) can be supported for lathe cuts to be made on the end or between the chuck and steady rest. In the case of tubular stock, internal boring or threading operations may be performed in addition to external operations or facing cuts. Center drilling, drilling, tapping, or reaming jobs may be performed on steady rest supported workpieces by mounting suitable tools in the tailstock drill chuck, also. The fixed steady rest is indispensable for supporting work that cannot go on centers because it is too long for the lathe bed or because a center drilled spot in the end would be objectionable.

From Photos 1 and 2, it is apparent that the workpiece must be located in the steady rest to coincide with the axis of the lathe. In setting up, every effort should be made to center the work carefully by adjusting the position of the

5

6

jaws. The workpiece must be smooth and round where it is in contact with the jaws, and lubricating oil *must* be applied at the contact point.

BILL OF MATERIALS

No.	Part	Material	Dimensions
1	Clamp	Aluminum	.25 × 1.00 × 2.00
2	Base	Aluminum	.62 × 1.00 × 2.88
3	Frame	Aluminum	.31 × 2.50 × 2.50
4	Jaw (3 req.)	Hard Base	.12 × .38 × 1.25
	8-32 × .88 Flathead machine screw (1 req.)		
	8-32 × .50 Flathead machine screw (1 req.)		
	¼-28 × 1.25 Socket head cap screw (1 req.)		
	4-40 × .38 Button head screw (3 req.)		

Small Keyways & Keyseats

Mention of cutting internal keyways automatically brings to mind the use of broaches, since broaching is the customary method by which keyways are cut. However, broaches and their necessary guides and presses are a bit on the expensive side for the relatively infrequent use they receive in the home shop. Furthermore, none of the tool catalogs on my book shelf lists broaches smaller than 1/16" in width.

Since I am particularly fond of the smaller sized projects, the commercially available broaches are a little larger than I really care to use on my engines or in my toolmaking projects. Refer to Photo 1, which illustrates my point fully. The round object in the photograph is a pulley of 1.25" diameter for a model engine. The blade of the square shown with it is calibrated in 1/64" increments along the lower edge and 1/32" increments along the upper edge. Notice that the internal keyway at the bottom of the central hole is just .043" wide, which makes it nicely proportioned for use on a small model.

The tooling I used to cut the internal keyway shown in Photo 1 is home built. Photo 2 shows the various parts making up the keyway tool along with a pair of V-blocks that I made for cutting the corresponding external keyseats in shafts. In Photo 3, you will see the tool at work on my Unimat DB 200 cutting an internal keyway. The purpose of this series is to run through a description of the steps I followed in making the tools, followed by a description of their use.

The actual cutting surface in the tool for cutting internal keyways is a Craftsman saber saw blade which sells for approximately 50¢. Check your catalogs to see how that compares with the price of broaching equipment, consider the neat keyway shown in Photo 1, and you are likely to be ready to start work on making a duplicate of my tool!

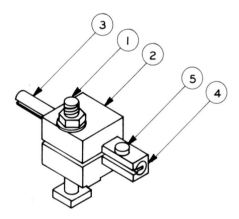

KEYWAY CUTTER ASS'Y.

Compare the isometric assembly drawing with the views shown in Photos 2 and 3 to obtain a clear understanding of the parts of the tool and how they go together. The accompanying bill of materials lists all stock requirements to build the tools exactly as shown. If you wish to build the internal keyway cutter for a lathe of some other size or make, you may have to make a change in the dimensions of parts 1 and 2, but this will be discussed as we go along. The material requirements are small in any case. Cut off ends are about all you will need.

1

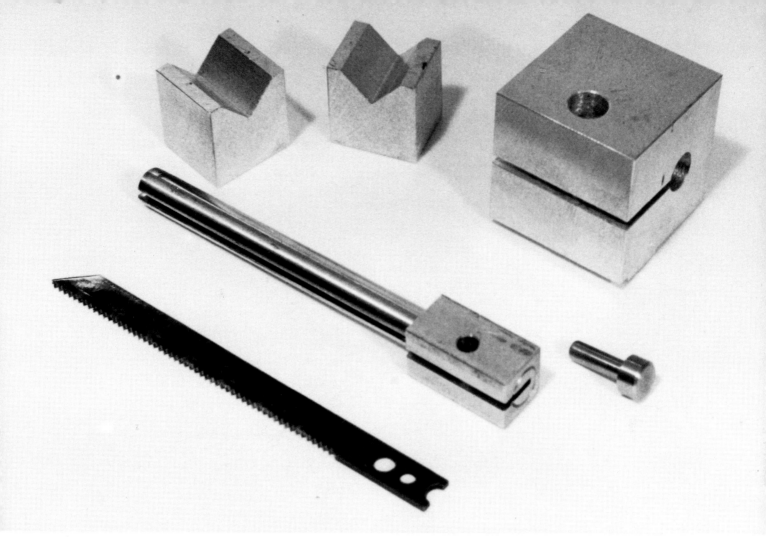

2

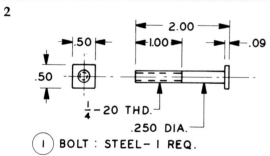

.50 ← → .50 ←

.50

$\frac{1}{4}$ – 20 THD.

2.00
1.00 → ← .09

.250 DIA.

① BOLT : STEEL – 1 REQ.

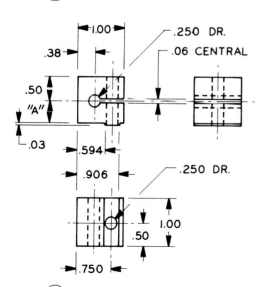

1.00
.38

.250 DR.
.06 CENTRAL

.50
"A"
.03

.594
.906

.250 DR.

1.00
.50

.750

② MOUNTING : ALUM. – 1 REQ.

3

4

I did all of the machining operations directly on the Unimat for which I was making the tool. Much of the work was done with the Unimat set up vertically for milling cuts and drill press work. Some of the work did entail a horizontal set up as a lathe, however.

If you have a suitable T-head bolt to fit the slot in the cross slide of your lathe, you may wish to skip making the bolt (Part 1). As drawn in the detail drawing, the bolt is dimensioned for use in a mounting (Part 2) that is 1.00″ tall. If your lathe is larger than the Unimat DB, make the bolt longer to compensate for whatever height you may have to add to the mounting. The machining procedure will be the same whatever the length. Chuck a suitable length of square stock in the four-jaw chuck. When you get it running centrally, it is a good idea to center drill the outer end so that you can support it on a tailstock center while turning it down. Use a knife tool for turning the shank to diameter. Be certain to leave a clean corner where the shank and the square head meet so that the head will pull up firmly in the T slot of the lathe. Cut the thread by using a die in the tailstock die holder. Now you can reverse the part, gripping it in the three-jaw chuck to take a facing cut across the outer face of the head. You may make the head thicker or thinner than the .09″ dimension to fit the exact dimension of the slot on your lathe.

Referring now to the drawing of the mounting

(Part 2), note the dimension marked "A." Dimension "A" corresponds to the height of the lathe's axis, or center line, above the top surface of the cross slide. On the Unimat DB, this height is exactly .47″, but it may be different on other models of Unimat or other lathes. Adding the height of .47″ for "A" to the .50″ and .03″ gave me an overall height of just 1.00″ for this part. Follow the same procedure to determine how high the part must be for your lathe.

The first machining operation is to face off all sides of the block so they are flat and at right angles to one another. This can be done conveniently by setting the machine up vertically as a milling machine. Use either a fly cutter or the small facing cutter previously detailed in this column to face off each side in turn.

Locate the position of the vertical .250″ diameter hole through which the bolt (Part 1) will pass. Start the hole with a center drill. Finish to diameter with a twist drill. Check to be sure the bolt passes through freely. The next job is to use an end mill to form the tongue across the bottom of the part. Mark out the location of the tongue as shown in the drawing. Clamp the block upside down on the milling table in a position similar to what is shown in Photo 4. You will notice that in Photo 4, I had already milled away the metal to form the tongue. You should be able to mill to the full depth of .03″ at once. Cut carefully as you approach the edges of the tongue, because you will want the tongue to be a close fit centrally in the slot on the lathe carriage.

If you are working on a multi-functional machine tool, return it now to its lathe configuration. Set up the bolt and incomplete mounting on the lathe cross slide in working position after marking the approximate position of the .250″ diameter horizontal hole. Put a center drill in the lathe chuck to start the hole, and finish it with a twist drill. The purpose behind drilling the mounting in place on the lathe is to guarantee that the hole through the mounting will coincide exactly with the axis of the lathe.

When the hole is drilled through, you are ready to set up vertically once again. Check Photo 4 where I was using a slitting blade to cut the horizontal slot. The exact width of the slot is not critical, as long as it is more than .050″ to clear the teeth of the saber saw blade. This is the final operation on this part. The slot will allow the mounting to clamp down firmly on the tool holder (Part 3) when the bolt is tightened.

The tool holder (Part 3) and the head (Part 4) must be machined as a unit. Begin by cutting a length of .250" diameter steel rod for the tool holder. Drill rod is excellent for this part, but other grades of steel are acceptable. Use a lathe setup to chuck the part in the three-jaw chuck. Face off each end to bring the rod to length. All other machining on this part will have to be done in place in the head.

Cut a length of .38" square stock for the head (Part 4). I used a piece of keystock, which was very convenient. Chuck the part in the four-jaw chuck to face off both ends to bring it to length. Now you are ready to drill the horizontal .250" diameter hole through which the toolholder will pass. Notice that this hole is *not* centered in the side-to-side direction. Mark out the hole location carefully, because its position will determine how accurately the saber saw blade fits into the slot and how accurately the hole in the blade will line up with the .125" diameter hole in the head. Start the hole with a center drill. Drill it through with a .250" twist drill.

At this point, try the fit of the tool holder into the hole in the head. Mine was a light press fit, which was perfect. Fit the parts together, mark out the location of the .125" diameter hole. Keep the two parts together as you center drill and drill the hole. If you try to drill them separately, you are certain to come to grief because the holes intersect and cross one another. By drilling through both parts at once, the drill cuts as though it were going through one solid piece of metal with no deflection or skidding from the curved surfaces. After drilling the hole, cut a .31" length of .125" diameter soft steel rod and put it into the hole to insure that the toolholder cannot rotate during subsequent machining operations.

Refer now to Photo 5 which shows the vertical setup I used to cut the slots in the head and toolholder. Be very careful in making your setup to clamp the head/toolholder subassembly in a position exactly parallel to the motion of the carriage along the ways. This is important, because you want the slot to be cut to a uniform depth. It is a good idea to use an indicator to check this setup for the parallel condition. It is also a good idea to check with the indicator to be sure the parts are truly horizontal to prevent the slot from wandering off center. Notice in Photo 5 that I had one clamp holding the head down and a second clamp behind the toolholder to back it up

5

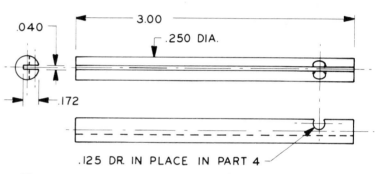

.125 DR. IN PLACE IN PART 4

(3) TOOL HOLDER : STEEL – 1 REQ.

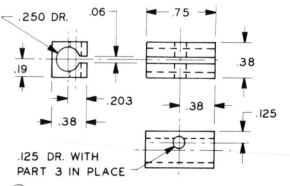

.125 DR. WITH
PART 3 IN PLACE

(4) HEAD : STEEL – 1 REQ.

against the pressure of the cut. As in the mounting, the width of the slot in the head is not critical, as long as it is greater than .050" to clear the teeth of the blade. I used a slitting blade of .053" width to cut through the head until the slot just reached the surface of the toolholder. At that point, I changed to the thinner slitting blade shown in Photo 5 to finish the slot in the toolholder. The saber saw blades measure .039" in thickness behind the

The Shop Wisdom of Rudy Kouhoupt   39

teeth. I cut the slot in the toolholder to a width of .040" so that the saber saw blade just fits into it. With the slots machined, you can remove the parts from the milling table and push the remains of the .125" diameter soft steel pin out of the hole.

The last part of the internal keyway cutter is the pin (Part 5) which is a plain lathe job. Chuck a piece of steel rod in the three-jaw chuck. Face off the end. Turn down the .125" diameter part to an easy fit in the hole of the head/toolholder. Part off to length. You can now insert a saber saw blade in a position where the larger hole in the blade coincides with the .125" diameter hole through the head. Put in the pin to secure the blade.

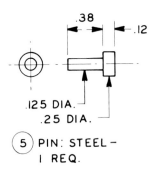

5) PIN: STEEL — 1 REQ.

6

Now your keyway cutter is ready for work. Assuming that you have machined a part, such as a pulley, and have the central hole drilled and reamed, set up the keyway cutter on the lathe cross slide as I had done in Photos 3 and 6. Use the longitudinal feed to advance the tool into the hole, as in Photo 3. Now use the cross-feed to pull the tool back toward you until the teeth of the saber saw blade just touch the surface of the hole. By retracting with the longitudinal feed, the saw teeth begin to cut away a little metal. Repeat the process, using the cross-feed to increase the depth of cut by about .002" to .003" on each pass. Continue until the desired depth of cut has been reached, as in Photos 6 and 1.

The internal keyway represents only one part of the job in fitting a key, of course. The other part, cutting the external keyseat in the shaft is simpler and requires less tooling. Refer to Photo 8 which shows the way I had set up the crankshaft of an engine to cut the keyseat. In this case, the cutter doing the work is a small Woodruff type of cutter that is sold by Dremel for use in their hand tools. The V-blocks supporting the crankshaft were home built to the dimensions shown in the accompanying drawing.

7

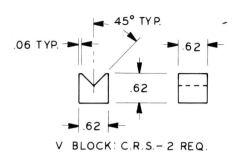

45° TYP.

.06 TYP.

.62

.62

.62

V BLOCK: C.R.S. − 2 REQ.

8

Notice in Photo 7 that I was cutting the pair of V-blocks in one piece of metal to insure that they were identical with regard to the shape of the V and its position in the blocks. Begin by cutting a length of stock long enough to contain both V-blocks. Fly cut or face cut all sides to produce a block that has flat sides all at right angles to one another. Clamp the block at a 45° angle as I had done in Photo 7. Position your milling cutter as shown so that its end cuts one side of the V and its side cuts the other side of the V. You will thus be sure that the surfaces of the V intersect at a 90° angle. When you have milled the V to full depth, cut the block in half, and face off the cut side of each half.

Returning to Photo 8 which shows the V-blocks in use, note that it is a good idea to use the indicator to get the crankshaft positioned parallel to the motion of the cross slide to insure uniform depth of cut in forming the keyseat. The width of the keyseat may be increased by raising and lowering the cutter on subsequent passes to cut away more metal, if needed. Since the V-blocks were machined simultaneously, there will be no problem with the horizontal alignment of any shaft of uniform diameter mounted in them.

A matched pair of V-blocks is very handy in the shop for many machining operations. In addition to positioning shafts for keyseat cutting, they are useful for accurate cross drilling setups, end milling setscrew flats, and other machining operations in which the round shape of a shaft makes it difficult to position accurately and hold securely.

BILL OF MATERIALS

No.	Part	Material	Dimensions
1	Bolt	Steel	.50 × .50 × 2.00″
2	Mounting	Aluminum	1.00 × 1.00 × 1.00″
3	Tool holder	Steel	.25 dia. × 3.00″
4	Head	Steel	.38 × .38 × .75″
5	Pin	Steel	.25 dia. × .50″
	V-blocks	CRS	.62 × .62 × 1.25″
	Saber saw blade	Craftsman No. 28702 or equivalent	

Building A Rotary Table

Frequently, milling and drilling operations call for the ability to move the workpiece at precisely controlled angles to locate or position holes, grooves, slots, or other features. Such cuts are conveniently made on a vertical mill or multi-functional machine tool which can be set up vertically. They do require, however, that you have a rotary table on which you can clamp the work securely and accurately. The table must be calibrated in order that the table and workpiece can be rotated to known angular positions for the cuts to be made.

The home-built rotary table that I use for such jobs is shown in Photo 1, where it is mounted on the cross slide of my Perris lathe. You will notice from the photograph that this is the machine setup I recently described in a short series showing how I mounted the Unimat DB200 column and head in conjunction with the Perris lathe bed for use as a vertical milling machine.

Refer to the accompanying bill of materials for a complete listing of the types and sizes of metal I used in building the original rotary table. The part numbers correspond with those shown on the isometric assembly drawing which will help you to visualize the relationship between the parts and how they fit together. Note I have made use of commercially available, nominal 4″ protractors which I modified to make the scale. The scale, assembled from two 180° protractors, is calibrated in increments of 1° of angle which takes care of just about anything that comes along. I have never had a need to do it, but I feel certain that eye approximations of ½° settings would prove sufficiently accurate for most jobs encountered in the home shop.

Before describing the construction and use of the rotary table, a word may be in order concerning its size. The 3.50″ diameter of the table shown in this series is in keeping with the size of the machine on which it is used and the projects that I make on it. I have absolutely no doubt, however, that any prospective builder applying a factor of 1.5X or 2X to all the parts detailed in the accompanying drawings would be able to build a similar rotary table of 5.25″ or 7.00″ diameter. Protractors are available in nominal 6″ and 8″

1

sizes at most stores handling drafting or engineering supplies. Scaling the job up in size and building a larger unit would be straight-forward. The availability of 360° protractors in 6″ and 8″ sizes would simplify the fitting of the scale. I was unable to locate a 360° protractor in 4″ size; this fact explains my using a pair of 180° protractors to make the scale.

The table (Part 1) is obviously the heart of the rotary table assembly. Work carefully on it, because the accuracy of the entire tool depends upon how accurately you make this one part. I made the table from a slice of 3.50″ diameter aluminum rod, as I have indicated in the bill of materials. There is no reason it could not be made from a piece of .62″ thick aluminum plate, if you prefer.

Select one side of the disc to be the top surface of the table. Using the center head of your combination square, locate the center, and make a light punch mark. Set your dividers to the appropriate distances to mark out the locations of the eight holes which are tapped size 10-32. Make a light punch mark at the center of each hole. Start each hole with a center drill. The four holes on .88″ radius may be drilled all the way through. You will notice in Photo 2 that I had drilled and tapped these holes all the way through in order to be able to mount the part on the lathe faceplate for machining. If you have a chuck large enough to handle the part by its outer edge, you may wish to drill and tap all eight holes to a .38″ depth, as I have indicated to do with the holes on the 1.38″ radius. These eight holes are for clamping workpieces or fixtures to the table in use. By restricting their depth to .38″, you will assure that chips cannot get in between the bottom surface of the table and the top surface

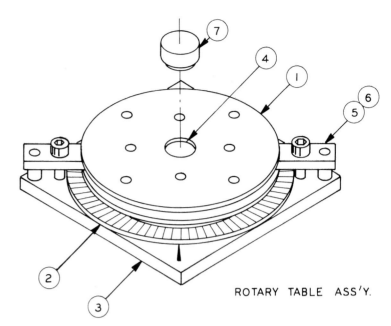

ROTARY TABLE ASS'Y.

of the base (Part 3). In no event should the holes on 1.38″ radius be drilled all the way through, because to do so would cause them to break into the step which supports the protractors on the underside of the table.

After drilling and tapping the eight size 10-32 holes, use a center drill to cut into your center mark on the top surface. Drill the central hole out to a diameter of .50″. Now you are ready to attach the part of the faceplate by means of bolts passing through the faceplate into the tapped holes on the .88″ radius. Mount the part on the faceplate with the *top* surface turned

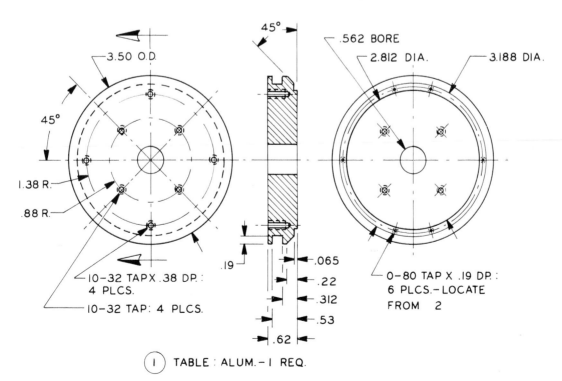

45°
3.50 O.D.
45°
1.38 R.
.88 R.
10-32 TAP X .38 DP.: 4 PLCS.
10-32 TAP: 4 PLCS.

45°
.19
.065
.22
.312
.53
.62

.562 BORE
2.812 DIA.
3.188 DIA.
0-80 TAP X .19 DP.: 6 PLCS.- LOCATE FROM 2

(1) TABLE : ALUM. – 1 REQ.

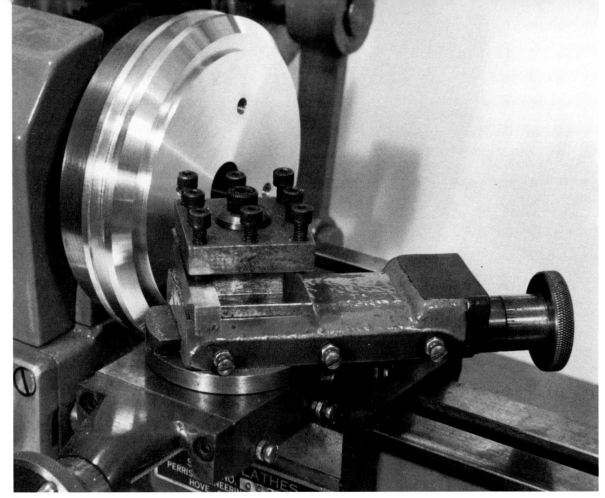

2

outward for the first lathe cut. Get the part running true on the faceplate, using the central hole as the reference surface. Take a facing cut to get the top surface true. De-burr the edges of the eight tapped holes to be sure no inaccuracies are incurred by chips getting under the part when you reverse it on the faceplate.

Reverse the part on the faceplate so that you can carry out the rest of the machining operations from the underside of the part. Be certain that the workpiece is hard up against the faceplate; this will insure that the top and bottom surfaces of the table will be parallel to the accuracy of your lathe. Once again, center the part by reference to the central drilled hole. Now you can take a light facing cut across the bottom surface to true it up. Remove as little metal as possible. When the bottom surface is machined flat, put on a short boring bar to bore the central hole out to finished size. The central hole and the bottom surface of the table are its aligning surfaces.

Turn down the periphery of the table to remove any roughness and to bring it to the desired diameter. Use a tool shaped like a parting tool to machine the groove in the edge. The purpose of the groove is to accept the ends of the clamps (Part 5), as you will notice in

Photo 1 and the isometric assembly drawing. The removal of the metal to form the groove is a relatively heavy cut. Therefore, it is a good idea to run the lathe in back gear or at its lowest belt speed while cutting the groove.

Use a tool shaped like a knife tool to cut the 2.812″ diameter step which will fit inside the protractors (Part 2). My protractors measured .055″ thick. By cutting the step to a depth of .065″, as indicated on the drawing, I allowed a clearance of .010″ between the bottom surface of the protractors and the base. Check your protractors for thickness, and adjust the depth of the step to allow this clearance if your protractors happen to be of a different thickness.

Turn your compound rest to the 45° position, as I had done in Photo 2, to machine the sloped undercut which will make it easier to read the markings on the protractor. Deburr the edges of the four bolt holes, and remove the table from the faceplate.

The commercially made protractors I used on the Protractor Modification (Part 2) were nominally 4″ Helix model No. HO4. They actually had a radius of 1.97″ that I included on the drawing as a reference dimension. Refer to Photo 3 which shows the underside of my table with the two protractors I modified to fit it. In the photo, you will notice you are seeing the underside of the protractor that was attached to the table and the upper side of the one that was not mounted. The plastic used in the protractors is clear but slightly tinted. I have no doubt that other makes of 4" protractors would work out just as well as the Helix brand. Anyone using a different make would be prudent to check, however, to be sure it is not oversize, which could lead to an interference with the bolts that pass through the Clamps (Part 5). Previously, I pointed out the importance of checking the thickness in order to machine the step in the underside of the table to the corresponding depth.

3

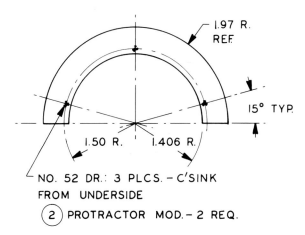

① 1.97 R. REF

15° TYP.

1.50 R.   1.406 R.

NO. 52 DR.: 3 PLCS. – C'SINK FROM UNDERSIDE

② PROTRACTOR MOD. – 2 REQ.

Use a very small center drill running at high speed to cut a very shallow dimple in the back of the protractors where the centering marks intersect. The dimple will be used with your dividers to mark out the locations of the three No. 52 screw holes on 1.50" radius. I marked the curved center line with the dividers and located the angular positions by reference to the angular markings on the protractors. Use the small center drill running at high speed to mark the location of each screw hole. Put in the No. 52 drill to finish each hole to size. Then, countersink each hole from the back of the protractor to accept the head of a size 0-80 flathead screw.

By doing all of the marking out and drilling on the protractors first, you have minimized chances of splitting them with the drilling and countersinking cuts. While I don't know the composition of the plastic in the Helix brand protractors, I found it to cut cleanly and freely. The protractors, as supplied, are semicircular in form with solid centers, which necessitates cutting away a lot of plastic to form the 1.406" inner radius. I did all of the cutting away and

fitting to the table by hand. To avoid breaking or marring the plastic, I supported the protractors in a bench vise with a thick cardboard sheet on either side. During the cutting work, I kept moving them around in order to keep the cut very close to the vise jaws for maximum support.

Begin the cutting away of the plastic by gripping each protractor in turn in the vise jaws with the horizontal center line parallel to the top of the vise jaws. Use a fine flat file to file away the plastic until you reach the horizontal center line that runs through the 0°, center, and 180° marks. I found that a second cut file had less tendency to clog on this cut and did the neatest job. Use a fine toothed saw blade in a frame, like a coping saw or jeweler's saw, to remove the bulk of the plastic inside the curve. In doing this type of cut on thin material, I always put the blade in the frame in reversed position so that it cuts on the draw stroke rather than the push stroke. This little trick tends to overcome the tendency for the blade to chatter or skip around. After sawing away the bulk of the plastic, file to the mark using a file of half-round section. Fit the protractor sections to the 2.812" diameter shoulder on the underside of the table so their inner curves fit tightly against the shoulder when the 0° and 180° marks at the ends of the protractors are exactly in line with each other. Carefully clamp the modified protractors in place on the underside of the table. Spot through the screw holes to locate the hole positions on the table. Use a .047" diameter drill to drill the holes to depth, and then tap

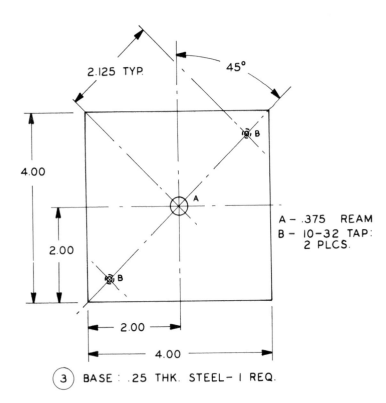

2.125 TYP.

45°

4.00

2.00

2.00

4.00

A — .375 REAM
B — 10-32 TAP:
2 PLCS.

(3) BASE : .25 THK. STEEL— 1 REQ.

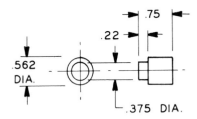

.75

.22

.562
DIA.

.375 DIA.

(4) PIVOT: STEEL—1 REQ.

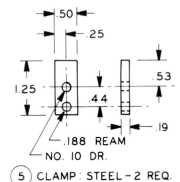

.50

.25

1.25

.44

.53

.19

.188 REAM
NO. 10 DR.

(5) CLAMP: STEEL — 2 REQ.

them with the 0-80 thread. Your table will now be finished as mine was in Photo 3, and it will be ready for mounting.

The Base (Part 3) is a simple 4.00" square cut from a piece of .25" thick steel plate. Saw the part to outline, and deburr the edges with a fine file. Rub the top and bottom surfaces flat on a piece of wet or dry paper spread flat on a plate glass surface. It is very nice for these surfaces to be exactly flat and parallel to each other, but it is not quite so important as on the table. When you are setting the rotary table up on your milling machine, you can use bits of shim between the base and the milling table to compensate for lack of parallelism in the base, if that proves to be necessary. There is no way to compensate for lack of parallelism in the table, because it rotates on the top surface of the base.

It is possible to finish the saw cut edges of the base by either filing or milling. I did them on the vertical milling setup to be sure they are really straight and at right angles to one another. It is much more accurate to position the rotary table for use when the base has sides that are straight and square.

Use your combination square and dividers to mark out the lcoation of the three holes in the base. Drill and ream the central hole for the Pivot (Part 4). Drill and tap the B holes for the socket head cap screws that will pass through the clamps (Part 5).

It is necessary to provide some means of attaching the base to your milling machine in order to use the rotary table. If you have a milling machine with a large flat table, you will probably be able to clamp the base flat in position on the surface of your milling machine table with toe clamps. If you are using a machine like my Perris lathe or one of the small multi-functional machine tools, you will probably have to devise some way of mounting the base on your cross slide. Refer now to Photo 4 which shows the underside of my rotary table. Notice that I have attached a round dovetail shaped piece which fits into the spot on the cross slide normally occupied by the compound rest of the lathe. Photo 5 shows the underside of the rotary table next to the cross slide for comparison purposes. Notice that I pass a screw through the cross slide to secure the base at the far end of the cross slide, as well. Since there are so many makes and models of machine tools around and in use these days, I have no way to provide exact mounting details that would prove universally applicable in type or dimension. Therefore, I am forced to let each reader who builds the rotary table devise a means of securing the base on each specific machine.

Chuck a short piece of .62" diameter steel rod in the three-jaw chuck to make the pivot (Part 4). Face off the end. Turn down a .75" length to a diameter of .562", checking its fit in the central hole of the table (Part 1). While it is important that the table rotate freely on the pivot, it is equally important that the table *not* be free to shift laterally. In other words, a close running fit is the proper state of affairs for the table and the pivot.

When you are satisfied with the fit that you have between the pivot and the table, turn down the .375" diameter part of the pivot to fit into the central hole of the base (Part 3). Since the hole in the center of the base was reamed, it is possible to make the end of the pivot a press fit into the hole. In doing this, I allowed an interference of slightly under .0005" between the parts. If you prefer to use an anaerobic adhesive, allow a little clearance in the fit rather than interference. Saw the part off from the rod. Reverse it in the three-jaw chuck, and face it off to length.

You can now mount the pivot in the base. Having an interference fit, I pressed it into place using the jaws of the bench vise. It could be done using an arbor press, of course.

The clamps (Part 5) are simple rectangles of .19" thick steel. Mark their outline and hole positions on a piece of suitable stock. Punch and center drill the spots where the holes are to be located. Drill and ream the holes before cutting the parts out to facilitate holding them against the stress of the drilling and reaming operations. Cut the pieces out. File them to dimension.

Machine the posts (Part 6) in the three-jaw chuck in the same way as you did the pivot. I turned the .188" diameter part of each post to be an interference fit in the reamed hole of the clamp. You will notice in Photos 1, 6, 7, and 8 that I made the .188" diameter parts a little longer than the thickness of the clamps. I used a fine file to "crown" the tip of each post where it stands above the top surface of the clamp. It looks neat that way. Actually, I put a slight "crown" shape on the end that contacts the base, also. In this case, the slightly rounded off shape makes an excellent aligning shape when tightening the clamps to lock the table in position.

4

5

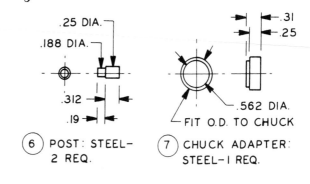

⑥ POST: STEEL— 2 REQ.

⑦ CHUCK ADAPTER: STEEL—1 REQ.

At this point, your rotary table is complete. It can be fully assembled, as mine was in Photo 6. The index mark in the lower corner of the base is a fine wedge-shaped piece cut from a black vinyl tape. You could make a little metal pointer, if you prefer. The vinyl tape pointer

6

was fitted to try it out and has been so durable that I never bothered to change it.

Photo 7 shows the rotary table set up on my machine with a workpiece clamped directly to the top surface of the table. In this case, the workpiece was a small casting for an instrument flange. The operation in progress was to mill slots in the surface at an accurate angle so they would align with positioning keys in the mating part. As an example of how this work was set up, I began by positioning the central hole in the casting accurately over the center of the table and clamping it in place. Then, measuring from a flat reference edge of the casting, I obtained an angular reading from the scale of the rotary table. With the angular reading as a base reference, it was a simple matter to rotate the table to the correct angular position to end mill each slot in turn. The milling cuts were made by using the longitudinal and cross travel as the X and Y motions, respectively. Tightening the 10-32 screws in the clamps (Part 5) secured the rotary table at the desired angular positions.

It frequently happens, however, that work cannot be conveniently clamped flat on the surface of the table. To get around this problem, I made the chuck adapter (Part 7) which is shown in Photo 6. Note that the chuck adapter has a small diameter end that is a close fit into the central hole of the table. The large diameter end is a close fit into the back of my three-jaw chuck when the backplate is removed. The screws that normally pass through the chuck to secure the backplate are used to attach the chuck to the rotary table

7

TABLE OF ANGLES

No. of equal divisions	Angular separation	No. of equal divisions	Angular separation
2	180°	24	15°
3	120°	30	12°
4	90°	36	10°
5	72°	40	9°
6	60°	45	8°
8	45°	60	6°
9	40°	72	5°
10	36°	90	4°
12	30°	120	3°
15	24°	180	2°
18	20°	360	1°
20	18°		

with the chuck adapter holding the chuck exactly central to the table.

The chuck adapter is a simple lathe job that you can do in the same way that you made the pivot and the posts. Work very carefully, as you did on the pivot to be sure the chuck adapter is a close, aligning fit in both the table and the back of your chuck. When you finish the lathe work on the chuck adapter, put it in place on the table, and mount the chuck on it.

Clamp the chuck securely in place with parallel jaw clamps after taking the table off the base. Spot through the bolt holes in the chuck body. Drill the spots and tap the appropriate thread in the holes. The holes for the chuck bolts are the ones close to the central hole in the table in Photo 6. The chuck adapter is always used and left in place when the chuck is mounted on the table.

Photo 8 shows a job I was doing with the three-jaw chuck and chuck adapter on the rotary table. In this case, I was center drilling a small wheel to position eight evenly spaced holes in the web of the wheel. Since eight equal spaces were required, I rotated the table exactly 45° between each drilling operation. In the accompanying table, there is a listing of the number of equal radial divisions and their corresponding angular separations. As an example of its use: If your work requires that you produce fifteen equal divisions, a check of the table shows that you can obtain the proper spacings by advancing the rotary table 24° for each operation.

There is almost no limit to the ways the rotary table can be used or to the ways the work can be mounted on the table to obtain angular accuracy in positioning holes, milling slots, milling polygonal shapes, sectoring round shapes and objects, or in a variety of other applications.

8

BILL OF MATERIALS

No.	Part	Material	Quantity	Dimensions
1	Table	Aluminum	1	3.50 dia. × .62″
2	Protractor	Plastic	2	Nominal 4″ (Helix Model HO4 or equivalent)
3	Base	Steel	1	.25 × 4.00 × 4.00″
4	Pivot	Steel	1	.62 dia. × .75″
5	Clamp	Steel	2	.19 × .50 × 1.25″
6	Post	Steel	2	.25 dia. × .50″
7	Chuck adapter	Steel	1	1.00 dia. × .31″
	Socket head cap screws		2	10-32 × .75″
	Flathead screws		6	0-80 × .125″

Fly Cutter and Angle Plate

The versatility of any machine tool is greatly enhanced by having a few simple accessories that either hold the workpieces or cut them. Many such accessories are really quite simple things to make. The work involved in making them is pleasurable in itself, since it provides absorbing experience in running the machine tools and produces something useful without making dents in the family budget.

It is frequently true that while using a fly cutter in a milling setup for machining flat surfaces on a piece of work, it is convenient to mount the work on an angle plate bolted to the milling table. Because the tools are so closely related, it seems reasonable that their construction be presented together in this article. The tools are pictured together in Photo 1 along with the cutter bit which fits the fly cutter. Make the fly cutter first; you will be able to put it right to work to do much of the machining on the angle plate.

THE FLY CUTTER

Begin by chucking a short length of 1.00" diameter steel rod in your lathe to make the body of the fly cutter. Take a facing cut across the end of the rod to form a flat surface. Use a center drill held in the tailstock drill chuck to locate and open the center of the piece. Drill it out with a suitable size twist drill to a depth that permits cutting a thread to match the nose of the spindle on your machine. Start the tap straight in by gripping it in the tailstock drill chuck. Pull the work around slowly by hand as you feed the tailstock forward with the other hand. When the tap is well started,

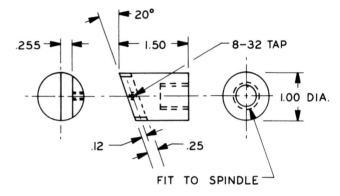

FLY CUTTER: STEEL - I REQ.

transfer from the tailstock chuck to a standard tap holder so that you can finish the thread to its full depth by hand.

Without removing the work from the chuck, you can try screwing it onto the spindle nose to see if it fits nicely. Notice that there is a short distance on the spindle that has no thread. This is an aligning surface to bring chucks, faceplates, and other attachments in straight against the thrust surface of the spindle. You will have to cut away a short length of the thread to clear this part of the spindle nose. This job is probably most accurately done by using a small boring bar mounted in the lathe tool post. Cut away just enough metal for the part to have a close fit when you screw it on the spindle nose.

Now you can remove the part from the lathe chuck to work on the opposite end. Hacksaw the end off to form the 20° angle. Check with your protractor to get the angle about right; it is not a critical angle. The angled end may be finished by filing or milling, as you prefer. Note in Photo 2 that the body of the fly cutter

1

2

3

was mounted on a vertical slide for end milling in the lathe. The T slot in the surface of the vertical slide took the place of a V block and held the work securely. After using the vertical slide in conjunction with the lathe cross-feed and longitudinal feed to mill the flat surface, the work was positioned at the proper height to mill in the groove that holds the tool bit.

Notice that one side of the slot is on the center line of the fly cutter. This places the cutting surface of the tool bit on center for the correct cutting position. Drill and tap the 8-32 hole for the setscrew which will secure the tool bit.

The form of tool bit shown in the detail drawing is a very useful shape for fly cutting flat surfaces. It may be ground from a standard ¼" lathe tool blank, or you may prefer to use one of the pre-ground carbide tipped lathe tools with a right-hand cut. My preference is for a cutter bit ground from a molybdenum/

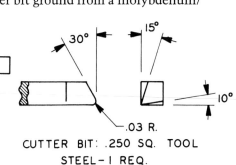

CUTTER BIT: .250 SQ. TOOL
STEEL – 1 REQ.

ANGLE PLATE: ALUM. – 1 REQ.

cobalt blank. Fly cutting usually involves a discontinuous type of cutting action that may chip or crack a carbide tool which is harder and more brittle.

Looking ahead a little, you can see the finished fly cutter at work on my Unimat DB 200 head in Photo 4. This picture clearly shows the position of the tool bit in fly cutter as it is presented to the workpiece.

4

removed at the intersection point. Advance the cut just a few thousandths of an inch at a pass. Referring to Photo 4, it will be apparent that the cut is advanced by lowering the spindle by the desired amout. Use the longitudinal feed to pass the work under the fly cutter on each advance of the spindle. When the tool bit is taking a full cut all the way across the flat surface, and the surface is smooth, you are ready to turn the piece for taking a similar cut across the other flat side.

Now you will have to work carefully, because the angular accuracy of the angle plate is determined by how accurately you fly cut the second side. If you are using a block for clamping as shown in Photo 3, you will probably find that the block is not quite so true as you would like. The solution is to slip a shim or two in place when you clamp the angle to it for fly cutting the second flat side. Check frequently with your square as you begin to fly cut the second side. Since you will be removing only a couple of thousandths on each pass, it will be easy to spot inaccuracies and use shims between the block and the angle to shift the angle to remove them. Time spent on this part of the operation will be well repaid when you put the angle plate to work.

With the surfaces fly cut, and the edges true, you can drill and tap the stud mounting holes in one side. Then you can drill and end mill the slots in the other side, as I was doing in Photo 3. Be sure to remove all burrs from the holes and slots, as burrs may upset all the accuracy of your best efforts.

Photo 4 shows a typical setup in which both the fly cutter and the angle plate are in use. Notice that the angle plate is clamped to the milling table by means of bolts through the slots, while the workpiece is clamped by a stud passing through the work into one of the tapped holes. In this case, I was using the fly cutter to form the flat sides on a cylinder casting for a small steam engine.

THE ANGLE PLATE

Cut a length of heavy aluminum angle stock for making the angle plate. The edges of this sort of angle stock are usually radiused. Saw the radiused edges away to leave the piece just a bit oversize. Now you can clamp the piece of angle flat on the milling table and use the fly cutter to smooth off the saw cut edge. When you get it true, reverse the angle to finish the opposite edge.

Refer now to Photo 3, and notice that I had clamped a solid block of metal to the milling table and was using it as a clamping block to finish the machining operations. The vertical threaded rods held the block in place on the table, while the parallel jaw clamps were used to clamp the unfinished angle plate to it. It is probably best to clamp the angle piece in position to fly cut each of the L-shaped edges first. Check with your square to position the angle squarely to the milling table for the cut, and finish off each edge.

At this point, you are ready to clamp the angle in the position shown in Photo 3 for fly cutting a flat surface. All of the rough angle stock available to me for checking had the flat surfaces intersecting at an angle of approximately 89°, which means that most metal had to be

BILL OF MATERIALS

Part	Material	Qty.	Dimensions
Fly cutter	Steel	1	1.00" dia. × 1.50"
Cutter bit	Tool steel	1	.25 × .25 × 2.00"
Setscrew	Steel	1	8-32 × .19"
Angle Plate	Aluminum	1	Nominal 3 × 3 × .38" thick × 2.50" long

A Micrometer Faceplate Attachment

Have you ever had a lathe job come along that required accurate spacing of holes in a workpiece after facing off the surface? Or, how about the case of placing some feature like a bored recess that must be off center by a precise amount? Perhaps the work requires that you turn a projecting part that is accurately centered with respect to a previous operation. If you are confronted with these or similar jobs calling for only one part, you can usually set up within the desired limits of accuracy by mounting the work on a faceplate or in a four-jaw chuck and using some sort of indicator arrangement to get the work running true. However, a job that calls for several parts to be produced identically brings up another problem. It is one thing to indicate in a single workpiece, but a job calling for several duplicate parts can become quite a chore

in which most of your time will be spent in measuring and indicating.

Facing the task of producing a matched set of four eccentrics for a steam engine project was the motivating force that led to the faceplate attachment shown in Photo 1. The immediate problem was to bore the hole for the crankshaft .141" off center in each eccentric, keeping them all within a close tolerance limit regarding their eccentricity. The idea behind the faceplate attachment being detailed here is a workholder that repeatedly holds the workpieces in a known position which can be controlled or located with micrometer accuracy by means of a calibrated screw arrangement.

You may be wondering why this tool is made as a faceplate attachment rather than a separate faceplate in its own right. The reason

1

2

is that reaming or boring centrally in workpieces usually requires that the end of the tool project through the work where it might contact and damage the nose of the lathe if it were screwed directly in place on the spindle. As a faceplate attachment, the additional thickness keeps the workpiece far out from the faceplate and spindle nose with plenty of clearance for the tool to pass through the work into the central bored hole in the attachment.

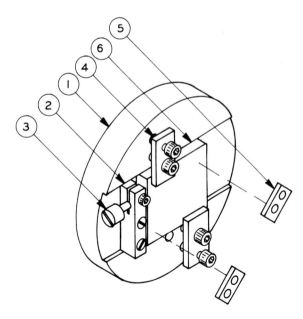

MICROMETER FACEPLATE ASS'Y.

While the faceplate attachment detailed in this article was intended for use on a rather small Perris lathe and is dimensioned accordingly, there is no reason that a scaled up version could not be built and used on a larger lathe. A larger version can be expected to handle workpieces of larger size with equal precision and efficiency. If you can anticipate that such an attachment will improve the ease of use and the efficiency of your lathe operations, take a look at the parts laid out in Photo 2, check over the bill of materials, and we will get on with describing how to build the attachment and set it up for use in a typical job.

The faceplate body (Part 1) is turned from a slice of aluminum rod. Using the center finder on your combination square, scribe two intersecting center lines across a flat face of the stock to locate the center of the slice. Put a mark on the intersection of the lines with a sharp center punch. With one leg of the divider in the center mark, locate the position of the holes marked "A" on the detail drawing. Punch these locations with a sharp punch, also. Center drill, drill, and tap the "A" holes in accordance with the hole schedule on the drawing.

Now you can attach the slice of aluminum to one of your lathe faceplates by passing ¼-20 bolts through the faceplate from the back and screwing them into the tapped holes. Check to

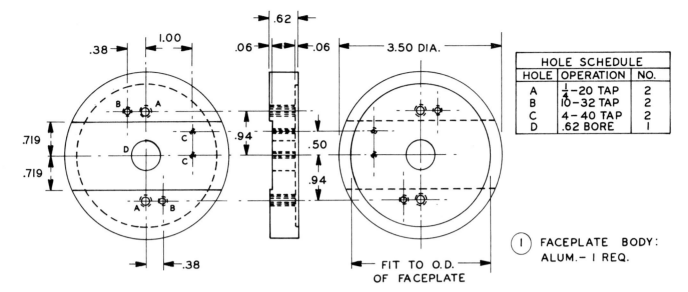

HOLE SCHEDULE		
HOLE	OPERATION	NO.
A	$\frac{1}{4}$–20 TAP	2
B	10–32 TAP	2
C	4–40 TAP	2
D	.62 BORE	1

FACEPLATE BODY:
ALUM.– 1 REQ.

be sure that the tips of the bolts are below the surface of the aluminum by .12″ or so. You may prefer to do this operation with the part mounted in a lathe chuck if you have one with ample jaw capacity. After putting the workpiece on the lathe, use a center finder to get the center punch mark in the aluminum running on the axis of the lathe. When it is running true and you have tightened the bolts, put on a round nose tool to take a facing cut across the work. Cut away as much metal as necessary to leave the face flat and smooth.

Using a center drill in the tailstock drill chuck, start the "D" hole in the center of the work. Open the hole with a .500″ diameter twist drill, cutting through about a half the thickness of the aluminum piece. Use a short boring bar to bore the hole out to its finished diameter. Be careful not to run the tool in too deep; you will actually finish the hole from the other side.

Put a left cutting knife tool in the tool post to machine the recess that will fit over the edge of the faceplate. Cut the recess to a depth of .06″ and to a diameter that will be a very close fit to the outside diameter of one of your faceplates. The closer the recess is fitted to the faceplate diameter, the more accurately you will be able to set it up later on.

If you are satisfied that you have a close fit of the recess to the faceplate you intend to use, seat the work in position on the faceplate, and bolt it there with the 1/4-20 bolts. Use the round nose tool to face off the second side. Work on the "D" hole again to finish it following the same procedure you used in starting it in the first side.

Now you are ready to transfer the part to a

milling setup to mill in the broad flat area across the face. Before removing the piece from the lathe, mark out the edges of the milled area. To do this, place your surface gage on the lathe bed, and set the tip of the scriber to the center height of the lathe plus .719″. With the work turned so that the center line through the "A" holes is vertical, scribe a line from side to side across the work by swinging the surface gage on the lathe bed. Turn the spindle 180° so the center line through the "A" holes is again vertical with the work turned over. Once again, scribe a line from side to side. This insures that the lines will be parallel to one another and straight across the part.

Remove the faceplate attachment from the faceplate. Set it up on a milling table with the scribed lines parallel to the direction of travel of the milling table. Put on a good sharp end mill to machine the broad flat area. Start the cut in the central hole. You will have to set the cross travel over between cuts to keep advancing the progress of the milling. Check to be sure it is all straight; continue milling until you have cut away the metal up to the scribed lines.

The straight edges of the milled area are good reference lines for locating the rest of the holes. Locate the "B" and "C" holes. Punch the spots with a sharp center punch. Start the holes with a center drill, drill them out, and tap the threads specified in the hole schedule. Remove all the burrs from the holes.

If you cut the adjusting bar (Part 2) from a piece of flat stock, mill all the cut edges to bring the piece to size. Mark out the locations of the four holes, and start them with a center drill. Drill and countersink the No. 33 holes for the

The Shop Wisdom of Rudy Kouhoupt 55

3

size 4-40 flathead bolts that will attach this part to the faceplate body. When you drill and tap the hole for the clamping screw that goes vertically into the part, run a No. 43 drill all the way through. Then drill the hole out halfway through the part using a No. 33 drill.

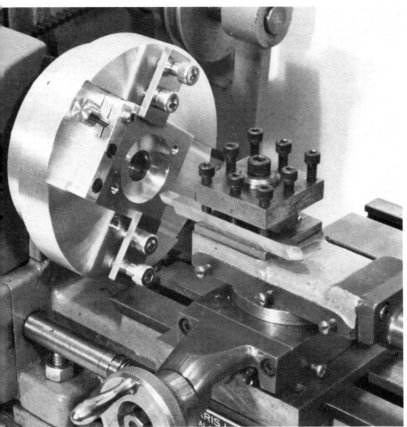

4

Finish the hole by cutting the 4-40 thread.

Now you are ready to tap the 5-40 thread crosswise in the part for the adjusting screw. You will note from the detail drawing that a thin slit runs in from the tip of the adjusting bar and passes longitudinally through the 5-40 hole. The slit must go all the way through the 5-40 hole and extend into the metal behind it to provide a clamping action on the adjusting screw used in the 5-40 hole. Cut it with a thin slitting blade of approximately .024″ thickness in a milling setup. Take care in cutting the slit so that it centers directly on the 5-40 tapped hole. Note from the drawing that the slit cuts across the 4-40 hole at right angles to it. The 4-40 hole is to be clearance size for a 4-40 socket head screw above the slit with the threads all below the slit. After you cut the slit, remove all the burrs that could interfere with the clamping action. Run the 5-40 tap through the threaded hole again to clear it of burrs from the slitting operation, also. Bolt the adjusting bar to the faceplate body in the position shown in the photos and the isometric assembly drawing.

Chuck a short length of steel rod for making the adjusting screw (Part 3). Use a knife tool to reduce the diameter to .312″ as shown. Continue to turn the part down to form the step for the 5-40 thread. With a 5-40 die held in the tailstock die holder, advance the tailstock with one hand while pulling the lathe spindle over with the other hand to cut the thread.

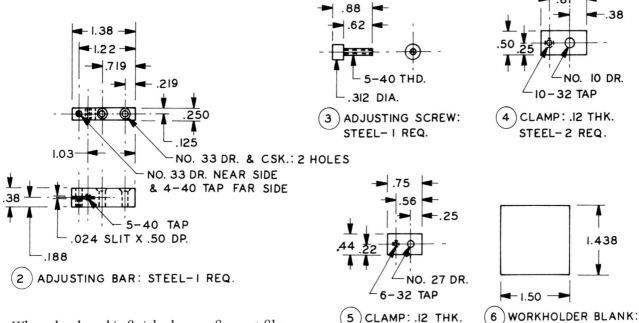

.88
.62
5-40 THD.
.312 DIA.

(3) ADJUSTING SCREW:
STEEL- 1 REQ.

1.00
.81
.38
.50 .25
NO. 10 DR.
10-32 TAP

(4) CLAMP: .12 THK.
STEEL-2 REQ.

1.38
1.22
.719
.219
.250
.125
1.03
NO. 33 DR. & CSK.: 2 HOLES
NO. 33 DR. NEAR SIDE
& 4-40 TAP FAR SIDE
.38
5-40 TAP
.024 SLIT X .50 DP.
.188

(2) ADJUSTING BAR: STEEL-1 REQ.

.75
.56
.25
.44 .22
NO. 27 DR.
6-32 TAP

(5) CLAMP: .12 THK.
STEEL- 2 REQ.

1.438
1.50

(6) WORKHOLDER BLANK:
.25 THK. ALUM.

When the thread is finished, use a fine cut file to remove burrs and to smooth up the tip of the screw leaving it with a slight radius on the tip.

Transfer the chuck from the lathe to the dividing attachment as shown in Photo 3 to mill the calibration marks on the .312″ diameter head of the screw. Since the screw has a forty pitch, it will advance .025″ on each complete turn it makes in the adjusting bar. Therefore, by milling 25 calibration marks equally spaced around the head, you will be able to gauge the advance of the screw at the rate of .001″ for each calibration mark. You will note in Photo 3 that the calibration marks were being cut with the corner of a small end mill to a depth of about .005″ into the metal of the head. The marks were milled to a length of .09″ with every fifth mark cut to the full length of the head. In use, the long marks make for easy spotting of .005″ increments and reduce the chances of making reading errors while working with the tool.

When you finish cutting the calibration marks, remove the chuck from the dividing attachment and put it back in the lathe. Now you can part the adjusting screw off. Clearances between the head of the adjusting screw and the milled face of the faceplate body are rather close when the adjusting screw is in place in the adjusting bar. Therefore, it is a good idea to use a thin saw blade to cut a narrow screwdriver slot across the head. The use of a slender screwdriver makes adjustment of the screw much easier.

The clamps (Parts 4 and 5) are very easy to make. Mark them out on a suitable piece of steel. Center punch all the hole locations. Start the holes with a center drill. Then drill and tap

5

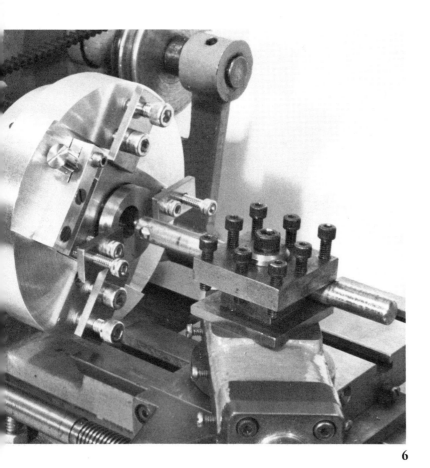

6

the drilled holes. The screws in the tapped holes of the clamps act as adjusting screws to exert pressure against the faceplate body to support the ends of the clamps.

Since it was desired to hold round eccentrics in the workholder, a hole was started in the center with a center drill, and a .500″ drill finished the hole all the way through. Next, the knife tool shown was used to machine the recess into which the eccentrics were a very close fit. Note that 6-32 holes were tapped on the diagonal of the workholder blank at a spacing from the recess which permitted the smaller clamps (Part 5) to secure the eccentric in the recess, as you can see in Photos 5 and 6. At the point shown in Photo 4, the recess in the workholder was still on center. To change its position, the screws in the larger clamps were slackened off a bit. The clamping screw in the adjusting bar was loosened so that the adjusting screw could be screwed in, thus moving the workholder off-center by the desired amount. When the adjustment of position had been made, the screws in the clamps were tightened again to secure the workholder and workpiece, and the clamping screw in the adjusting bar was tightened to hold the adjusting screw in position.

The tailstock drill chuck was used as in Photo 5 to start the crankshaft hole in the eccentric. A twist drill was used after the center drill to put the hole through the eccentric. Finally, the hole was finished to exact size with the single point boring bar shown in Photo 6. By loosening the smaller clamps, the eccentric was removed from the workholder without moving anything else. Each of the other eccentrics in the set was mounted in the workholder in turn for drilling and boring. Since the workholder was not moved between workpieces, it was assured that they would all be bored in exactly the same position.

them in accordance with the detail drawing. Saw them out, and finish them to size by either milling or hand filing.

At this point, the faceplate attachment is just about ready to go to work. You will need a workholder like the one shown in Photos 4, 5, and 6. Saw out a workholder blank (Part 6) a little oversize so that you can finish the edges by milling. The 1.50″ dimension is not critical. In fact, this dimension could be altered to suit a particular workpiece which would fit better in a workholder of a different size. The 1.438″ dimension is somewhat critical, however. You will realize that this is the dimension between the parallel edges of the milled out flat area on the faceplate body. Mill the edges of the workholder blank keeping them parallel to one another making the blank a close sliding fit in the milled out area.

Now you are ready to mount the workholder blank in the attachment as shown in Photo 4 where it was being prepared for the four eccentrics referred to last time. Set the adjusting screw in the adjusting bar back to a position where the workholder blank will be centered in the attachment. When the adjusting screw was set to the desired depth, the blank was clamped securely in place by the larger clamps (Part 4) by socket head screws in

BILL OF MATERIALS

No.	Part	Material	Quantity	Dimensions
1	Faceplate body	aluminum	1	3.50″ dia. × .62″
2	Adjusting bar	steel	1	.25 × .38 × 1.38″
3	Adjusting screw	steel	1	.312″ dia. × .88″
4	Clamp	steel	2	.125 × .50 × 1.00″
5	Clamp	steel	2	.125 × .44 × .75″
6	Workholder blank	aluminum	as needed	.25 × 1.50 × 1.50″

Time for an Overhaul

Years of continuous and hard use took their toll on my Perris lathe. Each time it was set up for a cut, a greater amount of attention was required to insure the production of accurate work. Clearly, the rotational axis of the lathe had shifted; it was no longer parallel to the ways. Furthermore, there seemed to be a disparity between the center heights of the headstock and the tailstock. Considering the state of affairs and remembering that the serial number on the builder's plate is the very early number of 0034 moved me to think along two lines: Should I replace the lathe, or should I refurbish it?

The idea of a nice, new, tight machine tool was very appealing. Several tool catalogs were obtained; prices of lathes and accessories were checked and compared. And the overhaul option became much more attractive! At least, it looked worth a try.

Photo 1 shows the appearance of the lathe when I started to refurbish it. First thoughts about the misalignment of the lathe axis had convinced me that the headstock bearings were at fault. Since these lathes don't seem to be in production any longer, there is no chance of obtaining spare parts. The possibility occurred to me that it might be necessary to rebore the headstock, or possibly even make a new one.

With some misgiving, I removed the drive gears and pulleys and used solvent to remove the lubrication residues along with the nameless black crud that had accumulated in various places. After the general cleanup and disassembly came the first opportunity to do some quantitative measurements. The spindle, without pulleys or gears, was returned to the headstock bearings. Note in Photo 2 that I was using an indicator to check out the alignment of the spindle. By placing the indicator stand on the flat upper surface of the lathe bed, I was able to determine whether or not the spindle was parallel to the ways. It was *not*! In fact, the threaded end was tipped down toward the ways by several thousandths of an inch. Next, I mounted the indicator on the lathe cross slide to check the spindle for parallelism with the longitudinal travel of the saddle. I was not surprised to find that the threaded end was pushed back by a couple of thousandths of an inch. This condition was expected, since the pressure of the tool is in that direction during most lathe work.

A certain measure of confusion arose at this point. The indicator readings confirmed that the spindle was off axis by quite a lot, but visual inspection of the split bronze sleeves in the headstock did not reveal uneven wear or anything out of the way. The headstock pedestals are split horizontally at the rear and

1

2

3

have adjustment screws for taking up wear. In order to check further into the misalignment, I opened up the adjusting screws fully.

Fortunately, I have acquired a short length of centerless-ground, hardened steel rod the same diameter as the lathe spindle, nominally .500″. The rod is very accurate, both for diameter and straightness, throughout its length. I obtained it because of its accuracy and use it as a standard for reference. Its accuracy was now a great help to me, as I put it in the headstock bearings in place of the spindle. Then I adjusted the bearings to what would be a running fit for the rod and repeated the indicator check.

Imagine my astonishment when the indicator readings showed the rod to be parallel to the ways within very close limits! The obvious conclusion was that nearly all the wear causing the misalignment was right in the spindle itself. Micrometer measurements of the spindle confirmed that there were over .005″ of wear at each of the points where the spindle was in running contact with the headstock bearings.

Having a direction in which to work made the

whole job take on a better air. The lathe was all put back together to as accurate a condition as possible. A piece of .75″ diameter rod was mounted between centers. Working very slowly, measuring progress frequently, and compensating as needed, I turned the profile of a replacement spindle. For reasons that will be discussed later, I made the replacement spindle a little longer than the original to overhang the change gears to the left of the headstock.

At this stage, the replacement spindle was essentially a solid two-step cylinder. The running portion was reduced to a diameter of .500″, but the nose end was still .75″ diameter. Once again, the procedure of taking down the headstock was repeated in order to insert the partially finished replacement spindle. Of course, the indicator readings were repeated. Happily, they showed that the new spindle was right on. Therefore, I put the pulleys and back gear components in place on the replacement spindle in the headstock and finished the machining operations on the spindle as it ran in place in the headstock.

The first job in finishing the spindle was to turn down the nose end to a diameter for the thread which is ½-20 pitch. Then I set up the change gears to cut the proper pitch and roughed the thread out using a standard lathe threading tool in the tool post. When the thread had been cut down to within a few thousandths of its finished size, I used a die held in the tailstock die holder to finish it off. By starting the thread as a lathe cut, its parallelism and concentricity to the spindle as a whole was guaranteed. Its accuracy of contour and interchangeability in faceplates, chuck backplates, and other attachments was assured by finishing it with a commercial die.

Of course, the center mark was still in the nose end from when it had been turned between centers. Working from the tailstock drill chuck, I drilled the clearance hole through the length of the spindle at a diameter of .31″. Finally, the question arose as to how to put in the center. The original Perris spindle had a very short but steep taper which matched a tapered section on the center point which also had a cylindrical portion that slid inside the spindle bore. Most metal lathes have a longer, more shallow taper, such as a Morse taper. Wishing to use a similar arrangement, but not having a reamer for a Morse taper, I used a standard taper reamer in the setup shown in Photo 3. The reamer is a hand reamer, but it

4

does have a center dimple in the handle end. By putting the lathe tailstock center into the dimple, I was able to start the reamer straight into the spindle bore and advance it to cut an accurately centered seat. While reaming the seat, I ran the lathe spindle at its lowest back-geared speed and used cutting oil generously to avoid chatter.

The turning of the center point became the first job of the lathe, using the spindle to make a separate part. With the three-jaw chuck on the nose gripping a short length of steel rod, the top slide was set to half the included angle of the reamer. The taper of the reamer I used was about 1.28″/foot which is a little over twice as steep as a Morse taper. When the taper had been turned to a good fit in the nose of the lathe, the part was removed from the chuck and put in place in the spindle nose. Then the top slide was repositioned to cut the 60° taper on the outer end of the center. By machining it in place in the spindle, its accuracy was also insured.

Turning the center with the new spindle demonstrated that the Perris was cutting well. I made a few more test cuts of various types, checked out the movements of the cross slide and longitudinal slide, and felt well satisfied with the results, since the performance of the lathe had been dramatically improved. This brought on thoughts of additional things to do to upgrade the capabilities of the machine still further.

One outgrowth of taking the measurements

from the Perris lathe during the fitting of the new spindle was knowledge that its longitudinal and cross feeds were dependably horizontal and at right angles to each other. This information is of importance for lathe work, but it has further implications with regard to milling. The bed of the Perris lathe is a nicely made iron box casting. Its vertical walls are deep and thick with ample webs and top joining to insure its rigidity. In all the work that I have ever done on it, I have never had any complaint concerning this aspect of the machine.

At this point, I must digress from the Perris lathe briefly to bring in my next line of thought. Regular readers of this column will be aware that my shop also contains a Unimat DB 200 which has been serving me faithfully even longer than the Perris. One of the features of the Unimat DB and SL models is a vertical column that can be mounted on the Unimat bed in place of the headstock. In this position, the headstock mounts on the vertical column to convert the machine into a vertical mill or drill press. There is one rather serious drawback in doing this, however: the location of the column restricts the movements of work on the slide and cross slide permitting only small amounts of travel. Any long work must be handled stepwise, which is not conducive to accuracy. Having seen the more recent Unimat 3 and other multi-functional machine tools in which the vertical column is positioned *behind* the lathe bed, the advantages of such placement for increased milling capacity became apparent. Therefore, my thoughts went to the possibility of mounting the Perris lathe bed to provide the X and Y motions with the Unimat head on its vertical column to the rear of the lathe bed. In all fairness to the Unimat, a similar arrangement could have been worked out with its lathe bed. The Perris offers a longer travel in both directions which accounts for my concentrating on it.

Refer now to Photo 4. In it, you will see the frame for mounting the Perris lathe with the Unimat column and a socket-type base for standing it on the frame. The rectangular steel frame is made from .38 × 2.00″ flat stock bolted together. Two bolts secure each corner, and the lathe bed is attached across the front by two more bolts at each end. Thus, the lathe bed becomes the front member of the frame playing a very active role in the rigidity of the frame. The four round holes in the corners of the frame serve no purpose; they just happened to be in the steel flats from some previous use.

5

There seemed to be no question that the frame that had been constructed would prove adequate in terms of strength and rigidity. My only doubts were whether or not the vertical column could be mounted accurately with respect to the lathe bed. While I felt it was possible, I was also aware that it would have to be mounted on an unmachined surface of the steel frame.

The Perris lathe got a good test when I made the rectangular block that mounts the vertical column on the frame. It can be seen in Photo 4 secured by four bolts to the rear crosspiece of the frame. Starting from a solid block of

aluminum, the side and end surfaces were faced off flat and square with the part held in the four-jaw chuck. It was bolted to a faceplate to face off the bottom and top surfaces. While it was still mounted for facing the top, the large central hole was bored to accept the stepped end of the vertical column. The hole was started with a ½″ twist drill and finished by boring with a single point boring bar mounted in the tool post. Boring in this way allowed for the closeness of fit essential for the column mounting.

On the Unimat DB, the vertical column is secured by a tapered threaded bolt that passes through a hole in the column and screws into the far side of the mounting. Therefore, it was necessary to turn the bored-out block by 90°, position it accurately on the faceplate, and make the hole for the tapered bolt. The hole was started in the usual way with a center drill and twist drill working from the tailstock drill chuck. This hole became the pilot hole for the 8 mm diameter × 1.25 mm pitch thread into which the tapered bolt screws in the near side of the aluminum block. The far side of the block was bored out to clear the large end of the tapered bolt. It was imperative for the center lines of these holes to intersect at right angles and at the correct height in order that the tapered portion of the bolt would engage the hole in the column and pull it tightly into position in the mounting block.

With the vertical column in place and the Perris lathe bed bolted to the steel frame, I was ready to follow the procedure shown in Photo 5 of using a square to determine how well the vertical column and the lathe bed lined up. Note that I was using the flat upper surface of the cross slide as the reference for squareness. This check showed that the column was leaning away from the lathe slightly. Therefore, the aluminum mounting block was loosened and a shim slipped between it and the steel frame toward the rear. A brass shim of .004″ thickness set everything right and settled the slight doubt I had experienced earlier. My next check was to turn the square by 90° from the position shown to check the squareness of the column in the X direction. Again, the comparison was made to the top surface of the cross slide. It proved to be accurate in this direction with no need for any more shims.

You will note from Photo 5 that I had disassembled the lathe bed completely at this point. This allowed me more finger room for working around the machine, and I intended to put on a fresh coat of paint, anyway. Therefore,

it was a matter of double convenience to have it all apart.

I did another small job on the Perris lathe bed while the spindle was out. Referring to Photo 5, you will note that there is a short threaded stub sticking up out of each bearing pedestal. Originally, the lathe had plain drilled holes for lubrication where the stubs stand. Being open at the top, the oil holes were always accumulating chips and other debris. I tapped them and screwed in the hollow threaded stubs to serve as oil reservoirs. You will be able to see in subsequent photographs that I screw an acorn nut on each to prevent the ingress of chips and other foreign matter between doses of oil.

With the Perris lathe bed reassembled, the vertical column in place, and the Unimat head mounted, I had reached the stage shown in Photo 6. Everything seemed to be in order, but I wanted to be certain nothing had been missed that could upset the accuracy of the milling setup. Therefore, I mounted my home-built milling table on the cross slide, as shown in Photo 7. By mounting the indicator on a round

6

7

8

lathe saddle by .0625″ for each revolution of the handle which has calibrations purported to be thousandths of an inch. Exactly how the manufacturer arrived at 62½ divisions, each of .001″, has never been clear to me! Some of the calibration marks are obliterated where the handle enters the ring; is it possible that the manufacturer did this to cover up the ½ division? At any rate, I did not think much of the system, so decided to make up a micrometer collar having 125 divisions, each of which is equal to .0005″. Each fifth mark is longer than those between. By advancing any two adjacent marks, the carriage moves .001″, and by advancing the equivalent of any two long marks, the carriage advances .005″. These are convenient units, and I always know where the carriage is without the positional break that was inherent in the missing marks.

There was one other feature of the Perris lathe that I did not find convenient. That was the cover which was supposed to fit over the train of change gears at the left side of the headstock. In most gear combinations, it did not fit in place and actually fouled the gear teeth. I made a small hood that can be seen in Photos 8, 10, 11, and 12. The hood is secured to the side plate by means of rivets. Its open sided construction permits assembly and use of any gear combination without interference. While its open construction is less safe than a fully enclosed cover, the hood is in the right spot to keep anything from entering the gears from the front. Side entry is possible only by reaching under the hood. In any event, the hood is clearly more safe than the original cover that had to be left off most of the time to avoid interefence with the operation of the gears. I do intend to fit a removable side plate in the interest of my own complete safety.

rod chucked in the Unimat head, I was able to make three very important checks. The indicator was lowered to the point where it was in light contact with the top surface of the milling table. As the table was traversed by the longitudinal feed of the lathe, I was able to determine that it was parallel to the lathe ways in the X direction. As the table was traversed by the cross slide feed, the parallelism to the cross slide ways was indicated in the Y direction. Finally, by rotating the spindle in the Unimat head, the sweeping motion of the indicator tip around the table checked out the alignment of the vertical spindle for perpendicularity to the X and Y axes.

Since the Perris lathe requires an outside power source, the whole mounting frame and lathe bed assembly had to be mounted on a board. Referring to Photo 8, you will note that I had drilled a hole through each of the short members in the steel mounting frame in order to bolt the assembly down and secure it with wing nuts. Clearance holes were cut in the board for the heads of the eight bolts that hold the frame together and keep the lathe bed in place.

The motor from which the lathe was to be driven was mounted on a separate smaller board that I fitted into wooden slides at right angles to the lathe bed. The purpose of the slides is to move the motor for releasing belt tension while changing the belt positions on the pulleys. When the motor is slipped back into running position, a small wedge locks it in place and keeps the belts at the desired tension.

The longitudinal feed screw of the Perris has an Acme thread of 16 pitch. It advances the

Photo 9 shows some accessory items that were made on the lathe for use with it. The center point for the headstock spindle has already been described. The collar and the end-threaded rod serve a purpose illustrated in Photo 10. Notice that the collar fits in place on the outer end of the lathe spindle; this fact explains why I made the spindle a little longer than the original, as referred to in Part 1 of this series. When the threaded rod is screwed into the collar, its tip engages a shallow keyway milled in the outer end of the lathe spindle. Thus, the collar is locked tightly in place on the spindle by the threaded rod which becomes a convenient handle for manual rotation of the spindle. This attachment is a great convenience in cutting threads and doing other heavily

9

10

stressed cuts best handled at very low speeds. Of course, the collar and rod are mounted only when a specific need arises for rotating the spindle by hand, and they are removed promptly when the job is finished. Notice I always remove the drive belt while using this attachment, as is shown in Photo 10, to eliminate any possibility of an unsafe condition resulting from the motor driving it.

The plain rod shown in Photo 9 was faced off true on each end. It is used as a depth stop, as shown in Photo 11. I tapped a hole for a setscrew in the side of the lathe spindle opposite the keyway for the threaded rod and collar. The depth stop can be locked in any desired position in the hole that passes through the spindle. It is convenient for quick, accurate positioning of any parts being made from rod gripped in the lathe chuck and extending into the hole in the spindle. For example, it permits accurate repetitive shouldering of locomotive axles by holding them in a known position. After the first one is machined, all the others will be identical if placed against the stop and machined to the same readings on the micrometer collars of the lathe.

One last item on the Perris lathe bed required attention. That was the clutch handle for engaging the lead screw for longitudinal advance of the carriage. It is the handle just to the right of the gear covering hood in Photos 10, 11, and 12. The handle rotates on a shoulder bolt to engage or disengage the dog clutch. There was a tendency for it to bind on the shoulder bolt and cause it to work loose. I machined a bronze bushing that is a close fit in the clutch handle and prevents the shoulder bolt from moving.

Quite a bit of work went into the refurbishing job. The result is shown all set up in Photo 12. Was it worth the effort? Within itself, it was an absorbing and enjoyable task to get it all together and functioning properly. The cost of materials used was so small as to be negligible. And the machine is working well, which is the bottom line after all is said and done. I have waited several months since finishing the job

11

12

to write up this short series describing it to give myself a chance to prove it out on some typical assignments. Two stationary steam engines have been built from parts machined using only this machine, and at the moment of writing, I am most of the way through a live steam locomotive. There is still plenty of life in the Perris lathe. In combination with the Unimat head, it makes a dependable and useful milling machine. Thoughts of buying a replacement for it have vanished.

Lever Operated Tailstock

The lever operated tailstock described here was specifically designed to fit my Unimat – one of the older models having round rods for ways. In Photo 1, you will see the tailstock being used in place of the original equipment with a drill chuck on the ram.

Several features of the tailstock are apparent from the picture. Most prominent is the fact that the tailstock is aligned to the lathe bed by means of the V-groove in the base that engages the near way. There is a clearance milled in the underside of the base to go over the longitudinal feed screw and rest flat on the way on the far side of the lathe. A flat clamp plate under the ways secures the tailstock in place on the lathe bed. The single V-groove contacting the near way provides positive alignment of the tailstock, while the flat clamping arrangement guarantees that the ways

are not moved laterally or otherwise deflected when the tailstock is clamped in place.

The lever operated tailstock is simple and accurate to set up, and is quicker in use than the screw operated tailstock provided with the lathe. It will accommodate the dead center of the lathe, a drill chuck, or the crotch center shown in the foreground of the photograph. All the machining operations involved in making the lever operated tailstock shown here and detailed in the drawings can be carried out directly on the Unimat for which it is made.

The original tailstock shown in Photo 1 proved so useful that variations were incorporated in the design, and a second one was built and fitted to the dovetail ways of my Perris lathe. A photograph of the modified form will be shown later on as a guide to

1

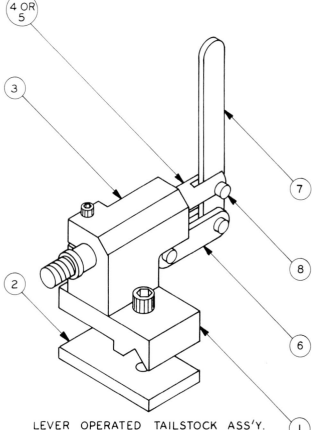

LEVER OPERATED TAILSTOCK ASS'Y.

anyone who may wish to adapt this type of tailstock to some other make of lathe.

Cut a rectangular block of aluminum for the Base (Part 1). Set up the Unimat in its vertical configuration to use it as a milling machine.

Clamp the block flat on the milling table to take a very light truing cut across the top surface with a fly cutter or similar tool. Using the top surface as a reference, mill the four edges of the block to get them straight and square to one another and square to the top surface. As you true the edges with the fly cutter, you will reduce the block to its final dimensions for length and width.

2

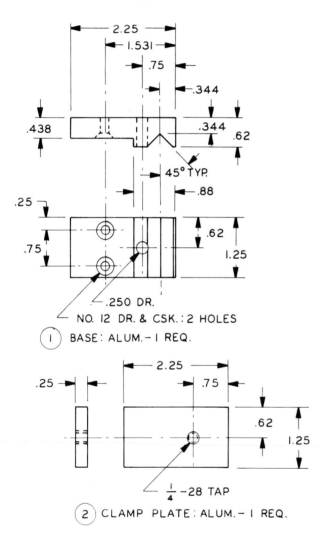

(1) BASE: ALUM.– I REQ.

(2) CLAMP PLATE: ALUM. – I REQ.

When you are satisfied with the overall dimensions of the block from which you are making the base, mark out the V-groove and the flat step which you will have to mill in the under surface. Be careful in marking out the V-groove and the depth of the step, because these features determine the accuracy of the position the finished tailstock assumes when it is clamped to the ways of the lathe.

Take a moment now to examine Photos 2 and 4 which illustrate an accurate means of obtaining the correct angles in the V-groove in the base. Note in Photo 4 that a large V-block having a 90° V was clamped to the milling table with the axis of the V exactly parallel to the X direction of travel of the milling table. In this setup, the two outer clamps secured the large V-block to the table. The central clamp pressed directly against the workpiece to press it down firmly in place in the V-block. As you can see in Photo 2, a short length of angle stock was used to transmit the force from the clamping bar to the base to hold it for the milling of the V. A milling cutter of .188" diameter was used for the cut which had just been finished in Photo 2. Use the quill feed of the Unimat head to get the cut down to the correct vertical position. Then use the Y feed to deepen the cut a little at a time as you traverse the work by means of the X feed. Be sure you advance the workpiece *against* the cut of the milling cutter; that is, from right to left in the setup shown in Photo 2.

When you get the V-groove finished to your satisfaction, clamp the base flat on the milling table to mill out the flat step. It can be cut using the same end mill as you used for the previous milling operation. At this point, you can mark out the locations of the three bolt holes. Punch them with a sharp center punch, start them with a small center drill, and drill them through. Finish the base by countersinking the two bolt holes from the underside of the flat step.

After you cut out the Clamp Plate (Part 2), mill the edges as you did on the base. Locate the position of the tapped hole. Drill it out, and tap the thread for the bolt that will pass through the base for the clamping action. Now you can clamp the base to the ways of the Unimat to be certain it clamps down flat and horizontal.

Cut out another rectangular block to make the Upright (Part 3). Fly-cut the edges to get them straight and square, paying particular attention to the bottom surface which will be in contact with the base. Mark out the areas on the sides where the Links (Part 6) are inset. This is shown in the detail drawing and shows up well in Photo 1. Clamp the part on its side on the milling table in the position shown in Photo 3 to end-mill the first side. Then you can turn the part over to mill the second side. You will note in Photo 3 that the second side was just being finished when the photograph was taken. Once again, you are ready to set up the large V-block on the milling table, as shown in Photo 4, to form the chamfers on the upper corners by end-milling. Notice that the chamfer on one side runs the full length of the upright, while it runs only partway back on the opposite side. This is to leave a flat spot for the 6-32 clamping screw. After finishing the chamfers, you can drill and tap the 10-32 holes in the bottom. Locate, drill, and ream the .125" diameter hole from side to

3

4

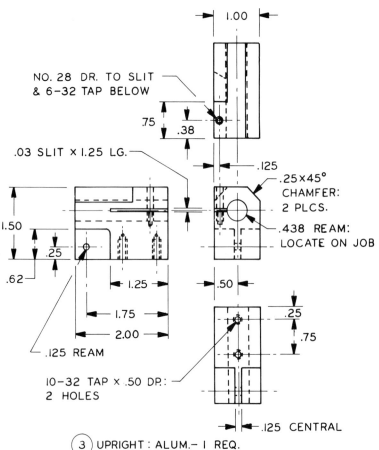

NO. 28 DR. TO SLIT & 6-32 TAP BELOW

.75

.38

.03 SLIT X 1.25 LG.

1.00

.125

.25 X 45° CHAMFER: 2 PLCS.

.438 REAM: LOCATE ON JOB

1.50

.25

.62

1.25

1.75

2.00

.50

.25

.75

.125 REAM

10-32 TAP X .50 DP.: 2 HOLES

.125 CENTRAL

(3) UPRIGHT : ALUM.— 1 REQ.

side in the milled out area. Finally, locate the 6-32 hole in the top surface. Drill No. 28 to a depth of .50". Continue drilling with a No. 36 drill to a depth of .75", and tap the deep part of the hole with a 6-32 thread.

Bolt the upright in place on the base as you prepare to locate the .438" reamed hole for the ram. As you refer to Photo 5, you will see at once that the hole is located and cut with the tailstock in place on the lathe bed. This is a point where you will have to pay attention to the lathe itself to be sure the headstock is

68   *The Shop Wisdom of Rudy Kouhoupt*

lined up properly. It is a good idea to place the tailstock that came with the lathe on the ways to get the head set with its axis parallel to the ways. Using a thin razor blade suspended between the center points has always worked well on my Unimat. The headstock and tailstock are in line when the razor blade is suspended in an exactly vertical plane and is exactly at right angles to the longitudinal ways.

Remove the tailstock from the ways when you are sure the headstock is accurately aligned. Slack off on the bolts that clamp the spindle advance motion in the Unimat headstock, and insert the spindle feed hand lever. Grip a center drill in the drill chuck. Clamp the unfinished tailstock on the lathe ways as shown in Photo 5. Use the spindle feed hand lever to bring the center drill into contact with the front surface of the upright to start the hole. By doing this operation with the tailstock clamped in place on the lathe ways, the hole will be right on the lathe axis. Change from the center drill to a twist drill to drill the hole all the way through the upright. The spindle feed hand lever cannot advance the headstock spindle far enough to drill the hole all the way through in one pass. When you have drilled as far as possible, let the spindle return to the starting position, advance the tailstock on the ways, and drill a little deeper until the hole goes through. Finally, chuck a .438" diameter reamer to open the hole out to its finished size.

The last operation that must be performed on the upright is to cut the slit down the side to permit the 6-32 screw to have its clamping action. Refer to Photo 6 which illustrates a convenient way to cut the piece with a slitting blade in a vertical setup. After completing the slit, use the .438" reamer again to be sure the hole is free of burrs.

Both the Drill Ram (Part 4) and the Center Ram (Part 5) are turned from steel rod. The drill ram has a threaded end suitable for mounting a drill chuck, the Crotch Center (Part 9), or similar accessories. The end of the center ram is bored to accept the dead center of the Unimat. Keeping the center ram relatively short provides greater rigidity to the tailstock center for lathe jobs handled between centers. The drill ram is longer to permit feeding the drill to greater depth in drilling operations.

Since the two rams are so similar, it is expedient to machine them both at the same

5

6

time. After cutting two lengths of .50" diameter steel rod, face off each end and center drill them for supporting them between lathe centers. While facing and center drilling the ends, support one end of the work in the

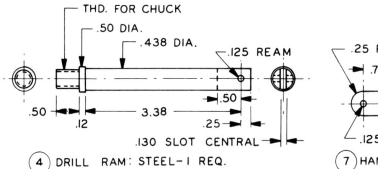

THD. FOR CHUCK
.50 DIA.
.438 DIA.
.125 REAM
.50
.12
3.38
.25
.50
.130 SLOT CENTRAL
④ DRILL RAM: STEEL–1 REQ.

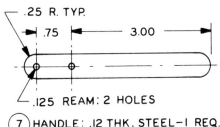

.25 R. TYP.
.75
3.00
.125 REAM: 2 HOLES
⑦ HANDLE: .12 THK. STEEL–1 REQ.

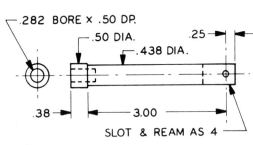

.282 BORE × .50 DP.
.50 DIA.
.438 DIA.
.25
.38
3.00
SLOT & REAM AS 4
⑤ CENTER RAM: STEEL– 1 REQ.

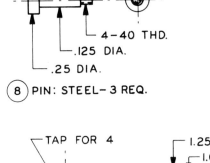

.12
.44
.12
4-40 THD.
.125 DIA.
.25 DIA.
⑧ PIN: STEEL– 3 REQ.

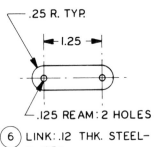

.25 R. TYP.
1.25
.125 REAM: 2 HOLES
⑥ LINK: .12 THK. STEEL–
2 REQ.

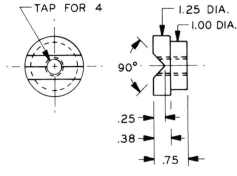

TAP FOR 4
1.25 DIA.
1.00 DIA.
90°
.25
.38
.75
⑨ CROTCH CENTER: ALUM.–
1 REQ.

three-jaw chuck with the other end running in a steady rest. Put each one between lathe centers to turn down the .438" diameter part. Try to obtain a smooth slip fit of the rams in the .438" reamed hole in the upright. The idea is to have them be a nice sliding fit, with no rattle or shake, while the 6-32 clamping screw is slacked off. Finish the .438" diameter part with fine emery paper to obtain a smooth surface. Now you can reverse the rams in the lathe, gripping the .438" diameter part in the chuck with the steady rest adjusted to produce true running of the center spot at the opposite end. Turn down the end of the drill ram and cut the thread with a die held in the tailstock die holder. Drill into the center ram with a .250" diameter drill, and finish the hole to exact size with a very slender boring bar. As you proceed with the boring, keep checking with one of the Unimat center

points until you have a very close fit with no shake or looseness.

A word about the thread on the drill ram may be in order. On the older model Unimats, the thread for the drill chuck supplied with the machine is 12mm diameter x 1.00mm pitch.

This would be a suitable thread to use, or you might prefer to use 3/8-24 to fit the standard drill chucks that are commercially available.

Once again, set up your machine vertically with a slitting blade on the nose, as you did for slitting the upright. Clamp each ram in a set of small V-blocks to cut the .130" slot in the outer end to clear the handle. The final operation is to drill and ream the .125" hole across the slot.

Mark out the Links (Part 6) and the Handle (Part 7) on steel flat stock. Drill and ream the

7

holes. Then cut the parts to length and file the radius on the ends.

Chuck a length of .25" diameter steel rod for making the Pins (Part 8). Turn down with a sharp knife tool to form the .125" diameter part and the threaded part. Cut the thread with a die held in the tailstock die holder.

Now you are ready to assemble the tailstock complete, as shown in Photos 1 and 7. Plain nuts on the pins will hold everything together very well; however, mine has acorn nuts which insure there are no sharp edges to bark my knuckles.

To improve the versatility of your lever operated tailstock, it is a good idea to make the crotch center (Part 9) which is shown set up in Photo 7. You will note that round stock supported in the crotch center is automatically held on the lathe axis permitting accurate cross drilling or other operations that must be done centrally on the work. Chuck a piece of aluminum rod in the three-jaw chuck. Take a facing cut to smooth it off. Reverse the part in the chuck to face off the second side and turn down the 1.00" diameter part. Start the central hole with a center drill in the tailstock drill chuck. Drill the hole out with a twist drill, and tap the thread to fit the thread on the drill ram. Screw the crotch center onto the drill ram as shown in Photo 7. Set your surface gage to the center height of the lathe, and scribe a horizontal center line across the face of the crotch center to locate the V-groove. Now you can mill the V-groove as you did in making the base. By aligning the V-groove with the center line, you will insure that it will always be in the horizontal position which is the most useful working position.

8

Photo 8 shows a lever operated tailstock fitted to the dovetail ways of my Perris lathe. The isometric drawing illustrates how the base was made with a fixed dovetail strip and a moveable clamping strip that provide firm clamping and accurate alignment on the lathe ways.

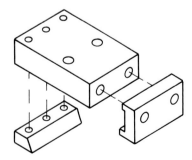

BASE ASS'Y. FOR
DOVETAIL WAYS

BILL OF MATERIALS

NO.	PART	MATERIAL	QTY.	DIMENSIONS
1	Base	aluminum	1	.62 x 1.25 x 2.25"
2	Clamp Plate	aluminum	1	.25 x 1.25 x 2.25"
3	Upright	aluminum	1	1.00 x 1.50 x 2.00"
4	Drill Ram	steel	1	.50" dia. x 4.25"
5	Center Ram	steel	1	.50" dia. x 3.62"
6	Link	steel	2	.12 x .50 x 1.75"
7	Handle	steel	1	.12 x .50 x 4.00"
8	Pin	steel	3	.25" dia. x .69"
9	Crotch Center	aluminum	1	1.25" dia. x .75"
	Flathead Screw	steel	2	10-32 x .75"
	Cap Screw	steel	1	6-32 x .75"
	Cap Screw	steel	1	1/4-28 x 1.25"

Other Features

Machining Your Own Spur Gears

Spur gears are the type on which the teeth are cut parallel to the axis of rotation of the gear. They make up the simplest form of gearing. Furthermore, spur gears are the most widely used type for transmitting power from one shaft to another which is parallel to it. As power is transmitted through spur gears, the rotation of the gear shafts is positively synchronized.

The simple nature of spur gears means that they can be produced in the home shop with relative ease. The calculations involved in preparing to cut a particular spur gear are straightforward. Anyone who understands the basic principles of spur gears should have no difficulty going through the calculations. While accurate work is called for, it is not difficult to make your own spur gears following the procedures shown in this article.

It is possible to produce spur gears with different forms of teeth. However, we will consider only involute-toothed spur gears in this article. The involute form is by far the most commonly used. All others, such as the cycloidal form, are outdated and unlikely to be encountered.

Figure 1 is a drawing of a sector of a spur gear on which the various parts and dimensions are identified. By referring to it, the terms used in describing gears will be easily understood.

Pitch Diameter

The pitch circle of a spur gear is an imaginary circle which passes through the teeth. It corresponds to the surface of a friction gear or toothless cylinder and may be thought of as the line of contact of two cylinders having the same diameter ratios as the gears under consideration. The diameter of the pitch circle is the pitch diameter.

Diametral Pitch

The most frequently used figure for specifying the pitch of gears is the diametral pitch. It is a dimensionless number indicating the number of teeth for each inch of pitch diameter. The diametral pitch system provides a series of standardized gear tooth sizes. In order to mesh properly, gears must be of the same diametral pitch, regardless of the overall size of the gears. It is general practice that when the word pitch is used alone, it refers to the diametral pitch.

Table 1 lists a number of formulas for calculating the various dimensions of involute spur gears. Referring to the formulas in the table, consider the following example. If a 16 pitch gear has 28 teeth, what is its pitch diameter?

$$PD = \frac{N}{DP}$$

$$PD = \frac{28}{16}$$

$$PD = 1.750''$$

Circular Pitch

Another way to express gear pitch is the circular pitch. The circular pitch is the distance from a point on one tooth to the corresponding point on the next tooth when measured along the pitch circle.

Consider again the 16 pitch gear having 28 teeth from the previous example. What is its

1

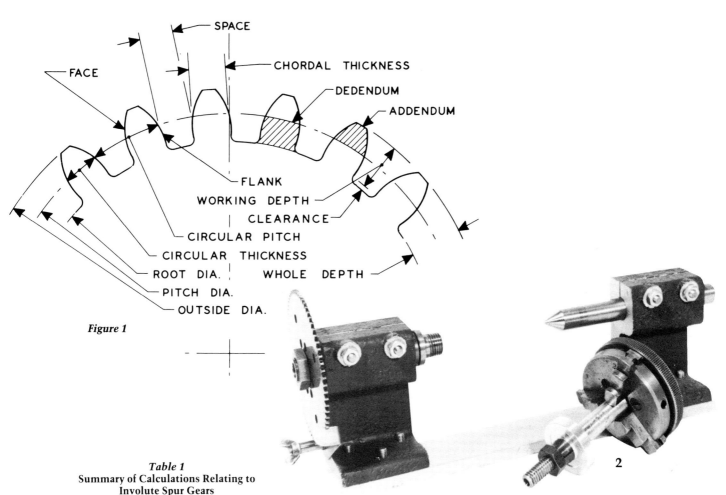

Figure 1

Table 1
Summary of Calculations Relating to Involute Spur Gears

Value to be found	Symbol	Rule for Calculation	Formula
1. Diametral pitch	DP	1a. Divide the number of teeth by the pitch diameter	$DP = \dfrac{N}{PD}$
		1b. Divide the number of teeth plus 2 by the outside diameter	$DP = \dfrac{N + 2}{OD}$
		1c. Divide π by the circular pitch	$DP = \dfrac{3.1416}{CP}$
2. Pitch diameter	PD	2a. Divide the number of teeth by the diametral pitch	$PD = \dfrac{N}{DP}$
		2b. Subtract 2 over the diametral pitch from the outside diameter	$PD = OD - \dfrac{2}{DP}$
3. Number of teeth	N	3a. Multiply the diametral pitch by the pitch diameter	$N = DP \times PD$
		3b. Multiply the outside diameter by the diametral pitch and subtract 2	$N = OD \times DP - 2$
4. Circular pitch	CP	4. Divide π by the diametral pitch	$CP = \dfrac{3.1416}{DP}$
5. Circular thickness	CT	5. Divide the circular pitch by 2	$CT = \dfrac{CP}{2}$
6. Addendum	A	6. Divide 1 by the diametral pitch	$A = \dfrac{1}{DP}$
7. Clearance	C	7. Divide .157 by the diametral pitch	$C = \dfrac{.157}{DP}$
8. Dedendum	D	8a. Add the clearance to the addendum	$D = C + A$
		8b. Divide 1.157 by the diametral pitch	$D = \dfrac{1.157}{DP}$
9. Whole depth	W	9a. Add the addendum to the dedendum	$W = A + D$
		9b. Divide 2.157 by the diametral pitch	$W = \dfrac{2.157}{DP}$
10. Outside diameter	OD	10a. Divide the number of teeth plus 2 by the diametral pitch	$OD = \dfrac{N + 2}{DP}$
		10b. Add the pitch diameter to 2 divided by the diametral pitch	$OD = PD + \dfrac{2}{DP}$

circular pitch? From Table 1:

$$CP = \frac{3.1416}{DP}$$

$$CP = \frac{3.1416}{16}$$

$$CP = .1963''$$

This same dimension can be found directly in Table 2 which lists the dimensions of involute gear teeth for the range of gear pitches that I feel are most likely to be produced in the home shop.

Addendum

By definition, the addendum is the length of the tooth measured from the pitch circle to the outside. In Figure 1, the addendum is shaded and is the part of the tooth which is between the pitch diameter and the outside diameter. For any given diametral pitch, the addendum has a constant dimension.

What is the addendum of our example gear of 16 pitch and 28 teeth ? From Table 1:

$$A = \frac{1}{DP}$$

$$A = \frac{1}{16}$$

$$A = .0625''$$

Or, refer to Table 2 to obtain the dimension without calculating.

Table 2
Involute Gear Tooth Dimensions in Inches

Diametral Pitch	Circular Pitch	Circular Thickness	Addendum	Working Depth	Whole Depth	Clearance
10	.3142	.1571	.1000	.2000	.2157	.0157
11	.2856	.1428	.0909	.1818	.1961	.0143
12	.2618	.1309	.0833	.1667	.1798	.0131
14	.2244	.1122	.0714	.1429	.1541	.0112
16	.1963	.0981	.0625	.1250	.1348	.0098
18	.1745	.0872	.0555	.1111	.1198	.0087
20	.1571	.0785	.0500	.1000	.1079	.0079
22	.1428	.0714	.0455	.0909	.0980	.0071
24	.1309	.0654	.0417	.0833	.0899	.0065
26	.1208	.0604	.0385	.0769	.0830	.0060
28	.1122	.0561	.0357	.0714	.0770	.0056
30	.1047	.0523	.0333	.0667	.0719	.0052
32	.0981	.0490	.0313	.0625	.0674	.0049
36	.0873	.0436	.0278	.0556	.0599	.0043
40	.0785	.0392	.0250	.0500	.0539	.0039
48	.0654	.0327	.0208	.0417	.0449	.0032

Dedendum

The dedendum is defined as the length of the tooth between the pitch circle and the root. Referring to Figure 1, the dedendum is the shaded part of the tooth between the pitch

diameter and the root diameter.

What is the dedendum of our example gear of 16 pitch? From Table 1:

$$D = \frac{1.157}{DP}$$

$$D = \frac{1.157}{16}$$

$$D = .0723''$$

Depth of Teeth

It will be noted from Figure 1 that the whole depth of the tooth is the full length of the tooth extending from the root diameter to the outside diameter. A number of extremely important points come together and are influenced by the whole depth dimension. The whole depth may be thought of as the sum of the addendum and the dedendum. Or it may be thought of as the sum of the working depth to which two gears are properly meshed plus the small amount of clearance which is allowed for running.

Continuing with our example of the 28 tooth gear of 16 pitch, what are the clearance and whole depth dimensions?

$$C = \frac{.157}{DP}$$

$$C = \frac{.157}{16}$$

$$C = .0098''$$

and

$$W = A + D$$

$$W = .0625'' + .0723''$$

$$W = .1348''$$

or

$$W = \frac{2.157}{DP}$$

$$W = \frac{2.157}{16}$$

$$W = .1348''$$

Tooth Thickness and Spacing

In order for the teeth of two spur gears to engage properly, the spaces between the teeth, as measured at the pitch diameter, must

coincide with the thickness of the teeth at the same point. The circular thickness of each tooth should be one half of the circular pitch. If the tooth thickness exceeds the space, the gears jam and do not mesh. If the space exceeds the tooth thickness, the gears mesh poorly and the difference between the space and tooth thickness becomes obvious as backlash.

Gear Tooth Surfaces

In the development of gear teeth, there are two different surfaces which come together at the pitch diameter. The surface of the gear tooth between the pitch diameter and the outside diameter is known as the face. The surface between the pitch diameter and the root diameter is known as the flank. A small fillet or reverse curve blends the flank into the root circle.

Pressure Angles

When two gears are properly engaged, their teeth come together and press against one another at a fixed angle which is the pressure angle. Involute spur gears usually have their teeth cut to produce a pressure angle of 14 ½°, as shown in Figure 2. Through experience, it has been learned that the greatest efficiency is obtained when the pressure angle is 14 ½°.

Other pressure angles, such as the 20° pressure angle shown in Figure 3, are possible. As the pressure angle becomes greater, the outward strain on the gear shaft bearings also becomes greater. Some advantages may be found by using a greater pressure angle for transmitting higher horse powers. It must be understood, however, that a gear of any pressure angle will mesh only with other gears having the same pressure angle. The general rule is that all involute spur gears engaged in a drive train must have the same pressure angle and the same diametral pitch.

Involute Gear Cutters

The number of teeth which may be used in involute spur gears ranges from 12 in a small pinion upward to any large number. This may even include a rack or straight gear. Some variations in the shape of face and flank surfaces are necessary to assure proper

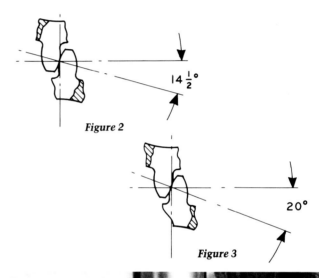

Figure 2

14 ½°

20°

Figure 3

3

4

engagement of any gears throughout this wide range. Therefore, a total of eight cutters are required in *each* diametral pitch to cover the full range or possible gear teeth which may be met with in that particular pitch. The cutters always have identifying marks on them. Photo 3 shows a group of involute gear cutters, one of which is mounted on a holder, ready for work.

Table 3 is a listing of the eight involute gear cutters making up a complete set. To continue our example of the 28 tooth gear of 16 pitch: What cutter would be used to cut the teeth on this gear? From the table, cutter no. 4 covers gears from 26 to 34 teeth, so a no. 4 involute gear cutter of 16 pitch will do the job.

The Gear Cutting Process

There are a number of operations which must be carried out in sequence to cut an involute spur gear successfully. For the sake of illustration, let's review the cutting of a gear that was required for use in a particular model and follow through the complete process. The gear required was to be of 32 pitch and to have a 14½° pressure angle. The gear had to have 36 teeth, a face width of .250" and a central hole to fit a ⅜" shaft.

In order to get started, the outside diameter of the gear was calculated. This dimension was needed to machine the gear blank prior to cutting the teeth. From Table 1:

$$OD = \frac{N + 2}{DP}$$

$$OD = \frac{36 + 2}{32}$$

$$C = 1.1875"$$

Since the specification was for a face width of .250", a piece of ¼" metal large enough for the 1.1875" OD blank was selected. After drilling and reaming the central hole, it was placed on a short mandrel in the lathe, as shown in Photo 1. The chuck mounting of the mandrel was important to keep the mandrel in a fixed position with respect to the spindle. The blank was turned to the calculated OD on the mandrel.

Next, the chuck with the mandrel and gear blank in position was transferred to the dividing attachment as a unit. This is shown in Photo 2. In previous articles in this magazine, the author has presented all details for the construction of this dividing attachment, as well as the use of the drill press as a light, vertical milling machine.

When the dividing attachment was positioned on the drill press for milling the gear teeth,

5

every precaution was taken to get the axis of the mandrel truly at right angles to the vertical axis of the drill press. Photo 4 shows a small indicator in the chuck measuring against the surface of the mandrel. If the indicator had not been available, it would have been possible to obtain true alignment by chucking a short piece of true rod and using a feeler gauge.

By checking Table 3, it was noted that a no. 3 cutter covers the range of 35 to 54 teeth. Therefore, the no. 3 cutter of 32 pitch was chucked and is seen ready for action in Photo 5. At this point, the "Z" motion had already been used to bring the cutting surface of the gear cutter down centralized to the axis of the mandrel.

Table 3
Involute Gear Cutters

Cutter No.	Range of teeth cut	
	Minimum	Maximum
1	135 teeth	Rack
2	55 teeth	134 teeth
3	35 teeth	54 teeth
4	26 teeth	34 teeth
5	21 teeth	25 teeth
6	17 teeth	20 teeth
7	14 teeth	16 teeth
8	12 teeth	13 teeth

6

7

The dividing attachment shown in the photos depends upon commercially cut spur gears to obtain its dividing action. The dividing gear shown in Photo 5 has 72 teeth which explains why it is marked with the number 72. Also, clearly shown in the photo are the reference marks which are used to avoid repetitious counting. To cut the 36 tooth gear required the use of alternate spaces on the 72 tooth dividing gear, and these are all marked. By examining the pattern of marks shown on the gear, it is apparent how it can be used to obtain several sets of radial divisions all without counting while using it. This virtually eliminates the possibility of making errors.

At this point, a check of Table 2 gave the proper dimensions of the gear tooth without further calculation. The important dimension was the whole depth which was found to be .0674". To obtain a good surface on the gear teeth, it is a good practice to cut them in two passes.

Using the "X" motion of the milling slide, the blank was advanced until its surface was barely contacting the cutter surface. The "Y" motion was used to move the blank away from the cutter. Then the "X" motion was advanced .060" to give this depth of cut on the first pass. The "Y" motion was used to feed the blank into the cutter. Each space was cut

in turn. In Photo 6, about one third of the tooth has been gashed out on the first pass.

After getting all the way around on the first pass, the "X" motion was advanced the remaining distance to obtain the desired whole depth. The procedure of advancing one tooth at a time was repeated all the way around to take the second pass, as shown in Photo 7. When the second pass had been taken all the way around, the gear was checked for dimensions and found satisfactory. The finished involute spur gear was removed from the mandrel and can be seen in Photo 8.

Building Your Own Dividing Attachment

The need frequently arises in the course of making parts for various engines, tools, and other shop appliances to obtain equal and uniform radial divisions. It may happen that the teeth have to be cut on a spur gear, for instance. Or the splines may have to be spaced out uniformly on a splined shaft. Or a wheel hub and rim may have to be drilled for spoke placement. The notches may have to be cut along the edge of a ratchet wheel for a lubricator, or a uniform set of wrench flats may have to be milled on some sort of head. The list goes on and on. Nearly every shop project seems to involve some sort of dividing job.

Like all other aspects of shop practice, there are different ways that dividing can be accomplished. Some ways are more accurate than others. Varying degrees of success are likely to be achieved, depending upon the method chosen and the nature of the work undertaken. Having been through the process of improvising several "make-do" setups for dividing, it became increasingly clear to me that I needed a versatile and accurate dividing attachment.

The unit which I designed and built to fill this need is shown in Photo 1. While it is a simple device, it is capable of good, accurate work. The dividing action is accomplished by counting teeth on a gear fixed to the spindle. The accuracy of the divisions produced is as good as the accuracy of the commercially cut gear used on the spindle. The flat base of the dividing attachment makes it simple to mount and accurate to position on any flat surface, such as the tables of vertical or horizontal milling machines, shapers, lathe saddles, or lathe milling slides. Light jobs may be supported from the spindle alone, but the best work results from mounting the workpiece on a mandrel supported from both ends.

CAST OR FABRICATE?

There are eight home-built components which go into the dividing attachment. All of them can be seen in Photo 2 taken during assembly. Since no bar stock was available to me in a size suitable for making the standards (Item 2), I determined from the outset that these would

1

2

3

4

have to be cast. Anyone having a suitable bar of aluminum or CRS could just as well duplicate the hole patterns and make an all-fabricated dividing attachment from the drawings included with this article. It is not necessary to cut away the large bulk of metal to form the vertical web, in this case. However, the resulting tool will be a bit boxy looking.

Photo 3 shows the wooden plate-mounted pattern which I used to produce the greensand mold shown in Photo 4. The small projection at the bottom of the pattern molded the pouring basin and in-gate where the molten aluminum entered the cavity in the mold. The molding flask is quite small, measuring just 4″ x 5″ on the inside.

My blast furnace is a small home-built unit which burns charcoal. As a matter of reference for anyone who wants to cast the parts, each of my standard castings weighed 7 ounces, and an additional 4 ounces of metal went into the runner and sprue. Unfortunately, my crucible holds only a pound of molten aluminum. A

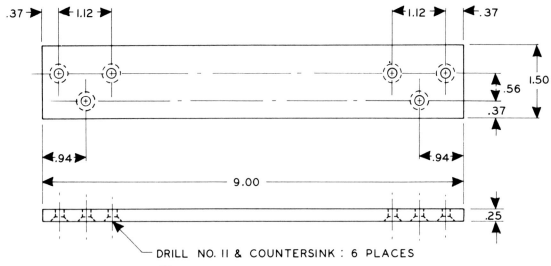

DRILL NO. 11 & COUNTERSINK : 6 PLACES

(1) BASE : ALUMINUM OR C.R.S.
I REQUIRED

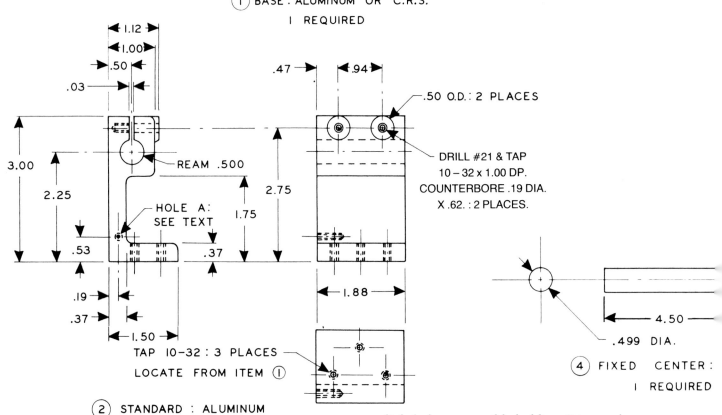

REAM .500

HOLE A:
SEE TEXT

.50 O.D. : 2 PLACES

DRILL #21 & TAP
10-32 x 1.00 DP.
COUNTERBORE .19 DIA.
X .62. : 2 PLACES.

TAP 10-32 : 3 PLACES
LOCATE FROM ITEM (1)

(2) STANDARD : ALUMINUM
2 REQUIRED

.499 DIA.

(4) FIXED CENTER :
I REQUIRED

.75 O.D.

.31 I.D.

THREAD 1/2-20
.499 DIA.

THREAD TO
FIT CHUCK

(3) SPINDLE : STEEL
I REQUIRED

slightly larger crucible holding 1½ pounds
would have been adequate to pour both molds
from a single melt.

CONSTRUCTING THE ATTACHMENT

Assuming that the prospective builder has all
the necessary materials on hand, the following
notes and instructions will summarize the
procedure I followed in machining the parts
and assembling them.

Begin by cutting a length of bar stock for the
base (Item 1). Either aluminum or CRS is
suitable for the base. After squaring the ends,
mark out the locations of the screw holes. Drill
through and countersink for the six No. 10-32 x
¾" flat-head screws which will hold the
standards in place.

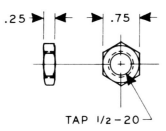

.25 → ← → .75 ←

TAP 1/2-20

(5) LOCK NUT : STEEL
1 REQUIRED

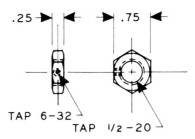

.25 → ← → .75 ←

TAP 6-32
TAP 1/2-20

(6) THRUST NUT : STEEL
1 REQUIRED

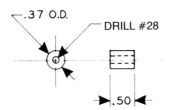

.37 O.D.
DRILL #28

.50

(7) SPACER : STEEL
1 REQUIRED

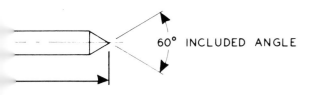

60° INCLUDED ANGLE

DRILL ROD

5

6

The same general procedure can be followed in machining the standards (Item 2), whether they are made from castings or solid blocks. In the chapter following this, I will describe my arrangement for using the drill press for doing light milling. All milling cuts required to machine the standards were taken on the equipment using the home-built toolholders and workholders to be described in that chapter.

The first operation is to flycut the two clamping bosses on the front of the standard castings. With these machined flat and parallel to the back surface, it is convenient to clamp the standards in the milling vise to flycut each side and the bottom. Referring to Photo 5, the

7

tool marks from the flycutting are visible on the side nearest the camera. At this point, both sides are already machined parallel to each other, and the part is inverted in the milling vise for flycutting the bottom surface.

After the bores have been reamed, the standards can be turned on their backs as in Photo 6 to drill and tap the clamping bosses for the No. 10-32 clamping bolts. The pilot holes for the tapping are not drilled all the way through. By leaving the holes blind, a firm mounting for the clamping bolts is provided with no further fastening necessary. Clear drill to a depth of .62", just adequate to clear the slit which provides the clamping action.

The exact width of the slit is not critical. The slitting blade being used in Photo 7 to cut it has a width of .032". The slit should be at least .020" wide and could reasonably be any width up to about .060".

Hole A on the drawing is drilled and tapped No. 6-32 x .50" deep. Its purpose is to mount the positioner (Item 8). Therefore, only one standard, the one which will carry the spindle (Item 3), will require hole A.

This is a good time to screw in the clamping bolts, which are nothing more than four short lengths of No. 10-32 threaded steel rod. Screw the rods in firmly against the bottoms of the blind holes. Cut them off with enough length projecting from the bosses to take a flat washer and No. 10-32 hex nut on each, as shown in Photo 2.

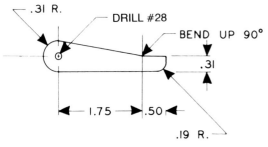

⑧ POSITIONER : 18 GA. STEEL
  I REQUIRED

Three No. 10-32 tapped holes have to be made in the bottom of each standard so they can be mounted on the base (Item 1). Slip a piece of straight, accurate rod (such as drill rod) through the bores of the standards, and stand them up squarely on a piece of plate glass or other truly flat surface. Spread the standards until their outer edges are exactly 9" apart. Tighten the clamping nuts so the standards clamp down tightly against the drill rod. This insures that the standards are exactly in line as determined by their bores.

Set the standards, with the drill rod clamped in them, in position on the base and clamp them to it. Now spot through the holes in the base with a No. 11 drill to mark the hole positions on the standard bottoms. Remove the standards. Drill each spot No. 21 and tap No. 10-32. Bolt the standards to the base. Check the bore alignment by slipping the drill rod through again. If necessary, adjust the alignment by adding shims or drawing the holes slightly.

The spindle (Item 3) is a simple lathe job, but some comments about it are in order. It is important that the standard be able to clamp very firmly against the spindle to prevent it from rotating while a workpiece positioned in the dividing attachment is being machined. Therefore, be careful that the .499" diameter is turned straight and true throughout its length. The ½"-20 thread is for the thrust nut (Item 6) and the lock nut (Item 5). I drilled the .31" diameter hole axially through the spindle so that it can accommodate long rods in the same way that a lathe spindle handles them. Some builders may not consider this feature important and will prefer a solid spindle in such case.

The thread on the spindle nose will have to be cut to fit the builder's chucks. In my case, this thread happens to be ½"-20 also. The .75" diameter thrust collar behind it is based upon the use of chucks fitting a thread in the .50" to .62" range. Should the builder require a larger thread, a proportional increase will be needed in the diameter of the thrust collar.

Drill rod is well suited to use for making the fixed center (Item 4). The diameter of this part is required to be a close fit in the standard bore in order to lend firm and unyielding support to mandrels mounting workpieces in the dividing attachment. The 60° angle on the pointed end corresponds to the tailstock center of a lathe.

The lock nut (Item 5), thrust nut (Item 6), and spacer (Item 7) are straightforward. Possibly commercial nuts could be adapted. I made my own from scratch to insure that the threads are on axis and square to the flat surfaces.

I used 18 gauge steel (0.48" thick) to make the positioner (Item 8). It could be thinner as long

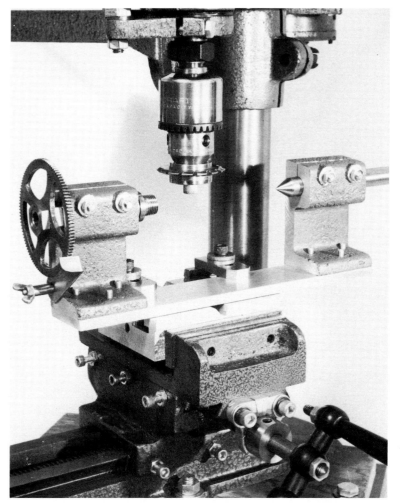

8

as it is stiff enough to engage the indexing gear teeth firmly and prevent rotation while clamping down on the spindle.

The remaining assembly work is quite simple. Slip the spindle into place in the standard containing hole A, and screw on the thrust nut. Do not over tighten the nut. Draw it up just to the point where the spindle has no end shake but rotates smoothly. When this adjustment has been made, put a brass No. 6-32 screw into the tapped hole in the side of the nut. Tighten the brass screw against the ½"-20 thread of the spindle to prevent the thrust nut from working loose, thus maintaining the spindle in adjustment.

Screw a length of No. 6-32 threaded steel rod into hole A. Cut it off at a length which is adequate to hold the spacer, positioner, and a No. 6-32 wing nut in the position shown in the photographs. Finally, slip the fixed center into place in the opposite standard.

USING THE DIVIDING ATTACHMENT
The commercial gears which I use as the indexing reference on the dividing attachment

9

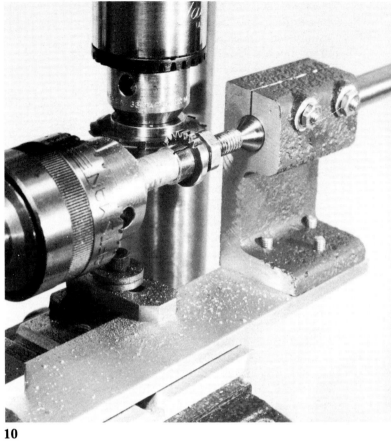

10

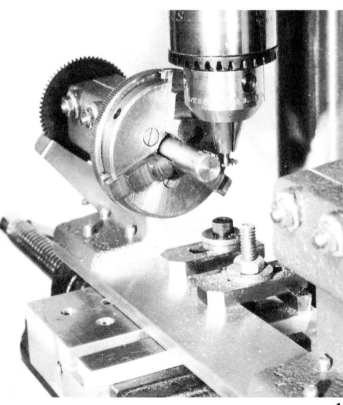

11

12

are from a variety of sources, including old phonographs, clocks, and appliances. Whenever a gear with a convenient and useful number of teeth is located, I put it on the lathe in a ring chuck that will center it accurately without damaging the teeth. Then it is a simple operation to bore out the central hole until it is a close slip fit on the ½"-20 thread of the spindle. In use, the indexing gear is held in place by tightening the lock nut.

At the present time, I have indexing gears with 40, 50, 60, 70, 72, and 110 teeth. Using the 40-tooth gear, for example, it is possible to obtain equal radial divisions of 2, 4, 5, 8, 10, 20, or 40 spaces. By counting off every fourth tooth, the 40-tooth indexing gear locates 10 equal divisions. In the same way, counting off every eighth tooth on the 72-tooth indexing gear locates 9 equal radial divisions.

In Photo 8, the dividing attachment is being set up to mill a spur gear. The 110 tooth indexing gear is already in place. It is important to put the dividing attachment in position on the milling table with its axis parallel to the axis of travel of the milling slide. A convenient means of doing this is shown in Photo 9. Here, a mandrel which is known to be straight is mounted between a chuck and the fixed center. An indicator mounted in the milling chuck is contacting the mandrel. As the milling slide is moved, the indicator will check the mandrel from end to end. Adjustments in the position of the dividing attachment can be made until the indicator shows that the desired parallelism has been attained.

The actual cutting of the gear is shown in Photo 10 where a suitable cutter is in place in the milling chuck. The cutter has been adjusted down until its cutting surface centers on the axis of the dividing attachment. The gear blank has been turned to the correct OD on a short mandrel in the lathe. Chuck, mandrel, and gear blank have been transferred as a unit from the lathe to the dividing attachment where the fixed center is supporting the tail end of the mandrel. The X motion of the milling slide has been set to bring the gear cutter to the desired depth of cut, and the Y motion is used to make the cut.

In this case, the gear being cut is to have 22 teeth. By counting off every fifth tooth of the 110-tooth indexing gear, the correct positions for the 22 teeth will be achieved. The positioner engages the desired locations on the indexing gear to position the gear blank for each cut. However, it is not wise to depend upon the indexing gear and positioner to hold the position during the cut. It is far better to draw up the clamping nuts on the standard to clamp the spindle securely while taking the cut. Between cuts, loosen the clamping nuts while the indexing gear is re-aligned and the positioner set for the next position. Then, re-tighten the clamping nuts.

Further examples of work in progress are shown in Photos 11 and 12. A short spline shaft is being machined in Photo 11. Here it is impossible to support the tail end of the shaft. Slow, light cuts are in order. A total of 14 splines are needed. Every fifth tooth of the 70-tooth indexing gear is being used to obtain the desired spacing.

In Photo 12, a wheel hub is being drilled radially for the placement of six spokes. Every twelfth tooth of the 72-tooth indexing gear is being used.

These are but a few examples of work which can be successfully undertaken on the dividing attachment described here. The proportions and dimensions indicated in the drawings are convenient for me, as they are well suited to my other tools and the projects turned out in my shop. If a need ever arises for a greater center height, it will be a simple matter to make flat spacers to go between the existing standards and base. Likewise, a new base of greater length could be made, if a job requiring more center length is to be undertaken. In the mean time, I shall continue to turn out many parts for engines and other tools using the attachment exactly as shown. And I am sure that anyone who takes the time to duplicate it will derive much satisfaction from building and using this handy dividing attachment.

Milling on a Drill Press

The lathe is often referred to as the "Queen of the Shop" because of its versatility. This is a valid statement, I suppose. However, the people who make it rarely tell you that the lathe's versatility arises mainly from the wide range of accessories and attachments available for it. With this thought in mind, any assessment of the versatility or general utility of a machine tool must include a consideration of what accessories or attachments the home shop machinist can make or buy to use with it and extend the capability of doing work on it.

It often happens that the first machine tool acquired for the home shop is a drill press. Devoid of glamour, it spends its life making small round holes (which are not *really* round!)

in work pieces which are usually hand held by the operator. However, by adding a few simple accessories to hold the work and do the cutting, the same drill press can be elevated from this lackluster role to an impressive position as a light, vertical milling machine.

As a light milling machine, the drill press is capable of producing flat surfaces on various work pieces. It can also cut grooves of varying shapes, widths, and depths, such as dovetails, keyways in shafts, or slots in surfaces which are flat or otherwise shaped. Even gear cutting can be done on a drill press which is equipped with a few simple attachments.

My setup for doing milling work on my drill press is shown in Photo 1. Some of the

1   **2**

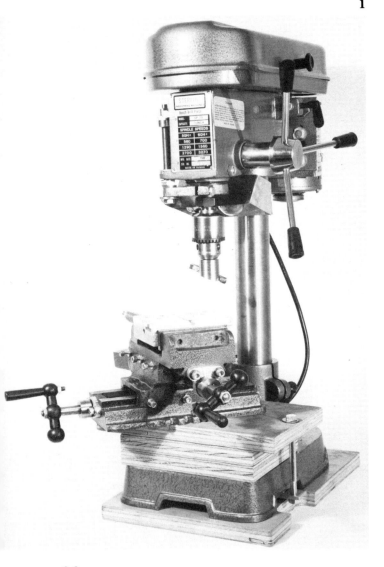

The Shop Wisdom of Rudy Kouhoupt

accessories are purchased items, but many are things which I made, myself. The work of machining the attachments was done on the drill press shown with some assistance from my lathe.

To begin doing milling work on the drill press, it is essential to provide some sort of slide which can hold the work securely while moving it from side to side and back and forth horizontally. These two motions correspond to the **X** and **Y** motions associated with the vertical milling machine. The photos show a cross slide, or compound slide, which I bought for this purpose from a *Home Shop Machinist* advertiser, Kitts Industrial Tools. As supplied by them, my compound slide had no means of measuring or indicating the motion imparted by its ⅛" pitch Acme leadscrews. Therefore, my first job was to make a pair of micrometer collars, one for each motion. My collars are divided and marked with 50 equal spaces, thus indicating .0025" of travel between adjacent marks.

The drill press provides the vertical or **Z** motion needed to place the cutting tool at the right level through its spindle advance mechanism. My drill press had the usual arrangement of a threaded rod passing through an external cast boss on the spindle housing to serve two functions. First, it mounted an adjustable pointer which indicates the spindle position on a two-inch scale. Secondly, the spindle could be locked in place or limited in its motion by the positioning of nuts on the threaded part of the rod.

While this was an acceptable way to control the position of the spindle, one serious problem arose. The thread supplied on the rod with the drill press was ⅜"-24. It was obvious that the 24 pitch screw has an advance of .04167" per turn making it impossible to fit a micrometer collar with evenly spaced divisions to indicate or control the vertical motion. To overcome this difficulty, I made up a new rod on which I cut a ⁷⁄₁₆"-20 thread. The 20 pitch thread has an advance rate of .050" per turn, which is quite convenient. I made a positioning collar with 50 equal divisions threaded internally for ⁷⁄₁₆"-20. Each mark on the collar shown in Photo 2 corresponds to .001" of vertical travel of the spindle.

When I installed the newly made rod on the drill press, it was necessary to ream out the boss so it would clear the slightly larger diameter of the ⁷⁄₁₆"-20 thread. In setting it up, I placed the positioning collar above the boss

and a locking collar below the boss. In use, I adjust the positioning collar as needed and then run the locking collar up to secure the spindle in position. The locking collar has wrench flats milled on it for use of an end wrench.

Proceeding now to how I mount the compound slide on the drill press: There are several possible ways. The particular method selected is usually dictated by the size and nature of the work at hand. The "quickest" way is simply to bolt the compound slide to the drilling table. This allows very convenient raising or lowering on the column. However, it is not well suited to the heavier cuts, since the cantilevered structure of the table is susceptible to some deflection which makes for unsteadiness and chatter. I feel that mounting the compound slide on the base of the drill press provides more rigidity. Even the simple stack of ¾" plywood blocks shown in Photo 1 provides a surprisingly stable and reasonable mounting for the slide. By using an indicator from the chuck, it is very simple to set it up truly. Thin shims are slipped in as required, but I find that everything stays put when the ⁵⁄₁₆"-18 clamping bolts are pulled up tight. On cuts requiring maximum rigidity, rectangular metal blocks take the place of the plywood blocks and are positioned by the same general procedure.

In discussing the cutting tools which I have made for use on my machine, it is important to keep one fact in mind. My drill press has a *male* taper on a *solid* spindle for mounting the chuck. This fact precluded the use of a drawbar to secure the tools in the spindle and forced me to make the tools in such a way that they can be chuck mounted. My end mills are all single-ended types with relatively short shanks, making them well suited to this form of use.

I needed to produce fairly broad flat surfaces, therefore the first tool which I made up was the fly cutter shown in Photos 3 and 5. As shown in Photo 3, it uses a ¼" carbide-tipped cutting tool held in place by two 8-32 set screws. Starting with a steel rod of 1" diameter and turning in the lathe, the chucking shank was reduced to ½" diameter for a length of 1". The rod was cut off at an angle of approximately 70° to form the head. Photo 4 shows the unfinished fly cutter set in a pair of V-blocks in the vise of the compound slide. The V-blocks were positioned at 20° to the vertical and repeated cuts with a ¼" end mill formed the flat face. It would have been nice to have a fly

3 4

6

cutter to use for
this job! Finally, the
groove for the carbide tool
was milled in with the same end mill.

The holders which I have made for slitting saw
blades and gear cutters are illustrated in
Photos 6, 7, and 8. Making these was purely a
lathe job. They were made from the same rod
as the fly cutter and have the same shank
dimensions. On the face of the head of the
holder, there is an accurately turned spigot
which fits into the central holes in the blade. I
have blades of this type with central holes of
both ⅝" and ¾" diameter, so I made up a holder
for each size. The holders differ from one
another only in the diameter of the spigots and
in the placement of the pin which engages the
keyway in the blade.

After turning the spigot to fit the hole in the
cutter closely, a suitable spot was located on
the face of the head. The spot was drilled and
reamed ³⁄₃₂" and a hardened pin pressed in and

5 ground off flush with the face of the spigot.

When the blade is placed on the holder, the pin fits into the keyway in the blade and insures that the blade cannot slip. The center of each holder is tapped ¼"-20 for the socket head cap screw which holds the outer cap in place and secures the blade. The outer cap has a shallow recess at the center so that the edge of the cap surrounds the spigot (clearing the driving pin), bears against the blade and presses it against the face of the holder.

Photo 7 shows work held in the jaws of the compound slide being slit off by a 2" diameter blade. The operation shown in Photo 8 is the cutting of a 40-tooth gear of 48 diametral pitch (DP). The blank for the gear was turned in place on the short mandrel in the lathe. The lathe chuck was transferred to the indexing head which was set up for milling the teeth on the drill press. In this small pitch, I am able to form the teeth to full depth on a single pass. I have not cut gears above 16 DP and must take the metal out in two passes on the larger size teeth.

An extremely useful accessory for clamping and holding work is the small milling table visible in Photos 8 through 12. It is a good example of a variety of milling operations, all of which were done right on the drill press, itself.

To make the table, I cut off a 3" x 4" piece of aluminum plate of 1" thickness. None of these dimensions are critical, but they happen to be convenient in fitting the table to my compound slide. The first machining operation was to hold the block on edge in the vise jaws of the compound slide and fly cut each side and end, in turn, to make them flat, smooth, and square to one another.

Then, using an end mill, repeat cuts were taken across the 1" x 4" faces to leave the ledges which can be seen to rest on the tops of the vise jaws on the slide. The ledges provide a quick and accurate means of positioning the table in the jaws when setting it up to hold other work.

7

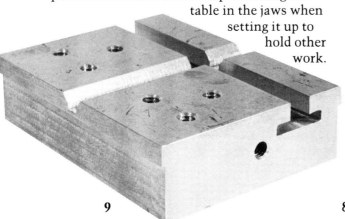

9

8

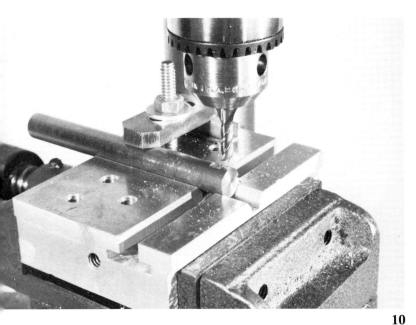

10

11

12

At this point in making the table, they were used to position the table accurately in the vise jaws while an end mill and ¾″ diameter Woodruff cutter were used, in turn, to cut the T-slot for clamping work to the table.

While I like the flexibility of T-slot clamping, I also like to use studs threaded directly into a table, so I made six holes tapped ¼″-20 for this use. The pilot holes for the ¼″-20 threads were drilled all the way through so that the chips from milling fall through the table and do not build up to clog them. Examples of clamping with fixed studs or T nuts can be seen in Photos 10, 11, and 12.

An interesting and useful feature of my small milling table is the V-groove which is at right angles to the T-slot. To form the V-groove, I first used an end mill to cut away the bulk of the metal. Then I ground a tool with a 90° V-shaped point and milled away the edges of the groove to form the V shape. The bottom of the groove was deliberately left flat and square, as formed by the end mill, to allow clearance for drills or other tools which pass through work clamped in the V-groove.

Photos 10 and 11 show two examples of jobs being done on the milling table where the V-groove positions round stock securely and eliminates the need for using a pair of V-blocks. In Photo 10, a small woodruff cutter was being used to cut a keyway in a rod. An end mill was being used in Photo 11 to form a flat seat for a set screw on the side of the same rod. Milling operations do not have to be confined to the top surface of the table, either. As Photo 12 shows, flat stock or long items may be clamped with some reasonable overhang for edge profiling with end mills or similar cuts.

At the time of writing these notes, I have had this particular drill press for somewhat more than a year. In addition to fitting it with the compound slide and making the tools and accessories illustrated and described in this article, I have been building a 1¼″ scale model of Geiser *Peerless* steam traction engine. All of the milling work connected with the model (including milling the gears in the drive train) has been done on the machine shown, using the tools and methods described. From my experience with it, I have no hesitancy to recommend that anyone needing the services of a light, vertical milling machine for building models or other things should look into the possibility of doing such work on a good drill press.

An Automatic Parallel

My drawing board is a commercially built unit that I bought several years ago. It is one of the smaller sized boards with a top surface of 23 x 31 inches. Despite its small size, it is very well built with solid oak framing and a genuine butcher block top which has metal-bound sides. While boards of such quality were not prohibitively expensive at the time I bought it, drafting machines and automatic parallels were. Having invested my money (wisely) in a sturdy, new board, I proceeded to draw with a conventional "T" square. It worked, of course, but a "T" square leaves much to be desired. Very little time passed before my mind was made up to make some sort of automatic parallel to use on it.

The automatic parallel described in this article is the result of that decision. All of the materials used in its construction are readily available and inexpensive. A check of local hardware stores at the time of writing this article indicates that my original automatic parallel, which can be seen clearly in Photo 1, can be duplicated today for less than $7.00. Not bad for these inflated times! By comparison, the local drafting supply shop prices a 30" automatic parallel at a figure that wipes out a fifty dollar bill.

The heart of the automatic parallel is the straight edge used for drawing the lines. Many hardware and discount stores have a display of aluminum straight edges made by a company in Milwaukee, Wisconsin, under the Johnson trademark. These are marked with inch marks, numbers, and fractions of inches in addition to other marks for use by the building trades. They range in size from 12" up to five or six feet. The one selected for my use was the 36" model which is designated J36. This particular straight edge is 2" wide and .075" thick.

As you would imagine, with these proportions, it was quite flexible from end to end. Therefore, I added a half-inch square maple stiffening strip to the top surface. The stiffener is 27" long. It is attached centrally to the straight edge by six No. 2-56 flathead machine screws which are spaced at 5" intervals. I match-drilled the stiffener and straight edge to get the holes in the right places. Then I countersunk from the underside of the straight edge to set the heads

of the screws just below the surface. The top of the stiffener is counterbored to accept the nuts. I used screws of ½" length to insure that they do not stick up through the top of the stiffener. In use, the stiffener provides a good finger grip for moving the parallel besides making a convenient pencil ledge. While the maple strip was available and convenient for me to use, there is no reason that some other material would not prove just as serviceable. Even a piece of aluminum angle of a small size would be worth considering.

1

The pulleys (Part 1) were turned for my parallel from a tight, hard grade of furniture plywood that was salvaged from some long-forgotten TV cabinet. I cut them from the piece of plywood using a circle cutter on a drill press. Then I put each of them in the three-jaw chuck on a lathe to true the central hole and turn the groove where the string runs. Lengths of brass tubing serve for the bearings (Part 3) in the pulleys. They are a press fit in the central hole of the pulleys, but they could have been made looser and secured with epoxy or other suitable adhesive. The journals (Part 4) were made at the same time as the bearings. The journals are a free-running fit in the bearings and are about

2

.06" longer than the bearings to give clearance for a washer between the pulley and the pulley mount (Part 2).

Cut the pulley mounts from steel flat stock. Mark out the hole locations, as shown in the drawings. Refer to Photo 2 for a close-up view of the pulley on the pulley mount. Note that a No. 8-32 machine screw passes through a close-fitting washer, then through the journal which is inside the bearing in the pulley. A larger, flat washer is between the pulley and the pulley mount for clearance, as noted above. The larger washer has a central hole big enough to fit over the journal. Note that two No. 6 x ¾" wood screws attach each pulley mount to the lower surface of the drawing board.

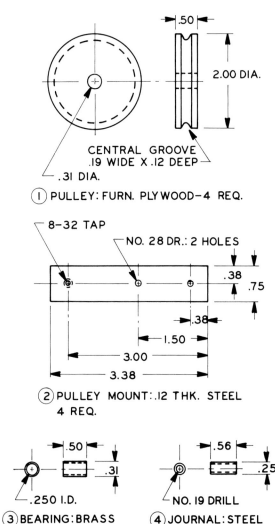

.50

2.00 DIA.

CENTRAL GROOVE
.19 WIDE X .12 DEEP

.31 DIA.

(1) PULLEY: FURN. PLYWOOD—4 REQ.

8-32 TAP

NO. 28 DR.: 2 HOLES

.38

.75

.38

1.50

3.00

3.38

(2) PULLEY MOUNT: .12 THK. STEEL
4 REQ.

.50

.31

.250 I.D.

(3) BEARING: BRASS
4 REQ.

.56

.25

NO. 19 DRILL

(4) JOURNAL: STEEL
4 REQ.

At this point, you will have to determine where to place the pulley mounts. Refer to Photo 3 to get the general idea. Pay particular attention to the crossed pattern made by the strings at the back of the board. It is necessary to place the pulley mounts in a position where the strings

3

can run parallel to the outsides of the reinforcing cleats under the board and still get around the ends of the cleats to pass diagonally across the center of the board. Obviously, the string has to be clear of the cleats at all points without rubbing, and the pulleys must not contact the cleats. When you are determining the positions for attaching the pulley mounts, hold them in place with small clamps. Then you will be able to stretch a string across the pulleys to be sure that the pulleys are located in a way to provide the necessary clearances. Once you are satisfied with the arrangement, you can put in the wood screws to hold them permanently.

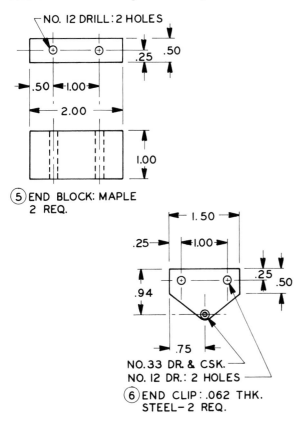

⑤ END BLOCK: MAPLE
2 REQ.

⑥ END CLIP: .062 THK.
STEEL— 2 REQ.

Now is the time to make the end bocks (Part 5) and the end clips (Part 6). The No. 12 drilled holes in these parts are clearance size for the No. 10-24 bolts that secure the parts to the straight edge as shown in Photo 3 and in the close-up view in Photo 4. The end blocks on my parallel were made from maple, as called out on the drawing. There is no reason that aluminum could not be used for this part. Use the end block and end clip assembly to locate the positions for drilling the clearance holes in the straight edge. Once again, clamp these parts in place to find the correct position. The parts detailed in the drawings are exactly to the dimensions I used. When the parts are all assembled, there is .25" clearance on each side of the board between the end block and the side

of the board. Also, there is .25" clearance between the end clip and the bottom of the board. The clearances are needed to permit moving the automatic parallel over the board freely and to give it a little "lift" to clear the papers, triangles, and other thin materials used in drafting. Note that the strings run parallel to the other sides of the cleats as shown in Photo 4.

The No. 33 drilled and countersunk hole in the end clip is for a No. 4-40 flathead screw. The countersink places the head flush and prevents it from digging into the lower side of the board. Cut a short piece of .125 ID brass tubing, about .25" long to fit on each 4-40 screw where it is held by a nut. Its purpose is to prevent the threads of the 4-40 screw from chafing the loops of the strings.

Two separate strings are required to set up the automatic parallel. Notice in Photo 3 that the first string starts out at the 4-40 screw in the end clip on the left. From the screw, it runs up around the top pulley, then diagonally across the board where it runs under the lower pulley and goes up to the 4-40 screw in the opposite end clip. The second string begins at the 4-40 screw in the end clip on the right. From the screw, it runs up over the top pulley and crosses the board on a diagonal to pass under the lower pulley and connect up to the 4-40 screw where the first string started. It is the crossed pattern of the strings that makes the automatic parallel stay in its parallel position.

It is important that both strings be of the same length to keep the parallel in a horizontal position. If the strings are of different lengths, the parallel will hold its position on the board, but it will always be at a slant. The twisted nylon twine which I used on my setup is size No. 12, which has a 106 pound test strength. It was manufactured by Wellington Puritan Mills, Inc., Madison, Georgia 30650, and has catalog number 10469 (G5112Z0300). It is sold in many hardware and other types of stores in this area, but the label information is included here for the convenience of anyone who has trouble finding it.

My first thought was that a spring would be needed somewhere in each string. Not so, however. The nylon strings are a bit stretchy which seems to be adequate. To find the exact length for the strings, make one as close as possible to correct length. Then stretch the second one into place and mark its loop-to-loop length. By taking the average of the two loop-to-loop lengths, you will know the exact length

4

needed for a proper pair of strings. Note in the close-up (Photo 4) that I did not tie any knots in the strings. Instead, I formed the loops around a rod and tied them off by wrapping with a tough button thread. When I was sure that I was satisfied with the fit of the strings, I coated each wrapping with epoxy and allowed it to cure for a permanent, tough job.

There is considerable variation between drawing boards with regard to their top dimensions. Also, there is likely to be quite a difference in the sizes and locations of the reinforcing cleats on the back of the boards. Because of the differences, it is not possible to give exact details for an automatic parallel that will fit every board that comes along. Anyone who wants to make an automatic parallel will have to examine the board first and possibly make some slight changes in the dimensions indicated in the drawings to allow for any variations between boards. However, the principles covered in this article are universally applicable, and the automatic parallel is equally useful for either right- or left-handers. It is much more pleasant and accurate to draw with an automatic parallel than a "T" square. In short, it is well worth the small amount of time needed to construct one and assemble it on the drawing board.

Engine Projects

Steam Engine

With the acquisition of a few tools, there usually comes a desire to put them to use on a project other than making more tools and accessories. Small engines, of one sort or another, make good projects for construction in the home shop since they give an outlet for doing reasonably precise work. Any home-built tools or accessories are certain to be useful on such projects, giving the builder the satisfaction of putting them to the test while further developing his skills.

With this thought in mind, I present the small steam engine shown in Photo 1 and detailed in the accompanying drawings. I hope the construction of the engine will appeal to readers as a small shop project. In the last section of this book, we have gone over a number of accessories that can be home-built, along with some suggestions for making a variety of setups in which they may be used. All of the tools and techniques that have been described are applicable to this engine and will be found helpful in its construction. All the materials used in the engine are readily available stock forms, such as rods, bars, flats, or angles.

Refer to the assembly drawing to obtain an overall view of what parts must be made for the engine and how they relate to one another.

The fabrication of the individual parts will be described in the same sequence as the part numbers appearing on the assembly drawing.

It is apparent from the drawing that this engine is of the single-action type. The piston-type valve admits steam to the cylinder during the outward stroke of the piston and opens to exhaust during the inward stroke of the piston. The importance of careful work and careful fitting cannot be overemphasized. For good performance, the parts of this engine, like any other engine, must fit together in such a way that all mechanical motions occur smoothly and evenly with no rubs, binds, or tight spots. This does not mean that the parts should fit loosely or have sloppy joints. It does mean that the extra time employed in obtaining proper fits will show up in the finished engine as reliable, trouble-free operation.

Begin the construction of the engine by marking the outline of the Bed (Part 1) on a piece of suitable flat stock. I used aluminum in the prototype, but there is no reason that brass or CRS could not be used just as

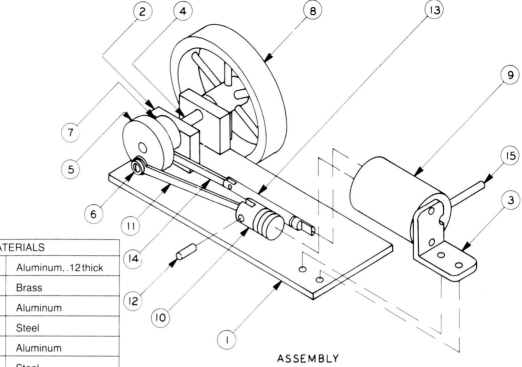

BILL OF MATERIALS		
1	Bed	Aluminum, .12 thick
2	Bearing (2 req.)	Brass
3	Cylinder Mounting	Aluminum
4	Crankshaft	Steel
5	Crank	Aluminum
6	Crankpin	Steel
7	Eccentric	Brass
8a	Rim	Steel
8b	Spoke (6 req.)	Steel
8c	Hub	Steel
9	Cylinder	Brass
10	Piston	Aluminum
11	Connecting Rod	Aluminum, .062 thick
12	Wristpin	Steel
13	Valve	Aluminum
14	Eccentric Rod	Aluminum, .062 thick
15	Steam Pipe	Copper Tube, .12 OD

ASSEMBLY

coincide with the bolt holes in the bearings and the cylinder mounting. Punch each hole location with a sharp punch, center drill to start the holes, and drill with a No. 33 drill.

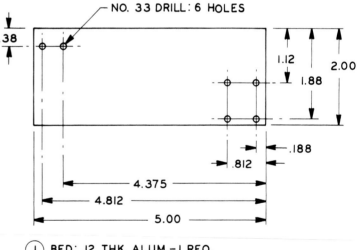

① BED: .12 THK. ALUM.—1 REQ.

effectively. Saw the part out staying clear of the lines to allow for finishing. It is a very desirable condition to have the edges straight and square to one another to provide accurate references for measurement and alignment of the components during the erection of the engine. Of course, there is no reason that careful work with files cannot produce accurate work, so the part may be finished to the marks in this way. However, a milling setup in which the piece is securely clamped to a small milling table can be arranged quickly and is very convenient to use for machining the part. If a milling setup is used to finish the edges, it will produce straight sides in which there is no fear of hooks or bellies.

After finishing the bed to outline, mark out the locations of the six drilled holes. Locate the positions carefully, since they will have to

It is important that the two Bearings (Part 2) be identical to ensure that the crankshaft will fit without binds. Mark the outlines on a piece of brass flat stock. Saw the parts out with allowance for finishing the edges, as with the bed. The bottom surface, which will contact the bed, requires the most accurate finishing. Take a light milling cut to finish it off straight and square to the flat sides. Locate the positions of the two tapped holes. Go through the usual procedure of punching, center drilling, pilot drilling, and tapping to form the threads for the mounting bolts.

Now you are ready to locate the position of the reamed hole. The height of the hole above the bed must coincide with the axis of the engine which passes through the cylinder and the crankshaft. It is a good idea to clamp the two bearings together with their bottom surfaces in line for the drilling and reaming operation to guarantee the alignment of the holes. After reaming, mount the bearings on the bed by means of 4-40 machine screws. Gently pass the reamer through them again; this will eliminate any tendency for the holes to run slightly.

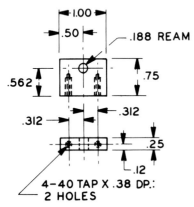

.188 REAM

1.00
.50
.562
.75
.312
.312
.25
.12

4-40 TAP X .38 DP.:
2 HOLES

② BEARING: BRASS—2 REQ.

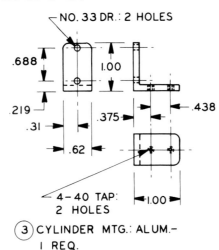

NO. 33 DR.: 2 HOLES

.688
1.00
.219
.375
.438
.31
.62

4-40 TAP:
2 HOLES
1.00

③ CYLINDER MTG.: ALUM.—
1 REQ.

Make the Cylinder Mounting (Part 3) from a short piece of aluminum angle that is .12" thick. A flycutter in a milling setup will do a nice job of finishing the edges. Locate the holes carefully. The tapped holes will be used to mount the part on the bed by means of machine screws passing through the bed. The drilled holes will clear machine screws passing into the cylinder. After drilling and tapping the holes in accordance with the drawing, radius the four corners with a file to improve the appearance of the part. Now refer to the assembly drawing. You will notice a curved notch in one vertical edge of the cylinder mounting. The notch is needed to clear the valve when the engine is assembled. I think it

is best to file the notch after making the cylinder, for then the valve chamber can be used as a guide. We will come back to this point later.

A short length of drill rod will make an excellent Crankshaft (Part 4), because drill rod is accurate to diameter, requiring no turning. Cut a piece of rod to length with an allowance for end facing. Chuck the rod in a three-jaw chuck to face off each end in turn. No further work will be necessary on this part just now. Slip it into the bearings mounted on the bed to check that it turns freely in the bearings.

Cut a slice from a 1" diameter aluminum rod for making the Crank (Part 5). Chuck the piece in the three-jaw chuck to take a facing cut across each side. Bring up the tailstock chuck with a center drill to start the hole in the center. Drill the hole through with a pilot drill. Then finish it with a reamer. Scribe a center line across the part. Measure from the central hole to determine the position of the 4-40 tapped hole. Use a sharp center punch to locate the hole. Center drill, drill, and tap. Next, locate the position and put the 6-32 tapped hole in the edge of the part. This hole is for a setscrew to secure the crank to the crankshaft. File a small flat on the side of the crankshaft to form a seat for the setscrew.

The Crankpin (Part 6) for this engine is held in place by a 4-40 machine screw passing through it. This saves doing the operation of cutting a thread on a solid crankpin. Chuck a piece of steel rod in the three-jaw chuck. Use a knife tool to turn down the .188" diameter part which will be the running journal in the connecting rod. Use a center drill and a No. 33 drill in the tailstock chuck to drill through the center. Part off to finish the crankpin.

Machine the Eccentric (Part 7) from a piece of brass rod mounted in the three-jaw chuck. Begin by taking a facing cut across the end of the rod. Then use a knife tool to turn down the .500" diameter part which will run inside the eccentric strap. If your lathe has the spine to part off, do so. If not, saw the piece off, reverse it in the chuck, and take a facing cut across the rough side. The facing operation on the first side will have left tool marks which will accurately locate the center of the piece. Scribe a line through the center mark. Measure along the line from the center mark to locate the position of the .188" reamed hole. Mark the location with a sharp punch. Then, center drill, pilot drill, and ream the hole. Working from the edge, put in the 6-32 tapped hole for the setscrew, as you did on the crank.

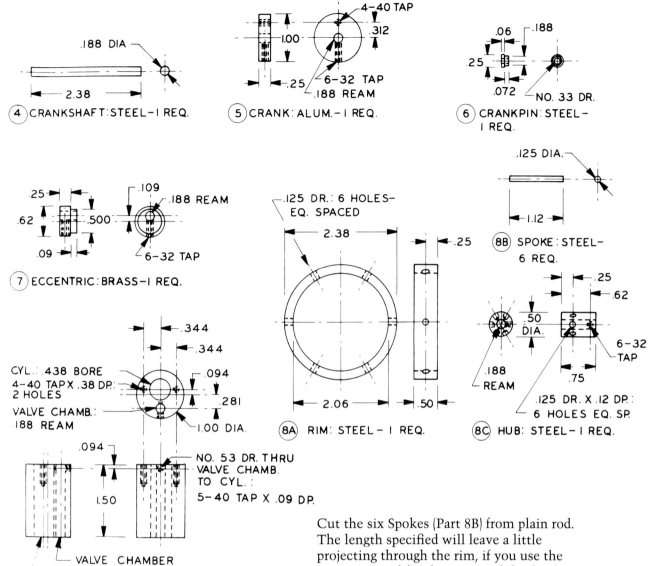

.188 DIA

2.38

4 CRANKSHAFT: STEEL—1 REQ.

4-40 TAP

1.00

.312

.25

6-32 TAP
.188 REAM

5 CRANK: ALUM.—1 REQ.

.06 .188

.25

.072

NO. 33 DR.

6 CRANKPIN: STEEL—
1 REQ.

.25

.62

.500

.09

.109

.188 REAM

6-32 TAP

7 ECCENTRIC: BRASS—1 REQ.

.125 DR.: 6 HOLES-
EQ. SPACED

2.38

.25

2.06

.50

8A RIM: STEEL—1 REQ.

.125 DIA.

1.12

8B SPOKE: STEEL—
6 REQ.

.25

.62

.50 DIA.

.188 REAM

6-32 TAP

.75

.125 DR. X .12 DP.:
6 HOLES EQ. SP.

8C HUB: STEEL—1 REQ.

.344

.344

.094

.281

1.00 DIA.

CYL.: .438 BORE
4-40 TAP X .38 DP.:
2 HOLES
VALVE CHAMB.:
.188 REAM

.094

1.50

NO. 53 DR. THRU
VALVE CHAMB.
TO CYL.:
5-40 TAP X .09 DP.

VALVE CHAMBER
CYL. BORE

9 CYLINDER: BRASS—1 REQ.

Anyone who does not wish to fabricate the spoked Flywheel (Part 8) detailed in the drawings may substitute a solid disk type flywheel for it. In my view, the spoked flywheel adds much to the appearance of the engine and is worth the small amount of extra work involved. I turned the Rim (Part 8A) from a slice of nominal 2″ water pipe. If you have access to some other heavy walled tubing, it would certainly be useable. The diameter specified looks about right for this size engine, but anything in the range of 2″ to 3″ would be acceptable. Chuck the rim with the three-jaw gripping it by the outer surface. Take a facing cut across the edge, and bore the inside with a short boring tool. Reverse in the chuck to take a facing cut across the opposite edge. Mark out the six equally spaced locations for the spoke holes. Follow the usual procedure of punching, center drilling, and drilling.

Cut the six Spokes (Part 8B) from plain rod. The length specified will leave a little projecting through the rim, if you use the same material for the rim as I did. Chuck a short piece of steel rod for making the Hub (Part 8C). Face it off on both ends. Use the tailstock chuck to center drill, drill through, and ream the central hole. Now you can mark out and drill for the six spoke locations. Also, put in the 6-32 tapped hole for the setscrew. Slip the spokes through the rim into the hub. Use a common propane torch as the heat source for soldering all joints between the spokes, hub, and rim. I used "Stainless Steel" solder, which is actually pure tin. When you are preparing to do the soldering, set everything in position as accurately as possible to minimize machining after assembly. Mount the soldered wheel on a mandrel between lathe centers after filing the spoke ends flush with the outside of the rim. Now you can take a truing cut across the face of the flywheel rim. If necessary, skim the edges of the rim, also, to get everything running true.

None of the machining operations on the Cylinder (Part 9) are difficult, but clearances are close. Work slowly and carefully. Cut off a suitable length of brass rod. Gripping it in the three-jaw chuck, face off both ends. Use the pattern left by the facing tool to locate the center, as you did on the eccentric. Scribe a line through the center mark. Using the center mark as a reference, locate the centers of the cylinder bore and the valve chamber. Working from the center of the cylinder bore, locate the two 4-40 tapped holes. Begin by putting in the tapped holes, as you did on the bearings and some of the other parts.

The small diameter of the valve chamber requires reaming in order to produce a suitable hole. If you have a .438″ diameter reamer, you can cut the cylinder bore by reaming, also. If not, this is a good place to use a boring bar between centers. This type of operation has been described earlier in this book.

The last operation is to locate the small hole on the side of the cylinder where the steam pipe screws in. Locate the hole very carefully, because its position relates to the valve timing. Use a sharp punch to mark the position, and start the hole with a small center drill. Drill through the valve chamber into the cylinder bore with a No. 53 drill to form the steam passage. Counter drill with a No. 38 drill into the valve chamber. Tap the

hole 5-40 to a depth of .09″ to accept the thread of the steam pipe.

Fitting the Piston (Part 10) to the cylinder bore is a job that requires precision. Chuck a short length of .50″ diameter rod with about an inch of the rod projecting from the chuck jaws. Take a facing cut across the end. Next, using a sharp turning tool, turn the part down. Don't go for a finished size just yet; it is better to stop when the part is about .010″ too large in diameter to fit the cylinder bore.

With the part still gripped in the chuck, locate the position of the reamed hole for the wristpin. Follow the usual procedure of center drilling, pilot drilling, and reaming to form the hole. At this point you will have to cut the groove where the connecting rod fits into the skirt of the piston. A convenient way to cut the groove is to make a setup in which the chucked part can be fed into a slitting saw blade. If your equipment does not permit such a setup, it may be necessary to cut the groove by hand using a fine saw and needle files.

In either case, the final turning to fit the cylinder can be done after the groove is cut. Use a very sharp tool with a slight radius for the final turning, trying to get as smooth a cut as possible. Advance the tool only a little at a time, and keep checking the part against the cylinder bore for fit. When you are satisfied that the piston will fit the cylinder bore nicely, but without slop, put on a pointed tool like a threading tool to cut the three shallow oil grooves. Now you can either part off the piston or cut it with a saw and face it to length.

Mark out the Connecting Rod (Part 11) on a piece of aluminum. Be careful in locating the two reamed holes, because of their positions

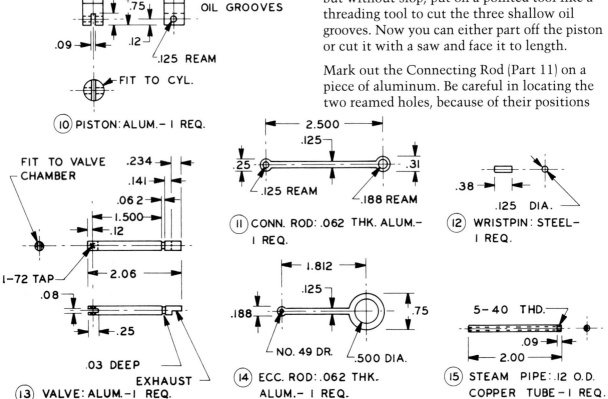

101 PISTON: ALUM.– I REQ.

11 CONN. ROD: .062 THK. ALUM.– I REQ.

12 WRISTPIN: STEEL– I REQ.

13 VALVE: ALUM.–I REQ.

14 ECC. ROD: .062 THK. ALUM.– I REQ.

15 STEAM PIPE: .12 O.D. COPPER TUBE – I REQ.

determine the travel of the piston inside the cylinder. Center drill, drill, and ream both holes before cutting the part out. Use a fine saw to cut it out. Finish to outline either by filing or milling.

The Wristpin (Part 12) is simply a short piece of steel rod. It requires no machining other than a facing cut on each end. Be sure that there are no burrs or sharp corners which could scar the cylinder walls or cause damage to the piston itself.

Turn the Valve (Part 13) from a piece of oversize rod. It will have to fit the valve chamber freely just as the piston fits the cylinder bore. Follow the same general procedure as you did on the piston to put in the 1-72 tapped hole and cut the groove in the end. The radial groove in the opposite end is the steam admission passage. Cut this groove in the lathe by using a narrow tool shaped like a parting tool. Be careful in positioning the groove, since its position relative to the 1-72 tapped hole is important to obtain good valve events. Now you can form the exhaust cavity by end milling. Note that the dimension between the exhaust cavity and the steam groove is also critical to the valve timing.

Construction of the Eccentric Rod (Part 14) is so similar to the construction of the connecting rod that no further description is really needed. Be careful in locating the centers of the two holes. The distance between them will also have an influence on the timing of the valve.

The last part to be made is the Steam Pipe (Part 15). Cut a length of .12" OD copper tube. Cut the 5-40 thread in the lathe using a die held in the tailstock die holder. Before chucking the tube in the three-jaw chuck, insert a short length of rod to protect the tube against the forces of the chuck jaws and the cutting of the thread by the die. If you do not insert the protective rod, you will surely find that the tube will collapse and break.

At this point all of the parts have been constructed, and the final assembly of the engine can begin. Refer to the accompanying photos as well as the assembly drawing while putting the engine together. When you have the crankshaft in place through the eccentric and the bearings, slip the flywheel into place and tighten its setscrew only slightly. This will mark the crankshaft so that you will know exactly where to file another small flat seat for the setscrew to bear against it, as you did for the crank.

Now you can reassemble the crankshaft and its components with the eccentric rod in place on the eccentric. Do *not* file a flat for the setscrew in the eccentric. You will have to adjust the position of the eccentric on the crankshaft for the valve timing. Put light machine oil on all the parts as you put them together.

When you put the cylinder on the cylinder mounting, you will be able to see where to file the notch in the mounting to clear the valve chamber. After filing the notch to clear the valve, make an oiled paper gasket to go between the cylinder and the mounting. Put all the parts together except for the steam pipe. Leave it off until the valve setting is completed. Rotate the flywheel slowly by hand checking to be sure there are no binds or tight spots. If anything "sticks" or feels uneven, take the time to find out why and remedy the situation.

When you are satisfied that everything is moving properly and has been oiled lightly, you are ready for the valve timing operation. Only one adjustment must be made; that is the angular relationship between the crankpin and the eccentric. With the eccentric in any position, rotate the flywheel slowly in the direction you want the engine to run while you watch the motion of the valve through the tapped hole where the steam pipe belongs. As you take it through a full revolution, you will see the steam admission groove in the valve move into position where it is fully exposed in the hole and then recede back into the valve chamber.

Continue to rotate slowly until the position is at its inward dead center position. Clamp the crankshaft in this position so the crankshaft cannot be moved inadvertently. Loosen the setscrew in the eccentric. Slowly rotate the eccentric around the crankshaft in the running direction until you can just see the edge of the groove in the valve about to open the hole and admit steam to the cylinder. Tighten the setscrew at this point and free the crankshaft. Run it through slowly again and check to be sure you are satisfied with the eccentric position. When you are sure it is correct, screw in the steam pipe with a bit of pipe dope on the thread.

Your engine is now ready to run on steam or compressed air.

A Horizontal Stationary Engine Project

Building a small steam engine without the useof castings is an interesting exercise in machining and other shop skills. Particularly so, if pains are taken to detail the finished engine in such a way that is has the appearance of having been built from castings. In designing the horizontal engine shown in Photos 1 and 2, I have attempted to do just that. No castings were used in the original model. Even the curved-spoke flywheels were built up. A variety of metals went into the original, depending upon the nature of the metal and the function of the part to be made from it.

I have broken the assembly of the model down into nine separate subassemblies which are identified in the large assembly drawing and its accompanying key. Each of the subassemblies has been given a number which identifies it. The .0 following the number refers to an isometric view of that particular subassembly. Each detail part of the subassembly is identified by its own number, such as 1.1, 1.2, and 1.3, which are the parts of the Flywheel Assembly, 1.0.

The specified tolerances are given as a guide for the sort of accuracy that seems desirable in making each part. Since each engine will be built on an individual basis with no requirement of interchangeability of parts, it is obvious that most parts will be made and fitted without being held to production standards. Each builder can exercise his own discretion concerning adherence to the tolerances.

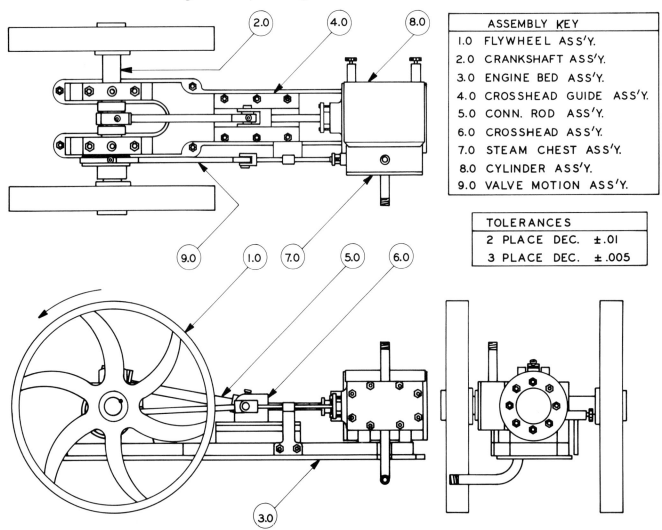

ASSEMBLY KEY	
1.0	FLYWHEEL ASS'Y.
2.0	CRANKSHAFT ASS'Y.
3.0	ENGINE BED ASS'Y.
4.0	CROSSHEAD GUIDE ASS'Y.
5.0	CONN. ROD ASS'Y.
6.0	CROSSHEAD ASS'Y.
7.0	STEAM CHEST ASS'Y.
8.0	CYLINDER ASS'Y.
9.0	VALVE MOTION ASS'Y.

TOLERANCES		
2 PLACE DEC.	±.01	
3 PLACE DEC.	±.005	

1

2

(1.0) FLYWHEEL ASS'Y.

4.06 I.D.

4.44 O.D.   .50

(1.1) RIM : STEEL — 2 REQ.

.69

.31

.62 DIA.

.75 DIA.   .375 REAM

(1.2) HUB : STEEL
2 REQ.

DIA. TO FIT 1.1

1.50 R. TYP.

.75 R.

.19 R. TYP.

.62 I.D.

(1.3) SPOKES:.075 THK. STEEL—2 REQ.

FLYWHEEL ASSEMBLY (1.0)

Begin construction of the Flywheels by cutting two Rims (1.1) from a piece of nominal 4" steel pipe. While this type of metal is not famous for its free-machining characteristics, it makes a serviceable job. There is no guarantee that the inside surface of the pipe will be round. The one I used was anything but round. To true the inner surface, I set it up on a lathe faceplate and took a boring cut. The plywood plate behind the rim in Photo 3 was used to prevent the boring tool from running into the faceplate. The ID indicated on drawing 1.1 may be varied somewhat, depending upon the condition of the steel pipe used. The important points are that the surface be clean steel all the way around for the subsequent soldering operation and that both rims be reasonably close to the same ID. Anyone having a chuck of ample capacity will likely find the setup easier using the chuck rather than the faceplate.

The Hub (Part 1.2) is an easy lathe job. Face off both ends, and turn down the reduced diameter. Don't put in the central hole at this point. The hole will be put in after soldering, to guarantee that it is true to the flywheel as a whole.

My own personal taste is to have the flywheels with curved Spokes, as detailed. Anyone who prefers straight spokes can make Part 1.3 by cutting out a disk of steel and marking out six straight radial spokes. There is no need to do any lathe work on this part. Mark out all spoke locations and shapes with reference to the center, cut out with a hacksaw, and file to the mark. Fit the OD of the spokes to the ID of the rim. Photo 4 indicates what the group of parts looks like for each flywheel just prior to soldering. The parts of my flywheel are joined together by soldering with a product sold as "stainless steel" solder which has a melting point of 450°F. Actually, this solder is lead-free, having a pure tin composition. Photo 5 shows the parts of one flywheel set up for the soldering operation using a common propane torch. In arranging the parts for soldering, I slipped the hub through the central hole of the spokes and placed it with the large diameter down to support both parts. Then the rim was slipped over with small bits of metal shim underneath the edge to support it at the proper height above the fireproof pad. Try to heat all the parts as evenly as possible to help prevent heat distortion or warpage. The type of solder I used has an extremely sharp melting point. I withdrew the heat as soon as the solder melted, because there was no plastic range to the solder, and further heating could serve no purpose.

3

4

5

6

Once the flywheels were cooled, each was returned to the faceplate, as shown in Photo 6. Again, a chuck could have been used. At this point, the already turned inside surface of the rim provided the reference. Mount the flywheel with this surface running true. Take a facing cut across the edge of the rim to get it true. Then shift attention to the outside surface which can be turned at a low speed. When both surfaces of the rim are running true, take a facing cut across the hub. Bring up the tailstock chuck, as shown in Photo 7. Center drill, drill through and ream the center hole. Turn the flywheel over on the faceplate for the final cut which is a facing cut across the opposite edge of the rim and the face of the hub. No further work is needed on the flywheels until the drilling and insertion of the round keys, but the crankshaft will have to be made first.

7

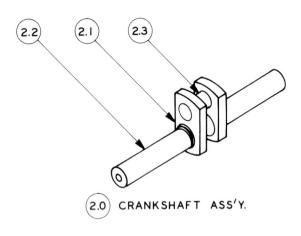

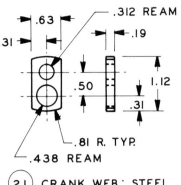
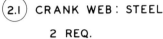
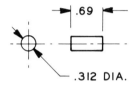

(2.0) CRANKSHAFT ASS'Y.

(2.1) CRANK WEB: STEEL
2 REQ.

.63
.31
.312 REAM
.19
.50
1.12
.31
.81 R. TYP.
.438 REAM

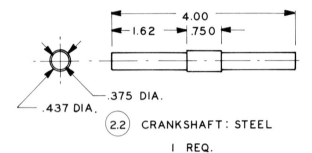

4.00
1.62
.750
.375 DIA.
.437 DIA.

(2.2) CRANKSHAFT: STEEL
1 REQ.

.69
.312 DIA.

(2.3) CRANKPIN: STEEL
1 REQ.

CRANKSHAFT ASSEMBLY (2.0)

There are several ways that crankshafts can be fabricated. The following procedure worked well for me on this and other engines. Cut a short piece of .50" diameter rod for the Crankshaft (2.2). Use the steady rest to face off and center drill each end so that the piece may be turned between lathe centers. Photo 8 shows the center drilling operation. The reason for putting the shaft between centers is to guarantee that the .437" and .375" diameter surfaces are concentric to one another and parallel throughout their length. The .437" diameter part in the center will fit into the Crank Webs (2.1). The .375" diameter parts will fit the hubs of the flywheels and be a running fit in the Main Bearings (3.5).

Next, cut the crank webs from suitable flat stock. Mark out the centers, and file to shape. It is important that these parts be made as a pair so they will have identical throws. Photo 9 shows the pieces set up for pilot drilling the holes. To insure that the holes would be parallel, I set them up, as shown, in my cross vise. After the first hole was drilled and reamed, I traversed the vise to the position of the next hole. Note the parallel jaw clamps holding the pieces together in the vise jaws. After the parts were reamed, they were separated. It is worthwhile to put witness marks on them so they can be kept in the same relative position to one another as the position in which they are reamed. Put a shallow countersink of about .03" on the *inside* of each web at the .438" diameter hole and on the *outside* of each web at the .312" diameter hole. The countersinks will help the solder to flow into the joints as the parts are put together.

A short piece of drill rod was used for the Crankpin (2.3). Drill rod runs true to diameter

8

9 **10**

11 **12**

13

14

and requires no turning. I cut it off about .06" longer than the required length to leave a little metal projecting on each side of the webs at assembly. Photo 10 shows the group of parts making up the crankshaft ready for assembly.

Slip the parts together for soldering. Reference to Photo 11 will give an idea of what the crankshaft should look like at this point. Note that the .438" diameter part of the shaft (2.2) projects about .03" on each side of the outer faces of the webs, forming a small shoulder. The measurement across the outer faces of the webs is .69". I used the same type of solder on the crankshaft as I did on the flywheel. I'm not certain whether or not it has adequate strength by itself. To be on the safe side, I pinned the four joints immediately after soldering. Photo 11 shows the operation of cross-drilling each joint with drill no. 52. The steel pins which I pressed into the holes were made from 16-gauge wire brads. After a few minutes of checking with the micrometer, I had selected several which were about .0005" oversize for a press fit into the holes. I found that easing the ends off a bit with a fine file helped them to start easily. My pins pass all the way through each joint and are filed flush at the surfaces of the webs. This is a good point to file off the ends of the crankpin to make it flush with the outer faces of the webs. Don't cut away the central part of the shaft, yet. There is one more operation to do first.

Refer to Photo 12 which shows one flywheel in place on the end of the crankshaft and the whole lot on end in the jaws of the cross vise. The drilling operation in progress is to make the ways for the round keys which secure the flywheels to the crankshaft. By careful drilling with drill no. 52, I drilled a hole to a depth of about .38" with the drill cutting half into the crankshaft and half into the hub of the flywheel, as indicated on the large assembly drawing. Actually, I drilled each end to a slightly different depth to insure that each wheel would always be returned to the same position on the shaft. The round keys were made from the 16 gauge brads, the same as the cross pins through the webs. Once the end pressure of drilling for the keys and fitting them to the holes is over, you can cut away the part of the shaft between the webs and file it flush and smooth. Note in Photo 13 that the end of the key is visible sticking out from the end of the shaft. I left them long to facilitate their removal. They can be pulled very easily with pliers despite the fact that they hold the flywheels tightly in place.

15

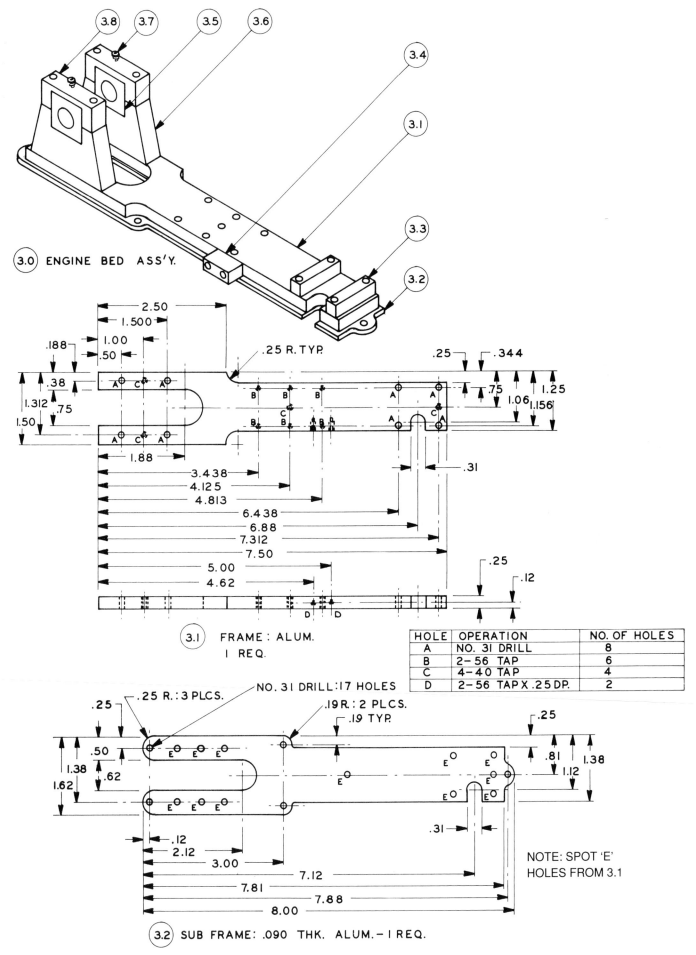

3.8 3.7 3.5 3.6

3.4

3.1

3.3

3.0 ENGINE BED ASS'Y.

3.2

2.50
1.500
1.00
.50
.188
.38
.75
1.312
1.50
.25 R. TYP.
.25 .344
.75
1.06 1.25
1.156

A C A
B B B
C
A A
A B B
C
A

.31

1.88
3.438
4.125
4.813
6.438
6.88
7.312
7.50
5.00
4.62

.25
.12

D D

3.1 FRAME : ALUM.
1 REQ.

HOLE	OPERATION	NO. OF HOLES
A	NO. 31 DRILL	8
B	2-56 TAP	6
C	4-40 TAP	4
D	2-56 TAP X .25 DP.	2

NO. 31 DRILL: 17 HOLES
.25 R.: 3 PLCS.
.19 R.: 2 PLCS.
.19 TYP.
.25
.50
.62
1.38
1.62
E E E
E
E E E
E
E
E E
E E
E

.81
1.12
1.38

.31

.12
2.12
3.00
7.12
7.81
7.88
8.00

NOTE: SPOT 'E'
HOLES FROM 3.1

3.2 SUB FRAME: .090 THK. ALUM.— 1 REQ.

16 **17**

18 **19**

ENGINE BED ASSEMBLY (3.0)

A length of .25 x 1.50" aluminum bar stock is ideal for making the Frame (3.1). Check to find one long edge that is straight. Use this as a reference edge, and square the ends to it. Lay out the various hole and edge locations using the straight side and one end as the reference surfaces for the dimensions shown on the drawing. Drill and tap the A, B, and C holes according to the hole schedule tabulated on the drawing. Now the piece can be cut and filed to shape. Don't forget to put in the holes marked D on the edge. These holes are needed for mounting the Guide Spacer (3.4), and part of the steam chest assembly at a later time.

Lay out and make the Sub Frame (3.2). The five holes dimensioned in the drawing of 3.2 can all be marked and drilled through. Clamp the frame and sub frame together as in Photo 14. Spot drill through the A and C holes of the frame to locate the twelve E holes in the sub frame. Drill no. 31 through the E holes. I countersunk all of the E holes from the underside to take the heads of 4-40 flathead screws. If you prefer to use some other head shape, do not countersink, but remember that it will be necessary to provide clearance for them in the base upon which you mount the finished engine. Make the Cylinder Mounts (3.3) and the guide spacer (3.4). These are just

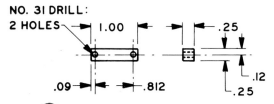

NO. 31 DRILL:
2 HOLES

3.3 CYL. MOUNT: STEEL - 2 REQ.

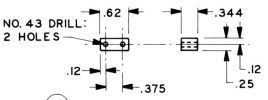

NO. 43 DRILL:
2 HOLES

3.4 GUIDE SPACER: ALUM. -1 REQ.

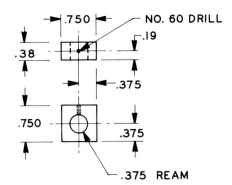

NO. 60 DRILL
.375 REAM

3.5 MAIN BRG.: BRASS - 2 REQ.

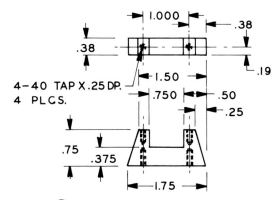

4-40 TAP X .25 DP.
4 PLCS.

3.6 BRG. PEDESTAL: ALUM. - 2 REQ.

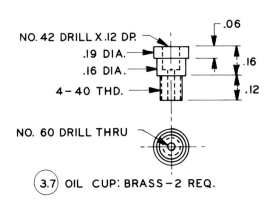

NO. 42 DRILL X .12 DP.
.19 DIA.
.16 DIA.
4-40 THD.

NO. 60 DRILL THRU

3.7 OIL CUP: BRASS - 2 REQ.

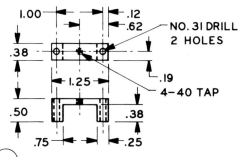

NO. 31 DRILL
2 HOLES
4-40 TAP

3.8 BRG. CAP: ALUM. - 2 REQ.

rectangular shapes with clearance holes drilled through them.

The Main Bearings (3.5) require careful work so they will line up well to support the crankshaft. I made them from pieces cut from a .75" square brass bar. Locate the centers accurately, and mark them with a light punch mark. Set them up on the lathe in the four-jaw chuck for the best accuracy. Use a center finder such as the one described by Kozo Hiraoka to position them truly on the lathe axis. Then proceed to center drill, drill, and ream, as shown in Photo 15. Don't forget to drill the no. 60 hole in the top so that oil can flow from the Oil Cup (3.7) to the crankshaft journal.

Set up the Bearing Pedestals (3.6) to make them as a pair. I used my drill press/milling machine to flycut all edges to the outline

shown. Then I set up the parts for end milling the recess which holds the main bearing (refer to Photos 16 and 17). Photo 16 shows the end milling operation, while Photo 17 shows how the main bearing was used as a gauge to get the recess the right width. The .375" dimension from the bottom is important. This plus the .375" center height of the main bearing

20

determines the center line height of the engine which is planned to be .750" above the Frame (3.1). A similar setup was used to machine the Bearing Caps (3.8). Of course, the depth of the recess is not critical to the main bearing position, in this case. I actually milled these to a depth of .370" to produce a clamping action when they are tightened down with the bearings in place. The oil cups (3.7), are straightforward lathe jobs. I turned them from .19" diameter brass rod.

It is important that the crankshaft be positioned at exact right angles to the midline of the engine. To accomplish this condition, I used the setup shown in Photo 18. The .75" brass bar from which the bearings were made was set in place in the recesses in the pedestals. The straightedge of the bar allowed me to check with a square to get the frame and pedestals aligned. Then I clamped the bar and pedestals as shown to spot-drill through the frame and sub-frame to locate the bolt holes in the pedestals. After tapping the holes, I put in studs cut from 4-40 threaded rod to arrive at the assembly shown in Photo 19. With the crankshaft in place, the assembly had reached the point shown in Photo 20.

21

CROSSHEAD GUIDE ASSEMBLY (4.0) AND CROSSHEAD ASSEMBLY (6.0)

As long as the holes are marked out and drilled accurately, there will be no problems with the parts of the crosshead guide assembly. All the parts are made from flat or bar stock. The thickness of the Spacer (4.3) is critical, inasmuch as it provides the needed clearance height for the Crosshead Slipper (6.1). Photo 21 shows the Crosshead (6.0) in place in the partially assembled Crosshead Guide (4.0). There is a thin shim on the board between the Guide Bar (4.1) and spacer, disassembled. I put

the shim in each side of the assembly to give the proper clearance for the crosshead. My reason for doing this is that, when overhaul time comes, a thinner shim (or no shim at all) is all that will be required to take up wear in the fit of the crosshead to the guide. The thickness of the slipper determines what you do about this. This is an area where each engine will have to be custom-fitted. Studs cut from 2-56 threaded rod hold these parts together on mine.

Cut the slipper (6.1) from half-hard brass bar or flat stock. True up all edges by milling or filing. A small piece of steel is required for the Upright (6.2). After cutting to size and truing the edges, I end milled the connecting rod clearance area in the setup shown in Photo 22. I used a .250" end mill for the cut and deliberately finished the clearance area to a width of .255" to give a bit of slack on either side of the connecting rod. Don't put the holes into the upright until after it is silver soldered to the slipper. The reamed hole for the Wrist Pin (6.3) and the tapped hole for the piston rod will both have to be on the center line height of the engine previously referred to. Therefore, measurements for the holes are most accurately made from the bottom of the slipper after doing the silver soldering. The wrist pin (6.3) is a simple lathe job requiring no explanation.

CONNECTING ROD ASSEMBLY (5.0)

The Rod Bearing (5.6) is split along the vertical center line for assembly on the crankpin. Therefore, it is essential that the bolt holes through the two bearing halves be in precise alignment. To do this, I squared off the end of a .31 x .62" brass bar, marked the hole locations, and drilled in from the end to a depth of .75".

Next, I mounted the brass bar in the cross vise, as shown in Photo 23. Two successive cuts with a slitting blade produced the bearing halves with their holes in perfect alignment. Use bolts through the holes to keep the bearing halves in place for the drilling and reaming operation shown in Photo 24. Take the bearing apart and put in the 2-56 tap for the Oil Cup (5.3). Note that the hole for the oil cup is slightly off center to allow a small amount of clearance for the oil to flow to one side of the bolt that passes through the bearing.

To machine the thrust rings on the sides of the bearing, I put the bearing halves on a mandrel in the lathe setup shown in Photo 25. The mandrel had been turned in place to a diameter that was a line-for-line fit in the bearing. This provided a good, non-slip fit for

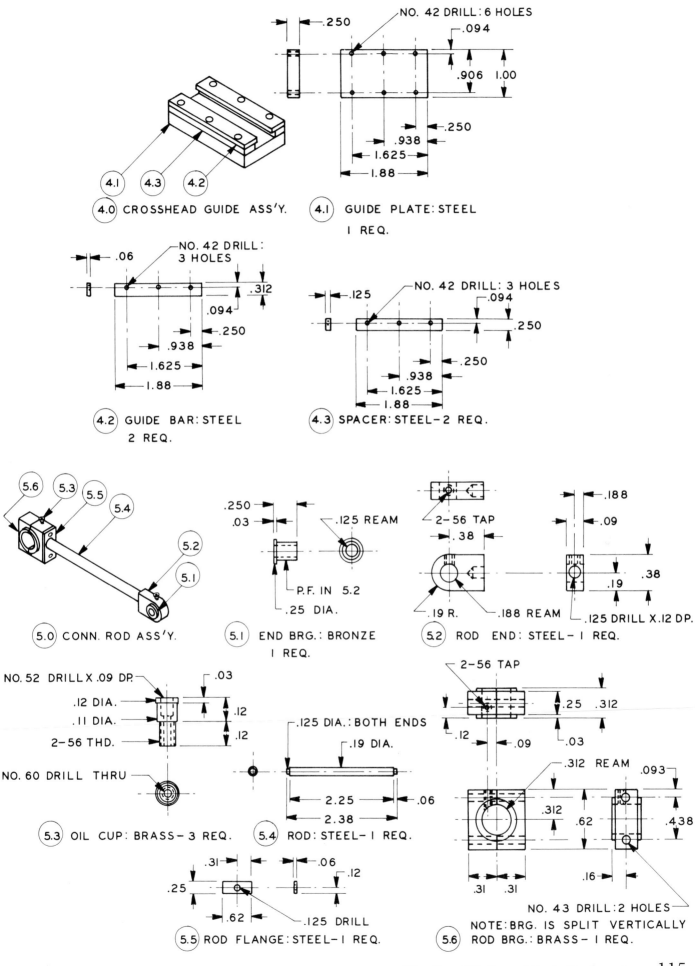

NO. 42 DRILL: 6 HOLES

.250 .094 .906 1.00 .250 .938 1.625 1.88

4.1 4.3 4.2

4.0 CROSSHEAD GUIDE ASS'Y. 4.1 GUIDE PLATE: STEEL
1 REQ.

NO. 42 DRILL: 3 HOLES
.06 .312 .094 .250 .938 1.625 1.88

NO. 42 DRILL: 3 HOLES
.125 .094 .250 .250 .938 1.625 1.88

4.2 GUIDE BAR: STEEL
2 REQ.

4.3 SPACER: STEEL – 2 REQ.

5.6 5.3 5.5 5.4 5.2 5.1

5.0 CONN. ROD ASS'Y.

.250 .03 .125 REAM P.F. IN 5.2 .25 DIA.

5.1 END BRG.: BRONZE
1 REQ.

2-56 TAP .38 .19 R. .188 REAM

.188 .09 .38 .19 .125 DRILL X .12 DP.

5.2 ROD END: STEEL – 1 REQ.

NO. 52 DRILL X .09 DP.
.12 DIA. .11 DIA. 2-56 THD.
.03 .12 .12

NO. 60 DRILL THRU

5.3 OIL CUP: BRASS – 3 REQ.

.125 DIA.: BOTH ENDS .19 DIA. 2.25 2.38 .06

5.4 ROD: STEEL – 1 REQ.

2-56 TAP .12 .09 .25 .312 .03 .312 REAM .312 .62 .31 .31

.093 .438 .16 NO. 43 DRILL: 2 HOLES

.31 .06 .12 .25 .62 .125 DRILL

5.5 ROD FLANGE: STEEL – 1 REQ.

NOTE: BRG. IS SPLIT VERTICALLY
5.6 ROD BRG.: BRASS – 1 REQ.

22   23

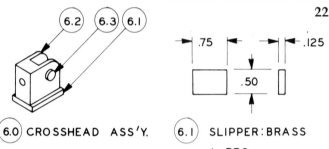

6.0 CROSSHEAD ASS'Y.

6.1 SLIPPER : BRASS
1 REQ.

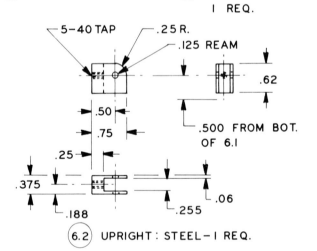

6.2 UPRIGHT : STEEL—1 REQ.

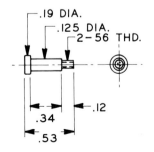

6.3 WRIST PIN : STEEL
1 REQ.

the light facing cuts required. The bearing was faced on one side and then turned for a duplicate cut on the opposite side.

The Rod (5.4) and the Rod Flange (5.5) require no explanation. When making the Rod End (5.2), mark out and punch the location of the 2-56 tapped hole, but don't put it in until the assembly is finished. The rod end and rod flange can be put in place on the rod and the two end joints silver soldered. Now is the time to clamp the halves of the rod bearing together with the rod flange to match drill the rod flange for the bolt holes. Note in Photo 26 that one hole had already been drilled. A bolt was in place through it, and the second side was being held by a clamp.

Turn the small End Bearing (5.1) from a piece of bronze or brass rod. Make the OD a press fit in the .188" reamed hole in the rod end. Center drill and pilot drill the bearing, but don't put the .125" reamer through just yet. It is better to press the bearing into the rod and then ream it in place. This is also the time to put in the 2-56 tapped hole for the oil cup, cutting through the side of the end bearing for entry of the oil into the bearing. The reason for making three of the oil cups (5.3) is that two are needed for the connecting rod assembly and one will also be needed later for the Valve Motion Assembly (9.0). The complete set of parts that make up the connecting rod assembly is shown in Photo 27.

STEAM CHEST ASSEMBLY (7.0)

The Steam Chest Cover (7.1) is made from .063" thick brass. Cut it to size, and square up

24

25

26

the sides. Select one side and one end as the base lines. Mark out the hole positions from these. Be very careful in doing the layout of the holes. There is very little clearance in the walls of the Steam Chest (7.2) and the cylinder, and the stud holes in these parts will be located by using the steam chest cover as a drilling jig.

To make the steam chest (7.2), cut a piece of brass bar to length and square the ends. Use the steam chest cover as the drilling jig to locate and drill the eight no. 43 holes for the studs that will secure the steam chest to the cylinder. Next, cut away the metal to form the hollow inside. This could be done by drilling followed by filing. I set up my drill press/milling machine and removed the metal by end milling. Then I used a setup like the one shown in Photo 28 to form the stuffing box by cutting away surplus metal with an end mill. Note that both glands on this model are plain types held in place by 1/72 hex head bolts passing through the gland flanges into tapped holes in the stuffing boxes. Use a setup like that in Photo 28 to drill for the gland and to ream through for the entry of the Valve Stem (7.10). I

27 traversed the part

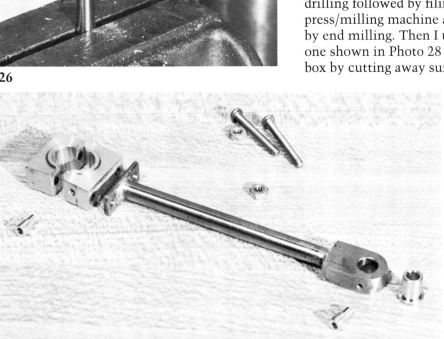

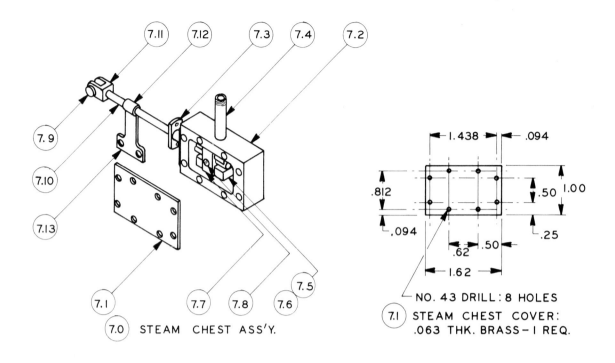

7.0 STEAM CHEST ASS'Y.

7.1 STEAM CHEST COVER: .063 THK. BRASS—1 REQ.

NO. 43 DRILL : 8 HOLES

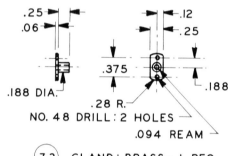

7.3 GLAND : BRASS—1 REQ.

.188 DIA.
.28 R.
NO. 48 DRILL : 2 HOLES
.094 REAM

7.4 STEAM PIPE : COPPER—1 REQ.

10–32 THD. : BOTH ENDS
.19 TYP.
3/16 O.D. TUBE
1.00

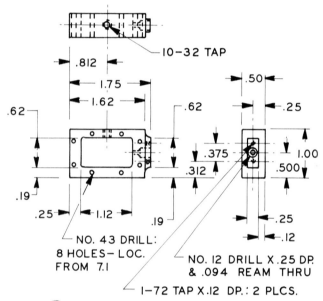

7.2 STEAM CHEST : BRASS — REQ.

10–32 TAP

NO. 43 DRILL:
8 HOLES—LOC.
FROM 7.1

NO. 12 DRILL X .25 DP.
& .094 REAM THRU

1–72 TAP X .12 DP. : 2 PLCS.

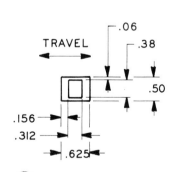

7.5 VALVE FACE : .062 THK.
STAINLESS—1 REQ.

TRAVEL

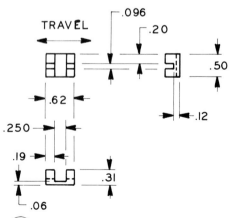

7.6 VALVE BACK : BRASS—1 REQ.

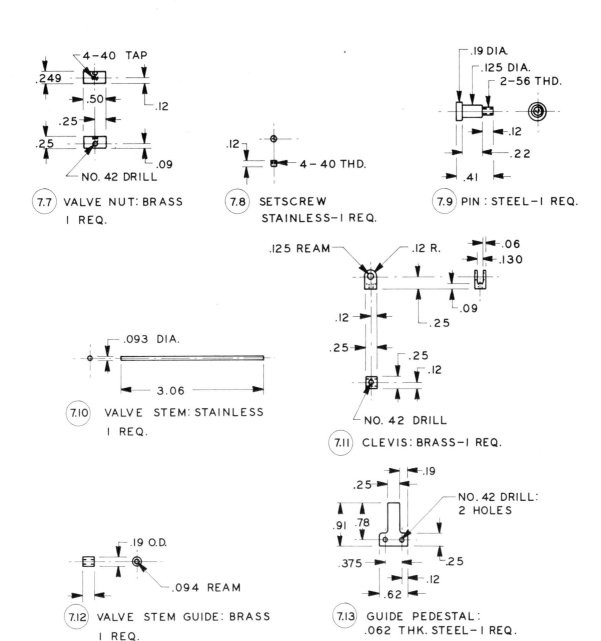

7.7 VALVE NUT: BRASS
1 REQ.

7.8 SETSCREW
STAINLESS-1 REQ.

7.9 PIN : STEEL-1 REQ.

7.10 VALVE STEM: STAINLESS
1 REQ.

7.11 CLEVIS: BRASS-1 REQ.

7.12 VALVE STEM GUIDE: BRASS
1 REQ.

7.13 GUIDE PEDESTAL:
.062 THK. STEEL-1 REQ.

to either side of the central hole to tap the 1-72 bolt holes for securing the Gland (7.3). Don't go too deep with the 1-72 holes lest they run into the previously drilled no. 43 stud holes in the end. Put in the 10-32 hole for the Steam Pipe (7.4) to complete the steam chest.

The gland (7.3) can be machined from a solid piece of brass rod. Or you may prefer to make it in two pieces, as I did. I made the cylindrical part from a piece of .188" diameter brass rod and the head from a length of .06 x .25" brass strip. I silver soldered the two pieces together. Then I chucked the part by the cylindrical end to complete the machining. This is a good time to chuck a piece of steel rod and make the Pin (7.9).

Quite a few of my engines have brass-over-stainless composite slide valves of the type that I am specifying for this engine. There are several advantages to using a valve with a

28

stainless steel face. To begin with, the exhaust cavity can be accurately cut to size by drilling and filing, thus eliminating a delicate end milling job. Secondly, the stainless face never galls the port face the way some brass valves do. None of my engines having the composite valve has ever worn enough to require relapping of the valve or port face surfaces. Mark out the Valve Face (7.5) on a piece of stainless. Drill through and shape the

29   **30**

exhaust cavity by filing away with needle files. Cut and file to the outside marks. Be careful about hitting the .625" dimension. This dimension is a factor in the steam lap of the engine and plays an important role in the valve events. Put the valve face aside and cut a piece of brass for the Valve Back (7.6). Don't cut the grooves in this part yet. First, silver solder the face and back together to make the complete valve shape. Then it is much easier to position the complete valve for end milling the grooves. The .250" groove engages the Valve Nut (7.7) and the .096" groove engages the valve stem (7.10). Use a short piece of stainless rod threaded 4-40 for the Setscrew (7.8). With a fine hacksaw, cut a shallow screwdriver slot across one end. Make the valve nut (7.7) from a piece of brass, and screw the stainless setscrew into the tapped hole.

The valve stem (7.10) is simply a piece of stainless steel rod cut to length. To make the Clevis (7.11) I drilled a no. 42 hole into the end of a .25" square piece of brass. Then I silver soldered the valve stem into the hole. Next, I located and reamed the .125" hole that engages the pin (7.9) and formed the .12" radius by filing. My milling arrangement for cutting the inside is shown in Photo 29. I simply clamped the part flat on the milling table and used a slitting saw blade to cut the metal away. The blade was relatively narrow, necessitating several passes to make the opening full width. The slide valve and its immediately associated parts are all shown in Photo 30.

You may wish to use some particular length for the steam pipe (7.4) to suit an installation you have in mind for the model. If not, the 1.00" length does nicely to connect to a steam

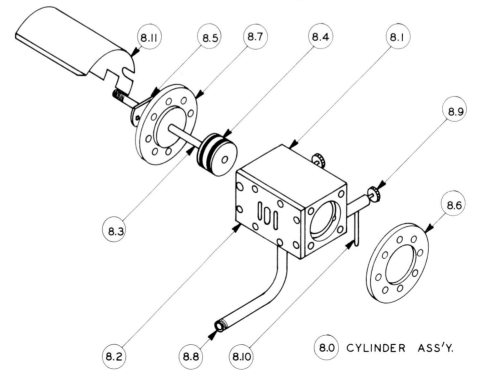

8.0 CYLINDER ASS'Y.

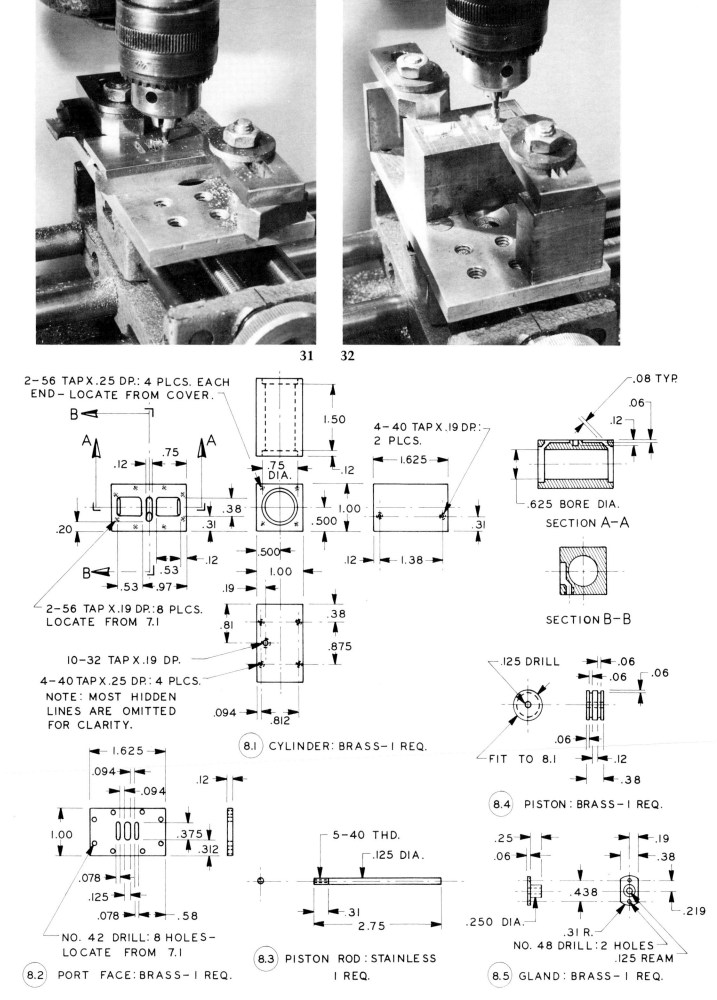

31 32

2-56 TAP X .25 DP.: 4 PLCS. EACH
END — LOCATE FROM COVER.

B

A   A
.12   .75

.20

B
.53   .97
.53

2-56 TAP X .19 DP.: 8 PLCS.
LOCATE FROM 7.1

10-32 TAP X .19 DP.

4-40 TAP X .25 DP.: 4 PLCS.
NOTE: MOST HIDDEN
LINES ARE OMITTED
FOR CLARITY.

.38
.31
.12

.53

1.50
.12

.75
DIA.

1.00
.500

.500
1.00

.19

.81

.38
.875

.094
.812

4-40 TAP X .19 DP.:
2 PLCS.

1.625

.31

.12   1.38

8.1 CYLINDER: BRASS—1 REQ.

.08 TYP.
.06
.12

.625 BORE DIA.
SECTION A-A

SECTION B-B

.125 DRILL   .06
.06   .06

.06
FIT TO 8.1   .12
.38

8.4 PISTON: BRASS—1 REQ.

1.625
.094
.094   .12

1.00

.375
.312

.078
.125
.078   .58

NO. 42 DRILL: 8 HOLES—
LOCATE FROM 7.1

8.2 PORT FACE: BRASS—1 REQ.

5-40 THD.
.125 DIA.

.31
2.75

8.3 PISTON ROD: STAINLESS
1 REQ.

.25   .19
.06   .38

.438

.250 DIA.

.31 R.

NO. 48 DRILL: 2 HOLES
.125 REAM

.219

8.5 GLAND: BRASS—1 REQ.

33   34

source. The cutting of the 10-32 threads is not as difficult as one might think. It is essential to insert a piece of .125" diameter rod into the 3/16" copper tubing to prevent the tubing from collapsing during the thread cutting. I chucked the tube with the rod in place and cut the thread with a die held in the tailstock dieholder.

Cut the Guide Pedestal (7.13) from steel, and silver solder it to the Valve Stem Guide (7.12). I waited until after the silver soldering to put in the final ream of the .094" diameter hole through the guide. The no. 42 holes will be used to bolt the part in position on the

guide spacer (3.4). The holes may be drawn or elongated with a round needle file if any alignment problems arise later on.

CYLINDER ASSEMBLY (8.0)

A good place to begin construction of the parts for the cylinder group is with the Port Face (8.2). Cut a piece of brass to outline, and finish the edges square by milling or filing. Lay out the positions of the two steam ports and the exhaust port. Measure these very carefully, because errors in the spacing or widths of the ports and the lands between them will show up in the valve events of the engine. My setup

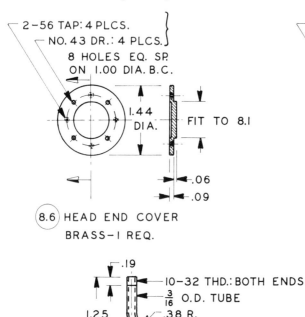

2-56 TAP: 4 PLCS.
NO. 43 DR.: 4 PLCS.
8 HOLES EQ. SP.
ON 1.00 DIA. B.C.

1.44 DIA.   FIT TO 8.1

.06
.09

(8.6) HEAD END COVER
BRASS—1 REQ.

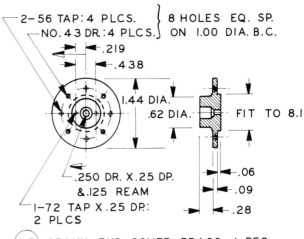

2-56 TAP: 4 PLCS.   8 HOLES EQ. SP.
NO. 43 DR.: 4 PLCS.   ON 1.00 DIA. B.C.

.219
.438

1.44 DIA.
.62 DIA.   FIT TO 8.1

.250 DR. X .25 DP.
& .125 REAM
1-72 TAP X .25 DP.:
2 PLCS

.06
.09
.28

(8.7) CRANK END COVER: BRASS—1 REQ.

.19
10-32 THD.: BOTH ENDS
3/16 O.D. TUBE
.38 R.
1.25
.19
1.50

(8.8) EXHAUST: COPPER—1 REQ.

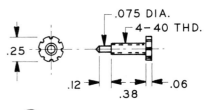

.075 DIA.
4-40 THD.
.25
.12   .06
.38

(8.9) DRAIN VALVE STEM:
BRASS—2 REQ.

for milling the ports can be seen in Photo 31. Note that the large exhaust port had already been cut when the photo was taken. One steam port was finished, and the second one was being cut. The cutter in use on the steam port is a Dremel no. 193, which cut the proper width of .078" in a single pass. For the exhaust port I used a Dremel no. 194 cutter. It produced the .125" width in a single pass, also. During this cutting operation, the brass piece was supported above the milling table surface on metal packing bars to prevent running the cutter into the surface of the milling table. Use the steam chest cover as a drilling jig once again to spot the eight no. 42 holes, and drill them through. After removing burrs from the piece, I lapped its flat surfaces on 600 grit wet or dry paper on a flat plate glass surface. At this time, I gave the valve face (7.5) a similar treatment to produce a smooth, flat valve with a smooth, flat port face to work against.

None of the machining operations involved in making the Cylinder (8.1) are difficult. However, there are a lot of steps involved. The clearances between the various holes and passages are tight in places, allowing very little room for error. Therefore, work slowly to insure that nothing gets away from you. The procedure I followed was to put in the steam passages first, most of the tapped holes second, and the bore last. All of the tapped holes are blind. When the tap reaches the bottom of a blind hole, it may exert a surprising amount of force at the tip. By putting in most of the tapped holes before the bore, I reduced the risk of distortion that might have occurred if a relatively thin wall, left by cutting the bore first, had been subjected to a localized force from the tap. The same thought applies to the milling operations that formed the steam passages.

Cut a block of brass to length. Mark out the locations of the steam and exhaust passages, as well as the seven tapped holes dimensioned

on the drawing. The tapped holes for the steam chest and cylinder covers will be located from these parts later on. Refer to Photo 32 to see the setup I used for milling the steam passages in the side of the cylinder. The cutter used was the Dremel no. 194. This was just right to cut the exhaust passage to full width on a single pass. Note that the exhaust passage is .12" deep and extends toward the bottom of the cylinder more than the steam passages. Its greater length allows the hole to be drilled at a 45° angle from the bottom of the milled passage to the 10-32 tapped hole in the lower surface where the Exhaust Pipe (8.8) screws in. I milled the steam passages to a depth of .06" using the same cutter. It was necessary to take repetitive cuts to get the passages out to full width. The second steam passage was being milled when Photo 32 was taken.

When the milling of the passages was done, I drilled and tapped the 10-32 exhaust hole in the lower surface. At this time, the four 4-40 tapped holes were put in the bottom to accept the bolts that would later mount the cylinder on the engine bed (3.0). Also, the two 4-40 holes were drilled and tapped in the side opposite the passages. These holes are for the Drain Valves (8.10). With the cylinder mounted on a large V block, as in Photo 33, I used a center drill to start the .125" diameter connecting hole between the bottom of the milled exhaust passage and the 10-32 tapped hole. Be very careful as the drill breaks through the bottom of the hole; it is likely to have a tendency to snatch at the metal, which could cause a big problem. Also, be sure that the drill does not damage the 10-32 thread as it breaks through. Use the steam chest cover (7.1) as a drilling jig to spot the eight holes around the steam passages. Drill and tap the eight spots for the 2-56 studs that secure the steam chest.

Now, direct your attention to the ends of the block. Mark out the location that will be the

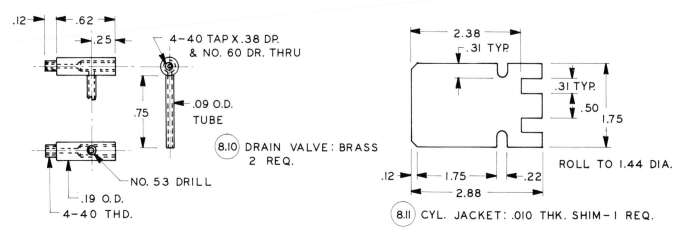

.12 ← → .62
→ .25 ←
4-40 TAP X .38 DP. & NO. 60 DR. THRU
.75
.09 O.D. TUBE
8.10 DRAIN VALVE: BRASS 2 REQ.
NO. 53 DRILL
.19 O.D.
4-40 THD.

2.38
.31 TYP.
.31 TYP.
.50
1.75
.12 ← → 1.75 → ← .22
2.88
ROLL TO 1.44 DIA.
8.11 CYL. JACKET: .010 THK. SHIM—1 REQ.

center of the bore. For boring cylinders, I like to use a boring bar between lathe centers, as in Photo 34. Note that I had placed some packing material in the form of metal blocks under the cylinder to get its bore center line to coincide with the lathe axis. Note, also, the solid clamping arrangement for securing the block to the lathe saddle. Before reaching the stage shown in Photo 34, the bore had been started by a center drill and opened out by a twist drill held in a chuck on the lathe spindle to make the hole to put the boring bar through. Light, successive cuts were taken with the boring bar to bring the cylinder bore out to the desired figure of .625". By using a finely sharpened tool with a small radius at the tip and taking the slowest feed rate possible, it was possible to obtain a very smooth finish in the cylinder bore by this method.

When I was satisfied with the .625" bore, I **38** advanced the tool and bored each end of the cylinder to .75" diameter for a length of .12" to form the recesses shown in the drawing. As the recesses were cut, they just broke into the pilot holes of the 4-40 tapped holes where the drain valves go, thus forming the way for the condensate to blow out. This is a good time to mill the .08" passages that connect the wide stream passages already milled in the side of the block with the recesses at the ends of the bore. I used the Dremel no. 193 cutter for this operation, with the block in the cross vise at an angle of 45°. The steam and exhaust passages of this engine are more than ample for full power. It is noticeable in the engine's performance. It runs with a clear, loud exhaust beat that is music to my ears.

The purpose of the recesses at the cylinder ends is to save work when overhaul time comes. The registers on the Covers (8.6) and (8.7) are fitted to the recesses. When a re-bore becomes necessary in the future, it can be done without upsetting the fit of the covers, glands, and associated parts. It is a little extra work initially, but it makes for a better engine.

I slipped the cylinder onto a mandrel between lathe centers and faced off each end to obtain true surfaces for the covers and bring the cylinder to the desired finished length. When Photo 35 was taken, the cylinder (8.1) and port face (8.2) were in place on the engine bed, and it began to look like an engine!

The Head End Covers (8.6) and the Crank End Cover (8.7) may be made from either flat stock or rod. Mine were made from slices cut from a brass rod of 1.50" diameter. Chuck each piece in turn. Face it off, and machine the register spigot that fits into the .75" diameter recess in the end of the cylinder bore. Take pains to make the register of the crank end cover a very close fit, as this determines the positional accuracy when fitting the Piston (8.4) and the Piston Rod (8.3). The machining cuts on the outer surfaces of the covers require that the covers be gripped accurately by the .75" diameter registers. Photo 36 shows a simple ring-type of chuck adapter I made to do this. I started with a piece of steel tubing that I faced off and bored to make it a close fit on the register diameters. When I was satisfied with the fit, I split the side of the ring with a fine hacksaw. The saw kerf shows in the photo between the number 2 and 3 jaws of the chuck. This is the position in which it was turned, and I always return it to the chuck with the kerf opposite the number 1 jaw to keep it accurate. Photo 37 shows the homemade "ring chuck" gripping the crank end cover for the drilling and reaming operations

on the stuffing box. It was used in this way to machine the outer surfaces of both covers.

With the lathe work finished on the covers, mark out the locations for the studs that secure the heads to the cylinder. Photo 38 shows the crank end cover setup in my home-built dividing attachment for marking out the eight holes that are equally spaced on a 1.00" diameter bolting circle. Four of the holes were tapped 2-56 for dummy studs, while four were drilled no. 43 to go over the studs in the ends of the cylinder. Don't forget to tap the two 1-72 holes in the stuffing box of (8.7) to secure the gland. Use the covers as drilling jigs to spot through the no. 43 holes to locate the studs in the ends of the cylinder. Tap the ends of the cylinder 2-56 x .25" deep for the studs. All the studs in my cylinder were cut from 2-56 threaded rod.

Make the piston rod (8.3) from stainless steel. Cut a 5-40 thread on one end to match the thread in the crosshead. I center drilled the opposite end to permit running the part with support from the tailstock center, as shown in Photo 39. At this point, the piston (8.4) had been silver soldered to the rod. By machining the piston on the rod, as shown, it was possible to obtain a very close fit of the piston to the cylinder bore with no doubts about the concentricity of the parts. I ground a tool very much like a parting tool to machine the packing grooves. This is the operation being done in Photo 39.

Machine the Gland (8.5) in the same way as was done on the smaller gland (7.3). Also, make the exhaust pipe (8.8) in the same way as (7.4). Cut the 10-32 threads before bending to shape. The bend can be put in smoothly by rolling the pre-threaded tubing over a former that fits closely against the sides of the tubing and prevents them from spreading out. Cut the Cylinder Jacket (8.11) from .010" thick brass shim stock or similar metal. Roll it to 1.44" diameter so it will be a snap fit over the cylinder covers. The jacket enhances the appearance, as is obvious in the pictures of the finished engine.

The two small drain valves are not difficult to make. Turn the Drain Valve Stems (8.9) from .25" diameter brass or bronze rod, and cut off the threads with a die. After parting off, use a needle file to make the little notches around the edges of the handle to improve the grip. The drain valve bodies (8.10) are also plain lathe jobs. When the drilling, tapping, and external threading operations are done, drill a no. 43 hole through the side. Insert a piece of

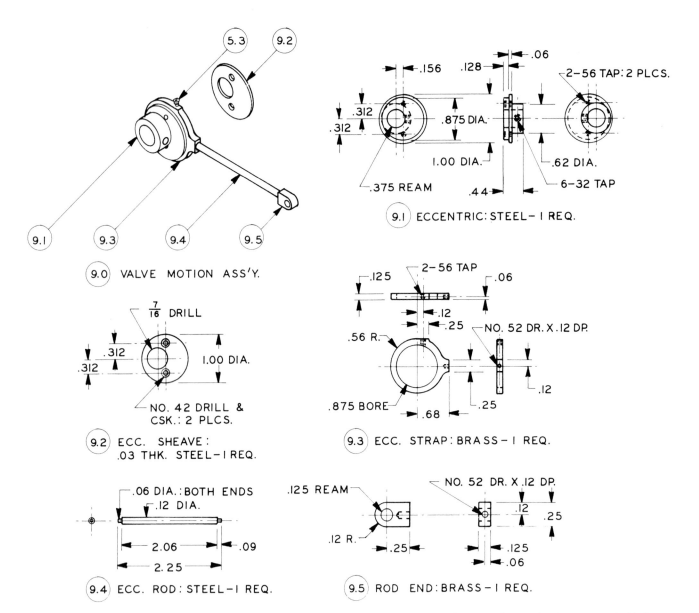

5.3 9.2

9.1 9.3 9.4 9.5

9.0 VALVE MOTION ASS'Y.

9.2 ECC. SHEAVE:
.03 THK. STEEL—I REQ.

$\frac{7}{16}$ DRILL

.312
.312
1.00 DIA.

NO. 42 DRILL &
CSK.: 2 PLCS.

.156 .128 .06

.312
.312
.875 DIA.
1.00 DIA.
.375 REAM
.44

2–56 TAP: 2 PLCS.
.62 DIA.
6–32 TAP

9.1 ECCENTRIC: STEEL—I REQ.

.125 2–56 TAP .06

.12
.25

.56 R.

NO. 52 DR. X .12 DP.

.875 BORE
.68 .25 .12

9.3 ECC. STRAP: BRASS—I REQ.

.06 DIA.: BOTH ENDS
.12 DIA.

2.06 .09
2.25

9.4 ECC. ROD: STEEL—I REQ.

.125 REAM

.12 R. .25

NO. 52 DR. X .12 DP.

.12 .25
.125
.06

9.5 ROD END: BRASS—I REQ.

.09" diameter brass tubing in the hole, and silver solder it in place. Put a no. 53 drill down the tube to be sure there is a clear way for the condensate to exit.

VALVE MOTION (9.0)

Mark the center of the Eccentric Strap (9.3) on a piece of hard or half-hard brass flat stock. Make a light punch mark on the center, and mark out the outline with dividers. Cut the part out with a hacksaw, and finish the outside with files. I put the part in the four-jaw chuck, as shown in Photo 40, for boring. If you set it up in the four-jaw, use a center finder in the punch mark to get it running true, as you did with the main bearings. I opened the bore with a center drill and twist drill. Then I proceeded to bore out the desired diameter with the boring bar shown in the photo. The reason for making the strap first is that it is easier to turn the eccentric to fit the strap than to bore the strap to fit the eccentric. After

removing the part from the four-jaw, drill the no. 52 hole for insertion of the Eccentric Rod (9.4) and put in the 2-56 tapped hole for the third oil cup (5.3). Make the eccentric rod (9.4) and the Rod End (9.5) as you did the similar parts for the connecting rod. Assemble the rod, strap and rod end, and silver solder them together.

The last parts to be made are the Eccentric (9.1) and the Eccentric Sheave (9.2). Chuck a piece of 1" diameter steel rod, and face the end off. Turn it down to a depth of .128" to form the running surface that fits inside the eccentric strap. Make this a free running fit, but be careful not to make it a sloppy fit. The facing cut leaves a pattern from the tool that accurately locates the center of the face with respect to the running surface. Scribe a line passing through the center as indicated by the facing pattern. Measure off .156" from the center, and make a light punch mark on the scribed line. The punch mark locates the center of the crankshaft hole. I placed the part in the four-jaw and once again adjusted to the lathe axis by using a center finder, as in previous cases. Once it was running true on the lathe axis, I center drilled, drilled through, and reamed as shown in Photo 41. With the bore in place, I transferred the part to a mandrel to turn down the .62" diameter hub. Locate and tap the 6-32 hole for the setscrew and the two 2-56 holes for the bolts to secure the eccentric sheave.

Make the eccentric sheave (9.2) from .03" thick sheet steel. The part is best filed to shape after drilling the holes. Countersink the no. 42 holes to accept the heads of 2-56 flat head machine screws. I found the depth of the heads to exceed the thickness of the metal by a few thousandths. Therefore, I carried the countersink cut on a little farther to take a little metal out of the eccentric itself. It is desirable that the heads of the screws be flush with or slightly below the surface of the eccentric sheave to be sure they do not contact the surface of the main bearing when the eccentric is mounted on the crankshaft.

FINISHING UP

At this point, the entire engine can be assembled except for the steam chest cover (7.1), which is left off until the valve setting is done. Put gaskets under each cylinder cover. Gaskets are also needed on each side of the port face and under the steam chest cover. Some years ago, a friend of mine gave me a small sample of .010" thick gasket sheet, which I used for my gaskets. They have worked out very well, but thinner gaskets probably would give satisfactory service.

Packings are needed in the piston and in both stuffing boxes. I used the traditional soft packing made from graphited string. Roll the packing into the grooves on the piston working on a glass surface. It is important to get enough packing into the grooves to form a resilient bed, but don't overdo it. Too much packing creates excessive friction and does more harm than good. This applies to the stuffing boxes, also. To make the rings for the stuffing boxes, I wind the string around a wooden dowel of the same diameter as the piston rod or valve stem. Then I cut across the wrap with a very sharp knife that cuts the string into short segments in ring form. I slip about three or four of the tiny packing rings into a stuffing boxes, being careful that the cuts are oriented at different angles where they cannot line up to form a built-in leak. Don't overtighten the glands. I have found that slipping in rings as described forms a good seal, even when the glands are relatively loose.

40

41

Apply oil to the piston, valve, rods, and all other moving parts. be certain that all the parts of the engine are free of mechanical binds or tight spots and that the piston stroke centers in the cylinder. It should be possible to turn the flywheels over without feeling any tendency to "stick" or stall at any position. When you are satisfied that everything is properly aligned, your engine will look like mine in Photo 42.

All is ready now for valve setting. It is normal practice for a full-size engine of this type to "run over." This is the direction of rotation indicated by the arrow in the large assembly drawing. During the valve setting operation, *always turn the crankshaft in the direction you want the engine to run.* The first adjustment to be made is the position of the valve nut (7.7) on the valve stem (7.10). When the adjustment is correct, the valve (7.5/7.6) travels in such a way that it uncovers each steam port, in turn, exactly equal amounts, as it reaches each end of its stroke. When this condition has been attained, the setscrew (7.8) can be tightened fully. The next adjustment is to the angular relationship between the eccentric and the crank. Turn the flywheel until the piston reaches dead center at the head end. Loosen the setscrew in the eccentric (9.1). Rotate the

42

eccentric slowly around the crankshaft in the running direction until the head end steam port is just about to crack open. Tighten the setscrew in the eccentric at this position. Now turn the crankshaft to bring the piston to dead center at the crank end. Check to see if the crank end steam port is just about to crack open. If not, go back and slowly check out each adjustment until the valve set is correct. When you are satisfied with the adjustments, put on the steam chest cover, and the engine is ready for running.

The designing and building of small engines is an especially rewarding pastime for me. I sincerely hope that everyone who undertakes the construction of this engine will derive as much satisfaction and pleasure from building and running theirs as I have had from the original.

An Overcrank Engine

All double-action steam engines require some sort of guide mechanism to keep the piston rod from being deflected and bent when the engine is running. As the load is taken up, it is a natural result of the angularity between the piston rod and the connecting rod that force is applied to the piston rod in a lateral direction. Many steamers have some sort of crosshead and guide bar arrangement in which the guide bars give lateral support to the crosshead, which is attached to the piston rod. By supporting the crosshead and guiding its travel in a linear path, the guide bar and crosshead arrangement prevents deflection and bending of the piston rod.

There are other means of accomplishing the same end, however. The small overcrank engine shown in Photos 1 and 2 does not have guide bars and a crosshead. In their place it has an assemblage of links, or levers, which are anchored by and rotate from two fixed points.

The lengths of the links and the positions of the anchors and bearings are all-important to the motion. All of the dimensions are laid out in keeping with geometric principles, so the resulting motion of the links interacting with one another is a straight line motion produced at one point in the assembly. The linearly traveling point in the guide assembly is designed to coincide with the wristpin and is attached to the wristpin. Thus, all of the necessary conditions for accurate and safe guiding and support of the wristpin in a straight line are fulfilled by the assemblage of links.

If the accompanying photographs, in two dimensions, give you the idea that this guide motion is a fascinating thing to watch while it is running, you are sure to get an extra charge from seeing the real thing working in three dimensions. As I worked on the design phase of this engine, I became evermore taken up by the desire to see it run. This made me impatient to get the chips flying. I hope you share my enthusiasm for the design.

One general idea is worth mentioning and bearing in mind; work carefully, so that all parts fit well and are free-moving. This does *not* mean sloppy fits: it *does* mean accurate fits. I say this because free movement, without binds or tight spots, is essential to slow operation of *any* engine. The beauty of this particular

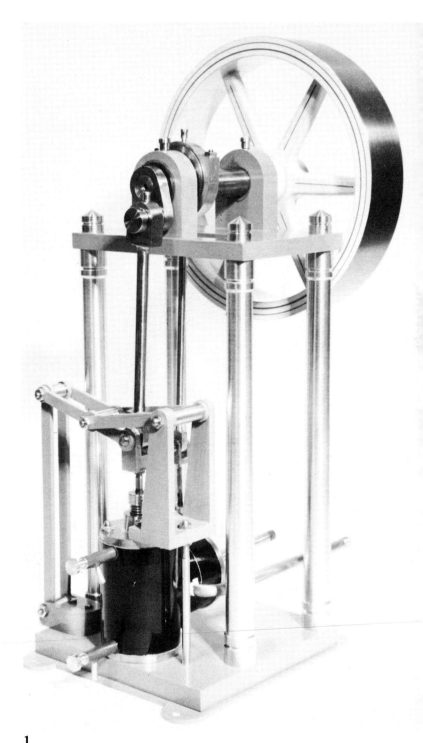

1

design, with its unusual guide motion, is most fully appreciated at low running speeds where the eye can follow the movements of the various parts.

None of the parts is difficult to make. In some respects, they are simpler than the more customary parts of guide bar assemblies. As

3

2   **4**

we proceed through each subassembly of the engine, I will describe various means I employed to build the original engine pictured. Also, I will attempt to alert you to any possible pitfalls.

The large assembly drawing accompanying this part of the project contains an assembly key. Use the assembly key to identify the nine subassemblies of the engine. The order in which they are numbered is the order in which they will be described.

ENGINE FRAME ASSEMBLY (1.0)
The shape of this engine, with its overhead

bearings and crankshaft, makes for a somewhat unusual frame structure. Begin by marking out the Base (1.1) on a piece of .312" thick aluminum plate. Cut the part out, and true the four edges by filing or milling to dimension. Be sure the reference edges you use for marking out the hole positions are straight and at right angles to one another. This guarantees that the holes are in the right positions with relation to one another, as well as with respect to the edges. Center punch each hole location. Start each hole with a small center drill. Drill through the "A" and "C" holes, which are

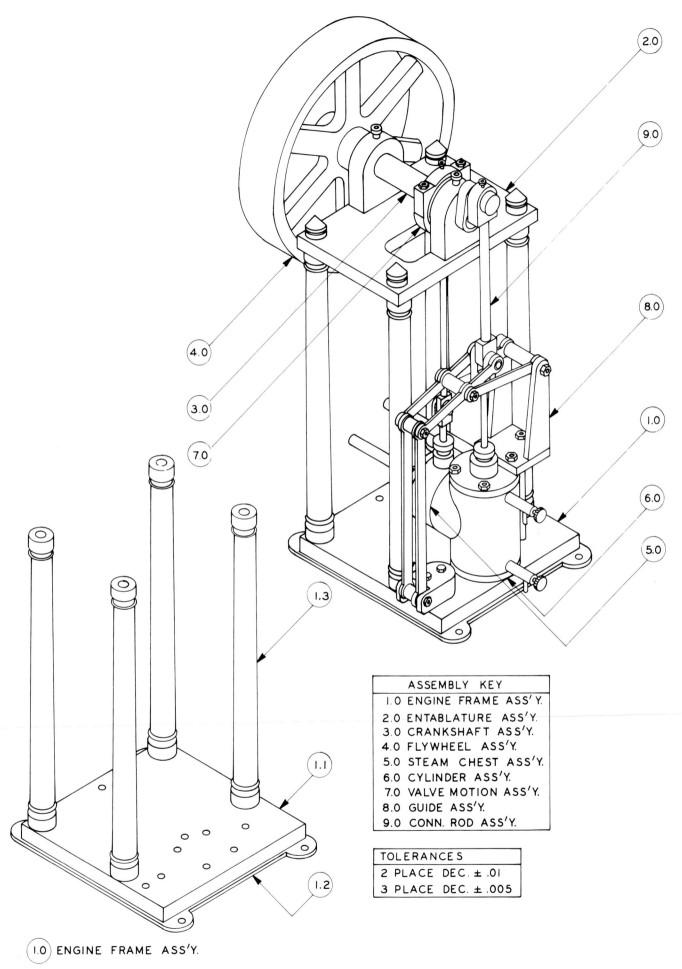

ASSEMBLY KEY
1.0 ENGINE FRAME ASS'Y.
2.0 ENTABLATURE ASS'Y.
3.0 CRANKSHAFT ASS'Y.
4.0 FLYWHEEL ASS'Y.
5.0 STEAM CHEST ASS'Y.
6.0 CYLINDER ASS'Y.
7.0 VALVE MOTION ASS'Y.
8.0 GUIDE ASS'Y.
9.0 CONN. ROD ASS'Y.

TOLERANCES
2 PLACE DEC. ± .01
3 PLACE DEC. ± .005

1.0 ENGINE FRAME ASS'Y.

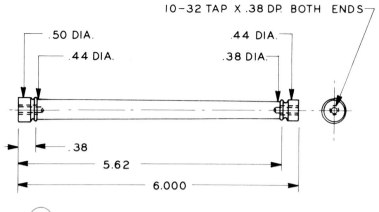

10-32 TAP X .38 DP. BOTH ENDS

.50 DIA.   .44 DIA.

.44 DIA.   .38 DIA.

.38

5.62

6.000

(1.3) COLUMN: ALUM. – 4 REQ.

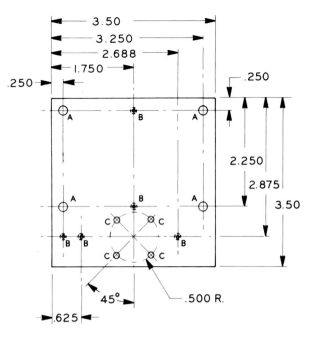

3.50
3.250
2.688
1.750
.250
.250
2.250
2.875
3.50
45°
.500 R.
.625

A   B   A
A   B   A
C   C
B   B   B
C   C

HOLE	OPERATION	NO. OF HOLES
A	NO. 11 DRILL	4
B	2–56 TAP	5
C	NO. 33 DRILL	4

(1.1) BASE: .312 THK. ALUM. – 1 REQ.

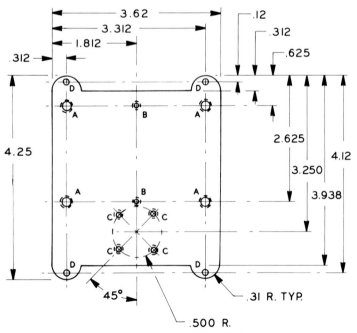

3.62
3.312
1.812
.312
.12
.312
.625
4.25
2.625
4.12
3.250
3.938
45°
.31 R. TYP.
.500 R.

D   D
A   B   A
A   B   A
C   C
C   C
D   D

HOLE	OPERATION	NO. OF HOLES
A	NO. 11 DRILL	4
B	NO. 44 DRILL	2
C	NO. 33 DRILL	4
D	NO. 31 DRILL	4

NOTE: C'SINK A, B, & C HOLES FROM UNDERSIDE

(1.2) SUB BASE: .062 THK. ALUM. – 1 REQ.

clearance holes for 10-32 and 4-40 bolts, respectively. Pilot drill and tap the "B" holes for size 2-56.

Mark out the Sub Base (1.2) on a piece of .062" thick aluminum. File or mill to outline as with the previous part. The "A," "B," and "C" holes of this part must align with the corresponding holes of the base. Part 1.1 is larger than part 1.2 so that it projects to form a .06" flange around the base structure with mounting bolts passing through the "D" holes. In making this part, I located and drilled only the "B" and "D" holes for starters. With the "B" and "D" holes drilled, I put two 2-56 bolts through the "B" holes to fasten the parts together. Then I match drilled through part 1.1 into part 1.2. This operation is shown in Photo 3.

I countersunk all "A," "B," and "C" holes from the underside to accommodate flathead screws. If you prefer to use some other head shape, you can leave the holes plain. In this case, you will have to make provision to clear the heads on whatever platform you use under the engine for running it.

While it is true that plain pieces of .50" diameter rod, cut to the proper length, would make serviceable columns for the engine, they would not be acceptable from an aesthetic point of view. Therefore, I designed the Columns (1.3) with head and foot turnings and a gracefully tapered shape. The exact taper and end shape of the columns is obviously not critical. However, it *is* important that all four columns be identical in shape. They must be identical in length, also, for the engine to stand straight.

Refer to Photo 4. It indicates how I used a steady rest to face the end of each column. After facing, center drill, so the part can be mounted between lathe centers. When the first end is done on each column, repeat the operation on the second ends with the lathe

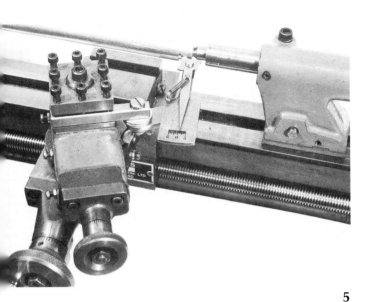

5　　**6**

7

carriage locked in position, to insure that all columns are faced off to the same length. Next, place each column between centers in turn to reduce the diameter of the head ends. Use a pointed tool with the carriage locked to machine the groove at each head end. Then, reverse each one to machine a similar groove at the foot end.

At this point, each of the four columns should look like mine in Photo 5. Here I was preparing to turn the taper by using the tailstock setover. It is relatively easy to get the right amount of taper by using an indicator against the workpiece mounted between centers to measure the tailstock displacement directly. After you have set the tailstock over by the proper amount, proceed to turn the tapers as shown in Photo 6.

The final machining operation requires that each column be returned to the lathe using the steady rest once again to pilot drill and tap both ends for the 10-32 mounting bolts. When the tapping operation is complete, parts 1.1, 1.2, and 1.3 can be assembled as in Photo 7.

ENTABLATURE ASSEMBLY (2.0)

The construction of the Entablature (2.1) is similar to that of the base. Cut the part form .25" thick aluminum and square up the edges. Locate the No. 11 drilled holes carefully. Their positions must match the "A" holes in part 1.1 for aligning the columns. I countersunk the No. 33 drilled holes from the underside and used flathead machine screws in them. If you prefer some other head pattern, do not countersink. The cutout is necessary to clear the eccentric and eccentric strap later on. Use a .375" diameter drill at each corner to leave the radius. Cut away the bulk of the metal with a small saw, and finish by filing or milling.

Cut two blocks of bronze for the Bearings (2.2). The first operation is to square the edges, paying particular attention to the bottom surfaces that will contact the entablature. I used the setup shown in Photo 8 to machine all the straight edges. This operation could be performed with either a standard flycutter or an end mill, depending upon your specific tooling. Note that I was taking the truing cut on both blocks, simultaneously. Next, mark out the hole locations. Drill and tap for the mounting bolts. Drill through with a pilot drill for the reamed holes, but don't ream them, yet. Form the curved shape by filing, followed by drilling and tapping for the Oil

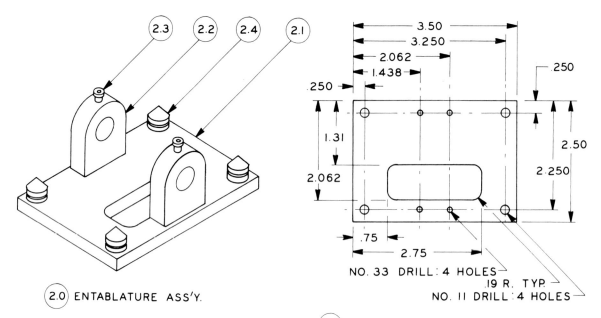

(2.0) ENTABLATURE ASS'Y.

(2.1) ENTABLATURE : .25 THK. ALUM. – I REQ.

NO. 33 DRILL : 4 HOLES
.19 R. TYP.
NO. II DRILL : 4 HOLES

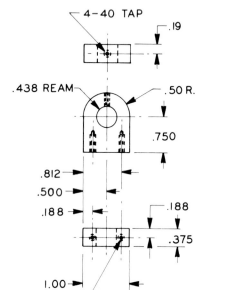

4–40 TAP
.19

.438 REAM
.50 R.
.750
.812
.500
.188
.188
.375
1.00

4–40 TAP X .38 DP.:
2 HOLES

(2.2) BEARING : BRONZE–2 REQ.

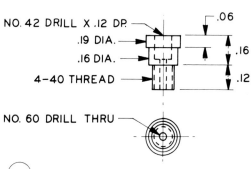

NO. 42 DRILL X .12 DP.
.06
.19 DIA.
.16 DIA.
.16
4–40 THREAD
.12

NO. 60 DRILL THRU

(2.3) OIL CUP : BRASS – 2 REQ.

Cups (2.3). Erect the bearings on the entablature. Now you can put the reamer through the .438" diameter holes, thus insuring that they are reamed in line.

To make the oil cups (2.3), chuck a piece of .19" diameter brass rod. Face it off and turn the end down for the thread. Cut the thread by using a die in the tailstock die holder. Turn down the .16" diameter section next, and part off to length. After doing this on two parts, chuck a split nut having a 4-40 thread. The split nut will hold the parts securely in the chuck without damaging the thread while you drill the no. 42 hole to form the oil reservoir and the no. 60 hole for the oil to enter the bearing.

Obviously, the fancy Cap Screws (2.4) will not hold the engine together any better than

8

plain machine screws. But they certainly do *look* better! This question of appearance and aesthetic appeal recurs in every subassembly in this engine. From my point of view, the extra machining time involved in obtaining a pleasing appearance is time well used. If you agree, chuck a piece of 38" diameter rod, face it off, turn it down, and cut the thread. Part off and shape the fancy heads by repetitive turning, as you did on the columns. Having turned fancy heads, I was unwilling to mill wrench flats on them. Instead, I drilled the no. 52 hole to a depth of .09". A 1" length of .062" diameter steel rod inserted into the hole gives more than adequate leverage for tightening or loosening the screws. Refer to Photo 9 for a view of all the parts of the 2.0 subassembly.

CRANKSHAFT ASSEMBLY (3.0)

The overhung Crankshaft Assembly is made up from three parts. Make the Crankshaft (3.1) from a suitable length of .50" diameter steel rod. I used the steady rest to face the ends to exact length and to center drill for mounting the piece between lathe centers. By using an oversize diameter rod and turning between centers, I was able to guarantee the concentricity of the .375" diameter and .438" diameter sections of the shaft. The .438" diameter part can be checked against the bearings (2.2) for a good running fit, as you bring it to the finish. Polish the .438" diameter portion with fine wet or dry paper for a smooth running surface.

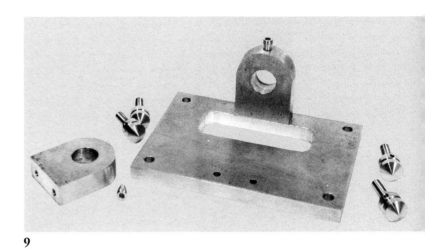

9

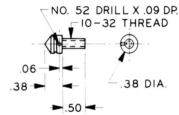

10

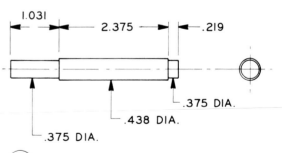

NO. 52 DRILL X .09 DP.
10-32 THREAD
.06
.38
.38 DIA.
.50

(2.4) CAP SCREW : BRASS-4 REQ.

1.031 — 2.375 — .219
.375 DIA.
.438 DIA.
.375 DIA.

(3.1) CRANKSHAFT : STEEL-1 REQ.

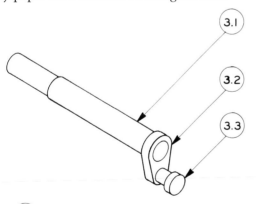

3.1
3.2
3.3

(3.0) CRANKSHAFT ASS'Y.

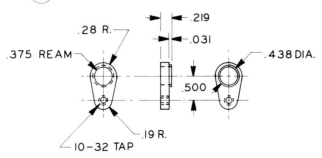

.219
.031
.28 R.
.375 REAM
.500
.438 DIA.
.19 R.
10-32 TAP

(3.2) CRANK : STEEL-1 REQ.

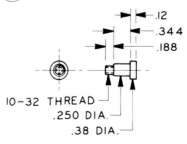

.12
.344
.188
10-32 THREAD
.250 DIA.
.38 DIA.

(3.3) CRANKPIN : STEEL-1 REQ.

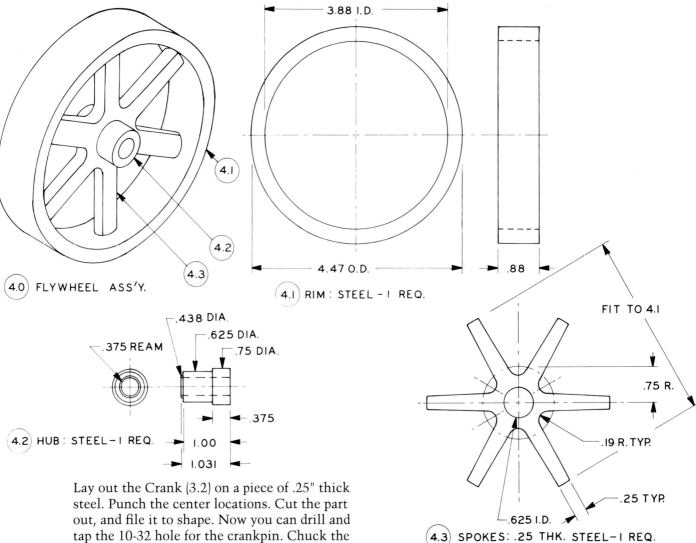

4.0 FLYWHEEL ASS'Y.

3.88 I.D.

4.47 O.D.

.88

4.1 RIM: STEEL – I REQ.

.375 REAM

.438 DIA.
.625 DIA.
.75 DIA.

.375

1.00

1.031

4.2 HUB: STEEL – I REQ.

FIT TO 4.1

.75 R.

.19 R. TYP.

.25 TYP.

.625 I.D.

4.3 SPOKES: .25 THK. STEEL – I REQ.

Lay out the Crank (3.2) on a piece of .25" thick steel. Punch the center locations. Cut the part out, and file it to shape. Now you can drill and tap the 10-32 hole for the crankpin. Chuck the part in the four-jaw chuck. Use a wiggler to center the part on the punch mark for the .375" reamed hole. Center drill, drill, and ream the 375" diameter hole. Take facing cuts to thin the part down to .219". Then face off another .031" to form the thrust shoulder that surrounds the reamed hole.

Machine the Crankpin (3.3) from a piece of .38" diameter rod by turning down for the thread and for the running journal. Cut the thread with a die in the tailstock die holder. Polish the running journal, as you did the crankshaft, and part off. Once again, the question of appearance: I did not want the wrench flats. Therefore, I drilled a no. 52 hole to a depth of .09", as on part 2.4, and used the same means of tightening.

The group of parts for the 3.0 assembly is shown in Photo 10. In machining the crankshaft, I turned the part that goes into the reamed hole of the crank to approximately .0005" interference for a press fit. Other means of assembly, such as *Loctite*, could be used with suitable allowance for proper fitting. After pressing 3.1 and 3.2 together, I cross drilled

with a no. 52 drill and pressed in a steel pin to secure the joint further. Photo 11 shows the center drill starting the hole for the pin. After pressing the pin in, I cut it off and filed the end flush with the crank. The pin fits so tightly that it simply cannot be seen after filing.

FLYWHEEL ASSEMBLY (4.0)

The material from which I made the Flywheel Rim (4.1) was a piece of nominal 4" "extra strength" steel pipe. The extra strength class of pipe has a wall thickness approximately double that of the standard class. The heavier grades of pipe seem to contain a better machining grade of steel than the usual types. If you are able to locate a piece of heavy wall industrial tubing, you are almost certain to have steel of better machining characteristics. The exact inner and outer diameters of the rim are not critical and may be varied a bit to suit your stock.

Cut a piece large enough for the rim. The first machining operation is to bore the inside to get it round. My setup is shown in Photo 12, where the rim was clamped to a faceplate

11   12

13   14

with a plywood pad to keep the boring tool from scarring the faceplate. After boring it out, measure the inside diameter and set it aside while you work on the other parts.

Make the Hub (4.2) by turning down a piece of .75" diameter rod to form the .625" diameter shoulder. Face off both ends, but do not ream the center hole or turn the .438" diameter thrust surface. Both of these will be done later to insure concentricity with the rim.

Mark out the Spokes (4.3) on a piece of .25" thick steel plate. Refer to Photo 13 which demonstrates how I marked the complete outline. This photo also shows how I center drilled and drilled with a .375" diameter drill to form the curves where the spokes run together. When the drilling is finished, use a saw to cut away the triangles between the spokes and to cut the spokes roughly to length. Allow the spokes to be a bit longer than

required for turning to an exact fit in the rim.

At this point, mount the spokes on a faceplate for boring and turning (Photo 14). Use a wiggler to center the part by reference to the center mark from which the piece was marked out. Use a short boring bar to bore the center to accept the shouldered part of 4.2. Then, put on a turning tool. Running the lathe at low speed, turn the ends of the spokes to fit the inner diameter of 4.1. Remove the part from the faceplate. Use a pillar file to radius the edges of the spokes. Refer to Photo 15 which shows all the parts prior to assembly.

Put the three parts together in their proper running position for soldering. I used stainless steel solder having a sharp melting point of 450°F. This product is actually pure tin. A common propane torch is more than adequate as a heat source. Try to heat the whole assembly as evenly as possible to minimize heat warpage.

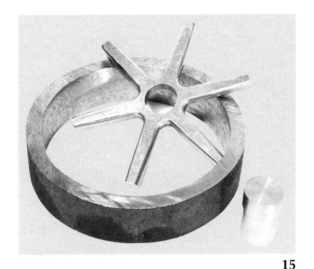

15

18

16

19

17

Let it cool to room temperature slowly.

Mount the wheel on a faceplate with the inner surface of the rim running true as your reference surface. Take a facing cut to true the edge of the rim, followed by a turning cut to get the outer surface true. Now you are ready to center drill, drill, and ream the central hole in the hub. My faceplate setup for doing this sequence is shown in Photo 16.

Reverse the wheel on the faceplate (Photo 17) for the final lathe operation of facing the other edge of the rim and machining the thrust shoulder on the end of the hub. Remove the flywheel from the faceplate. Slip it into place on the crankshaft. A key must be inserted to prevent the possibility of the flywheel slipping. Do this by drilling a no. 52 hole as is shown in Photo 18. Note that the drill is cutting the hole half in the hub of the flywheel and half in the crankshaft. Use a small center drill to start the hole. Drill to a depth of about .38" with the no. 52 drill. Make a round key from a bit of steel rod to be a press fit into the hole. It need not be a hard press fit, since it must be removed when removing the flywheel.

In Photo 19, you can see the end of the little round key projecting from the end of the crankshaft and hub. Everything that has been made thus far can now be put together. My assembly, at this point, is shown in Photo 20.

STEAM CHEST ASSEMBLY (5.0)

The Steam Chest Cover (5.1) is a good place to

begin on this assembly, because it will serve as a drilling template for the Steam Chest (5.3) and in later work on the cylinder. Make the cover from either flat stock or a slice cut from a 1.25" diameter rod. Mine was made from the latter. If you use a slice of rod, face it off on both sides to get the correct thickness and flat surfaces. Locate the position of the five holes, and drill them through.

The Steam Pipe (5.2) will be silver soldered in the central hole in the steam chest cover. The length shown is handy for general use, but you may vary it to fit a particular installation, if you have one in mind. Cut the 10-32 thread on one end by chucking the tubing in the lathe and cutting the thread with a die in the tailstock die holder. Be sure to slip a close fitting piece of steel rod inside the tubing before chucking or cutting the thread. To do this operation without internal support in the tubing is to invite disaster, as the tubing will be crushed and distorted. After cutting the thread, silver solder parts 5.1 and 5.2 together. Refer to Photo 25 which shows all the parts of the 5.0 assembly in a group.

Cut the circular steam chest (5.3) from a slice of 1.25" diameter rod. The circular shape of the steam chest is typical of some of the older steam engines. It makes for a neat looking design, as can be seen in Photos 1 and 2. To get around the possibility of making angular errors in the layout of the part, I set it up on my indexing attachment, as shown in Photo 21. By rotating the part quarter turns in the indexing attachment, it was possible to obtain perfect right angle measurements without any chance of slipping as might occur in using a

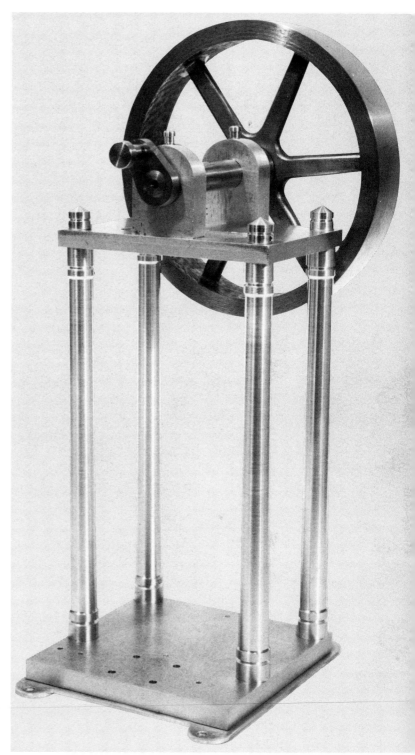

20

21

center finder and square. Mark out both center lines and the outline of the cavity. Carry the vertical center line over the edges to locate the .250" and .375" diameter drilled holes. The first operation after marking out is to drill these holes.

Next comes the cutting away of the metal to form the rectangular cavity. This could be done by drilling and filing to shape. I chose to end mill the cavity as shown in Photo 22.

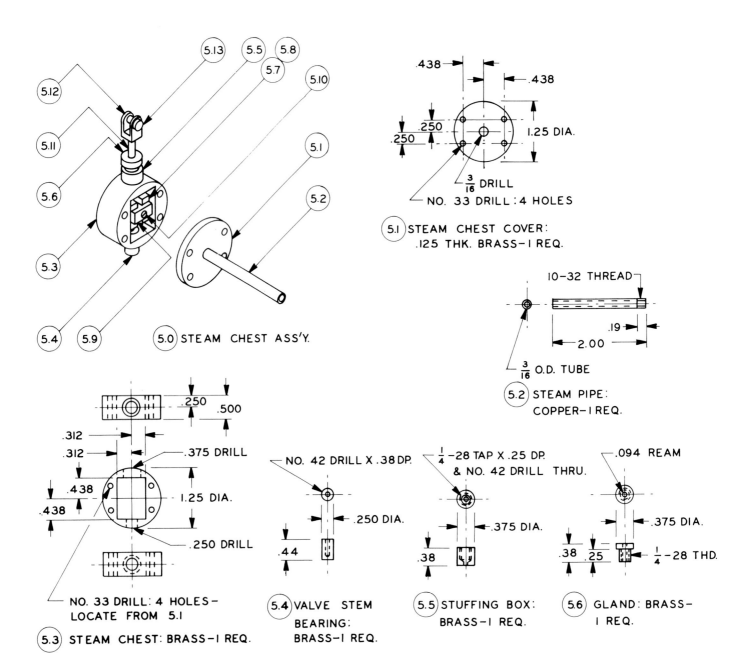

5.12 5.13 5.5 5.8

5.7

5.10

5.11

5.6

5.1

5.2

5.3

5.4 5.9 5.0 STEAM CHEST ASS'Y.

.438 .438

.250 1.25 DIA.
.250

$\frac{3}{16}$ DRILL

NO. 33 DRILL : 4 HOLES

5.1 STEAM CHEST COVER:
.125 THK. BRASS—1 REQ.

10-32 THREAD

.19
2.00

$\frac{3}{16}$ O.D. TUBE

5.2 STEAM PIPE:
COPPER—1 REQ.

.250 .500
.312
.312 .375 DRILL
.438 1.25 DIA.
.438
.250 DRILL

NO. 33 DRILL: 4 HOLES—
LOCATE FROM 5.1

5.3 STEAM CHEST: BRASS—1 REQ.

NO. 42 DRILL X .38 DP.

.250 DIA.

.44

5.4 VALVE STEM
BEARING:
BRASS—1 REQ.

$\frac{1}{4}$ -28 TAP X .25 DP.
& NO. 42 DRILL THRU.

.375 DIA.

.38

5.5 STUFFING BOX:
BRASS—1 REQ.

.094 REAM

.375 DIA.

.38 .25 $\frac{1}{4}$ -28 THD.

5.6 GLAND: BRASS—
1 REQ.

Note that there are .25" square packing bars under the part to prevent the end mill from cutting into the milling table. Naturally, there will be a small radius at each corner after milling. File the corners square with a small file of square section. Use the steam chest cover as a drilling template to locate and drill the four no. 33 holes for the studs.

Chuck a piece of .250" diameter rod to make the Valve Stem Bearing (5.4). Face off both ends, and drill the no. 42 hole which will support the valve stem. Use the same setup to machine the Stuffing Box (5.5) from .375" diameter rod. After facing off both ends, drill and tap carefully to maintain the concentricity of the thread and the through hole. Now you can insert parts 5.4 and 5.5 into the appropriate holes in 5.3 and silver solder them. Check

with a no. 42 drill through the parts to be sure they are properly aligned and will not cause a bind when the valve stem is inserted later on.

Make the Gland (5.6) next. While the drawings indicate to make the gland from round rod, some builders may prefer hexagonal stock to provide a natural set of flats for a wrench. In either case, chuck the stock and face the end. Turn the rod down and cut the thread. Then center drill and drill and ream for the valve stem to pass through. Part off to finish the machining. There is no need for a properly packed gland to be pulled up hard. I do not consider wrench flats very important on glands. Also, round headed glands look neater to me. I drilled four no. 52 holes equally spaced around the head to a depth of .09" and use a short bar as previously described for the cap screws and

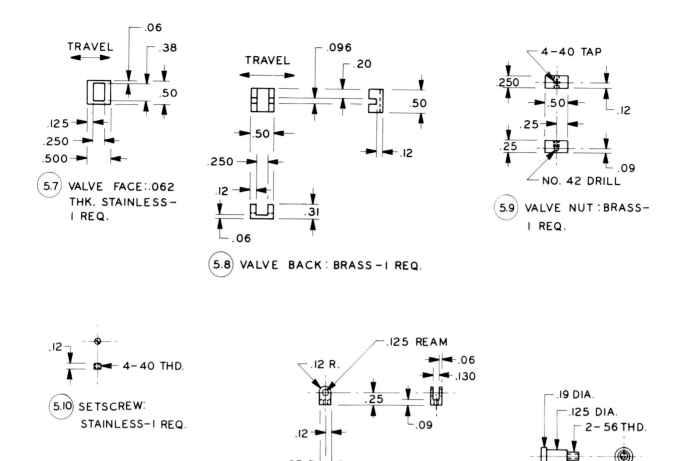

5.7 VALVE FACE: .062 THK. STAINLESS— I REQ.

5.8 VALVE BACK: BRASS—I REQ.

5.9 VALVE NUT: BRASS— I REQ.

5.10 SETSCREW: STAINLESS—I REQ.

5.11 VALVE STEM: STAINLESS—I REQ.

5.12 CLEVIS: BRASS—I REQ.

5.13 PIN: STEEL— I REQ.

crank pin. If you have a knurling tool, there is no reason that a light knurl on the head of the gland could not be used to provide a more than adequate finger grip, with no other means of tightening required.

Stainless steel seems to be the best material available for slide valves – at least for slide valve faces! It never seams to cause any galling or wear on the port face. None of my engines having stainless valve faces have ever shown any wear or need for a re-lap. Mark the shape of the Valve Face (5.7) on a sheet of .062" thick stainless. Drill through the central hole. Use needle files to file the hole out to its rectangular shape. Cut the part out with a saw. Finish carefully to the outline with a fine cut file. Work carefully to dimension on this part, since its length in the travel direction and the width of the exhaust cavity in the travel direction help determine the accuracy of the admission and exhaust events when the engine is running.

Any grade of brass is suitable for the Valve Back (5.8), since this part receives no wear. Cut a block of brass .50" square by .31" thick. Square up all the faces, but do not cut the grooves in the back just yet. First, silver solder parts 5.7 and 5.8 together. After cleaning up the parts , you can cut the grooves accurately by end milling. The setup I used is shown in Photo 23. Note that the cutter in use is a Dremel no. 194 for the wider groove. A Dremel no. 193 had already been used to cut the narrower groove. Both of these cutters give excellent cuts in brass. The last operation on the valve is to lap the stainless face flat. Do this on 600 grit wet or dry paper on a plate glass surface.

The Valve Nuts (5.9) is a simple rectangular brass part which fits into the wider groove in the back of the composite slide valve. Drill no. 42 for the valve stem to pass through. Drill and tap the 4-40 hole for the Setscrew (5.10). Make the setscrew from a short piece of

22   23

24   25

stainless threaded rod. Dress off the ends by filing, and cut a light saw kerf across one end to serve as a screwdriver slot.

No machine work is required on the Valve Stem (5.11), since it is simply a piece of plain stainless rod. Drill into the end of a square brass rod to make the Clevis (5.12). Insert the valve stem to a depth of .09", and silver solder the parts together. Now you can cut the brass to length. Ream through the .125" diameter hole, and file the radius on the end. Refer to Photo 24 to see the vertical arrangement I used with a slitting blade to cut away the metal to form the clevis. Note that the slitting blade was not thick enough to cut full width on a single pass; I had to repeat the cut to get to a full width. The Pin (5.13) which passes through the reamed hole in the clevis is very similar to the crankpin and is made in the same way. Once again, wrench flats may be milled on the head, although mine is arranged like the crankpin for tightening.

CYLINDER ASSEMBLY (6.0)

While the Port Face (6.1) is machined as a separate entity at the beginning, its identity is lost, and it becomes an integral part of the Cylinder (6.2). Begin by cutting off a 2.50" length of 1.25" diameter bronze rod. This is long enough for both parts 6.1 and 6.2 provided you keep your cuts straight. To machine the concave saddle shape, I mounted the 2.50" length of bronze rod on the lathe carriage in the setup shown in Photo 26. Note that the rod is very securely clamped down on top of some packing material which places the center line of the rod on a level with the center line of the lathe. Furthermore, the rod is positioned carefully at right angles to the lathe axis. The boring bar which is mounted between lathe centers has the tool set to sweep through a .625" radius. I used the power feed to feed the work as the cut was being made. On each pass, the cross-feed was used to advance the work a few thousandths at a

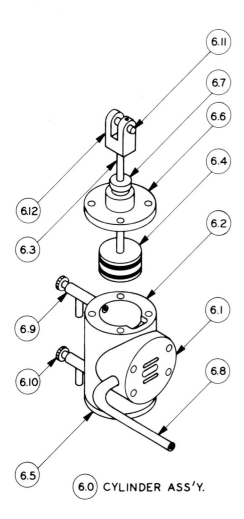

Labels in diagram: 6.11, 6.7, 6.6, 6.4, 6.2, 6.1, 6.8, 6.12, 6.3, 6.9, 6.10, 6.5

(6.0) CYLINDER ASS'Y.

26

27

time to deepen the cut. Check the progress of the work against the remainder of the rod from which you cut the 2.50" length to be sure that you have the radius of the tool set properly. It is important for the port face to fit snugly against the side of the cylinder. Refer to Photo 32 which gives a view of the finished cylinder. When you are satisfied with the fit of the port face and the depth of the cut, saw off the port face portion, leaving the other part for the main section of the cylinder. Silver solder these two parts together to form the rough assembly shown in Photos 27, 28 and 29.

None of the remaining machining operations involved on the cylinder are difficult, but there are a lot of them. In places, the clearances get pretty tight, also. Take your time, and work carefully so you will not come to grief.

It is imperative that the outer face of the port face be flat and parallel to the cylinder center line. To accomplish this condition, I set the rough cylinder assembly on the lathe carriage in the position shown in Photo 27. I positioned the cylinder axis parallel to the face plate by measuring between the face plate and the cylinder surface. Once again, note the secure clamping arrangement against the thin

packings. Using the facing cutter, I machined the port face flat and reduced its thickness to the dimension called out in the drawing. This is the same type of facing cut as that previously indicated in Photo 8. In this setup, the work was advanced to the tool by the longitudinal feed and the cut was made by using the cross-feed.

In order to put the bore into the cylinder, I rotated the cylinder to the position shown in Photo 28 where the axis of the cylinder is parallel to and coincides with the axis of the lathe. Begin by drilling out centrally as large as possible with twist drills. Then slip in a between-centers boring bar to finish the bore to size. Advance the tool in the boring bar by only a few thousandths at a time. By using a well-sharpened tool with a little radius on the

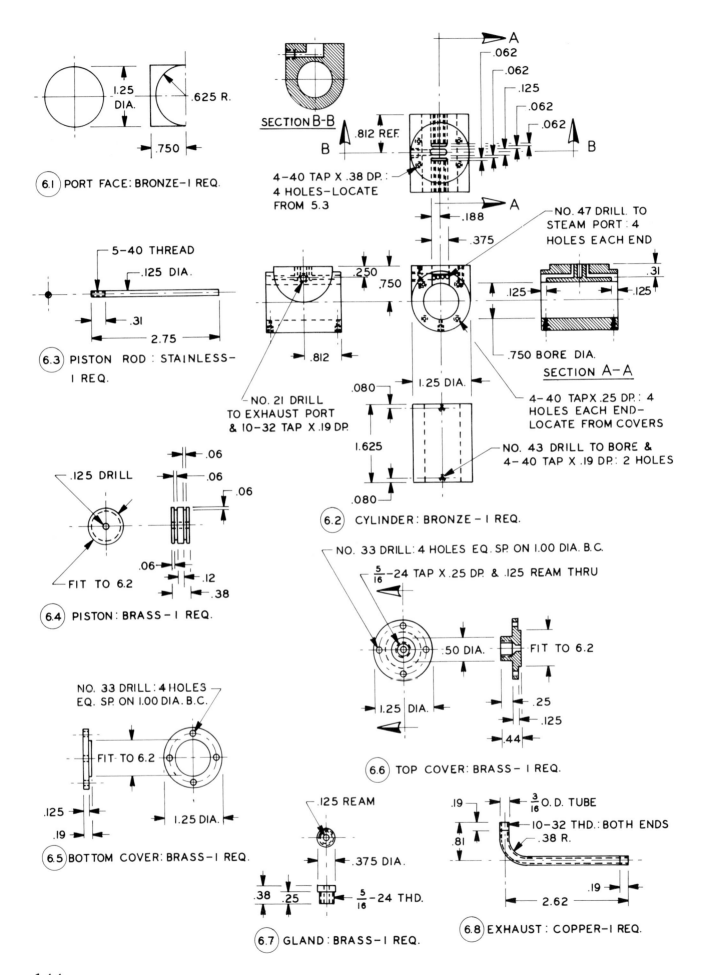

6.1 PORT FACE: BRONZE—1 REQ.

SECTION B-B

4-40 TAP X .38 DP.:
4 HOLES—LOCATE
FROM 5.3

.812 REF.

.062
.062
.125
.062
.062

NO. 47 DRILL TO
STEAM PORT: 4
HOLES EACH END

.188
.375
.250
.750

.31
.125
.125

.750 BORE DIA.
SECTION A-A

4-40 TAP X .25 DP.: 4
HOLES EACH END—
LOCATE FROM COVERS

NO. 43 DRILL TO BORE &
4-40 TAP X .19 DP.: 2 HOLES

.812

NO. 21 DRILL
TO EXHAUST PORT
& 10-32 TAP X .19 DP.

1.25 DIA.

.080
1.625
.080

6.2 CYLINDER: BRONZE—1 REQ.

6.3 PISTON ROD: STAINLESS—1 REQ.

5-40 THREAD
.125 DIA.
.31
2.75

.125 DRILL
.06
.06
.06
.06
.12
.38
FIT TO 6.2

6.4 PISTON: BRASS—1 REQ.

NO. 33 DRILL: 4 HOLES EQ. SP. ON 1.00 DIA. B.C.

$\frac{5}{16}$—24 TAP X .25 DP. & .125 REAM THRU

.50 DIA.
FIT TO 6.2
.25
.125
1.25 DIA.
.44

6.6 TOP COVER: BRASS—1 REQ.

NO. 33 DRILL: 4 HOLES
EQ. SP. ON 1.00 DIA. B.C.

FIT TO 6.2
.125
.19
1.25 DIA.

6.5 BOTTOM COVER: BRASS—1 REQ.

.125 REAM
.375 DIA.
.38 .25
$\frac{5}{16}$—24 THD.

6.7 GLAND: BRASS—1 REQ.

$\frac{3}{16}$ O.D. TUBE
.19
.81
10-32 THD.: BOTH ENDS
.38 R.
.19
2.62

6.8 EXHAUST: COPPER—1 REQ.

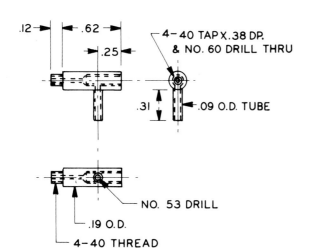

4-40 TAP X .38 DP.
& NO. 60 DRILL THRU

.12 .62 .25

.31 .09 O.D. TUBE

NO. 53 DRILL

.19 O.D.

4-40 THREAD

(6.9) DRAIN VALVE: BRASS—2 REQ.

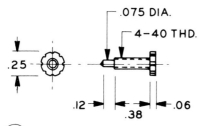

.075 DIA.

4-40 THD.

.25

.12 .38 .06

(6.10) DRAIN VALVE STEM:
BRASS—2 REQ.

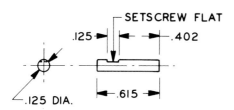

SETSCREW FLAT

.125 .402

.125 DIA.

.615

(6.11) WRISTPIN: STEEL—1 REQ.

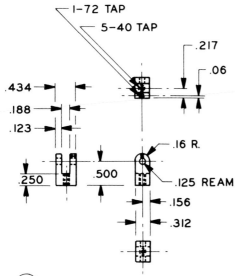

1-72 TAP

5-40 TAP

.217

.06

.434

.188

.123

.16 R.

.250 .500 .125 REAM

.156

.312

(6.12) CLEVIS: STEEL—1 REQ.

28

29

final cuts, the bore can be made very smooth with no need for reaming or lapping. Mount the cylinder on a close fitting mandrel between lathe centers to face off the ends. This leaves the ends smooth, and you can reduce the cylinder to its exact finished length. After removing the cylinder from the mandrel, stand it flat on the port face to locate, drill, and tap the two holes in the opposite cylinder wall for the drain valves.

Now you are ready to mill the inlet and exhaust ports in the port face. I did this milling in the vertical setup shown in Photo 29. Here I was using a .125" end mill to cut the exhaust port

The Shop Wisdom of Rudy Kouhoupt   145

30

31

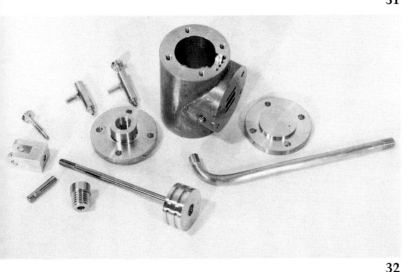

32

and had not started on the inlet ports. Mill the three ports all on the same setup to be sure they are all parallel.

Drill and tap the exhaust passage from the side of the port face to connect with the exhaust port. Stand the cylinder on each end in turn to drill the four No. 47 holes from each end. These connect the end of the cylinder with its steam port. I used a vertical milling setup once again to mill away the metal to a depth of .125" from each end where the steam passes from the drilled holes to the bore. Refer to Photo 32 which shows the finished cylinder in a position where all the ports and passages are visible. Clamp the steam chest (5.3) to the port face in its working position. Spot through the four bolt holes to locate them on the port face. Now you can drill and tap for the studs. Lap the port face flat on 600 grit wet of dry paper on a plate glass surface, as you did with the valve face.

The final operation on the cylinder is to drill and tap the ends for the cylinder covers. First, however, the covers have to be made. After making them, come back to the cylinder and locate the holes from the covers as you did from the steam chest.

Cut a length of stainless rod for the Piston Rod (6.3). Use the lathe with a die in the tailstock die holder to cut the 5-40 thread that screws into the clevis. Grip the rod in a collet or true-running chuck to center drill the opposite end. Cut off a short piece of .88" diameter brass rod for the Piston (6.4). Face both ends and drill a .125" diameter hole through the center. Slip the piston rod into the central hole and silver solder the parts together. To turn the piston to fit the cylinder bore, I used the lathe setup shown in Photo 30. Note that I had the threaded end of the piston rod in a true-running chuck while the center drilled end was supported by the tailstock center. Take light cuts to reduce the piston diameter to fit the bore. My tool for machining the packing grooves is ground like a parting tool. In Photo 30, the groove at the tailstock end had already been cut to full depth, and the other groove was being cut.

I used slices 1.25" diameter rod for making the Bottom Cover (6.5) and the Top Cover (6.6). The bottom cover is the easier of the two. Begin by facing off both sides. Then turn down the register which is a snap fit into the bore of the cylinders. After many years of strenuous use, my three-jaw chuck has lost some of its accuracy. Therefore, when doing a job requiring precise centering, I turn a split ring in the chuck, as in Photo 31, to grip the work truly. This sort of chuck adaptation is just about as good as using a collet – and a lot cheaper! In

Photo 31, I was working on the top cover. It had already been faced off on both sides, the register was turned to a snap fit in the cylinder, and the outer surface was turned to form the stuffing box. It is important that the stuffing box be accurately reamed and tapped on center. If it is off center, it will create intolerable binding on the piston rod. Drill the four bolting holes in each cover. Then transfer their locations to the ends of the cylinder. Drill and tap both ends of the cylinder for the bolts or studs.

There is little difference between the Gland (6.7) and the other gland (5.6). Follow the same procedure as you did on the earlier part, and cut the appropriate thread.

Making the Exhaust (6.8) is a somewhat tricky operation. Like the steam pipe, it does not matter exactly what length you make the exhaust. Cut off a piece of 3/16" OD tubing about 3.75" long. Cut a 10-32 thread on both ends in the same way you did the steam pipe. Don't try to put in the bend without annealing the copper by heating it to a dull red heat. Let it cool slowly; there is nothing to gain by quenching it in water. Turn a close fitting, grooved mandrel around which the tubing can be bent. The close fit of the groove will prevent the tubing from flattening or spreading out laterally in the bend area.

Drain Valves (6.9) are a great convenience on any engine for starting up. They are well worth the small effort involved in making them. Chuck a piece of .19" diameter rod. After facing off, turn down the end, and cut the thread. Part off and reverse in the chuck. Center drill the end using the tailstock chuck. Drill and tap as indicated. Drill through from the side to insert the .09" diameter tube. The tube may be silver soldered or soft soldered, as you prefer. Put a No. 53 drill through the tube after soldering to be sure there is a clear way for the condensate to exit. Two valves are required, of course, so you will also have to make two Drain Valve Stems (6.10). Chuck a piece of .25" diameter rod. Turn it down for the 4-40 thread and for the .075" diameter portion. Cut the thread using a die in the tailstock die holder. Now you can form the point on the tip by taking light strokes with a fine file as the piece rotates in the lathe. After parting off, use a needle file to make the little grooves around the edge of the handle. These do wonders for improving the grip.

Use a piece of .125" diameter steel rod for the Wrist Pin (6.11). Take facing cuts to machine it to the indicated length of .615". This length

figure insures end clearance when the guide assembly is put in place, later on. File the small flat for the 1-72 setscrew which locks the wrist pin in place in the clevis (6.12). The steps involved in making the clevis are very similar to those followed in making the other Clevis (5.12). Don't forget to tap the 1-72 hole for the setscrew just referred to for securing the wrist pin.

At this point, all of the parts for the cylinder assembly have been covered. The complete group of parts is shown in Photo 32. Refer, also, to Photo 33 in which the cylinder assembly has been put together and mounted on the base. I used countersunk bolts with their

33

heads under the base to mount the cylinder assembly. These bolts pass through the bottom cover into the tapped holes at the bottom of the cylinder. All other tapped holes in the top and port face of my engine are fitted with studs and nuts. Again, this is an aesthetic question. Roundheaded screws would hold just as well, but the studs and nuts look much better. I made all the studs in mine from 4-40 threaded stainless rod. After cutting them off, I machined the ends to give them a neat appearance. You will notice in Photo 33 that the two top studs next to the exhaust are .19" longer than the two studs on the opposite side. The extra length is needed, because these studs pass through a part of the guide assembly. The nuts raise another appearance question. On a small engine, standard 4-40 nuts look clumsy by virtue of their oversize proportions. Therefore, I used size 2-56 nuts which I drilled out and retapped with a 4-40 thread. While you are at it, do one with a 5-40 thread to lock the clevis in on the piston rod.

VALVE MOTION ASSEMBLY (7.0)

The heart of the valve motion is the Eccentric (7.1) which controls the motion and timing of the slide valve. A setup such as I used in Photo 34 is convenient for machining this part. Note that I had chucked a short piece of 1.00" diameter steel rod in the three-jaw chuck with the outer end supported by the steady rest. Begin the machining by taking a facing cut across the end of the rod. Next, machine the groove with a tool shaped like a parting tool. I had just finished the groove when I took Photo 34. Cut the piece off with an allowance for the setscrew hub. Chuck it again in the three-jaw, and face the opposite side to bring it to length. The facing operation leaves a pattern by which the center of the part can be located accurately. Measure from this pattern to position the center of the .438" reamed hole at a distance of .125" from the rotational center of the piece. Center drill, pilot drill, and ream the .438" diameter hole. Now you can mount the part on a tight fitting mandrel as I had done in Photo 35, where I was turning the setscrew hub to diameter. Finally, drill and tap the 6-32 hole in the hub for the setscrew.

Refer next to Photo 36, which shows how I marked out the Eccentric Strap (7.2) on a piece of .25 x 1.50" brass flat stock. In doing this, I marked not only the face, but also the edges

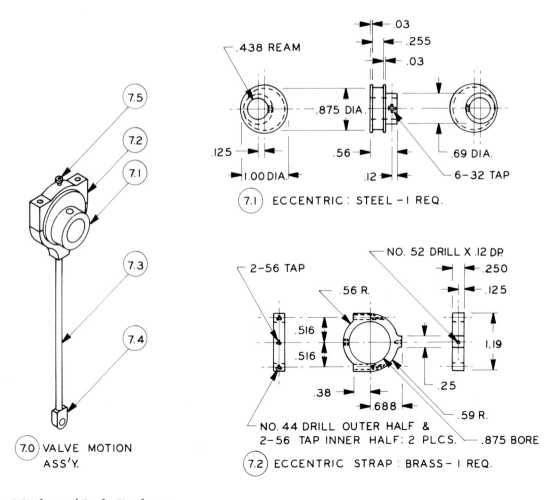

7.0 VALVE MOTION ASS'Y.

7.1 ECCENTRIC : STEEL – I REQ.

7.2 ECCENTRIC STRAP : BRASS – I REQ.

where the holes go for the eccentric rod, oil cup, and the securing studs. Note that I had left an area across the center wide enough to allow for the saw kerf. My first operation was to drill the four holes from the edges. The main reason for doing this was to guarantee the alignment of the stud holes in the two halves after they were separated. The holes I was drilling in Photo 35 were to form the short blending radius where the eccentric rod enters the strap. After doing this drilling, I sawed the part off.

Next, I set up a mandrel between lathe centers with a slitting blade as in Photo 37. Essentially, this converts the lathe into a horizontal mill. By clamping the part securely to the lathe carriage, I was able to slit off the unwanted metal at the bottom of the eccentric strap. In order to cut the part in half, I clamped it to the lathe carriage in the position indicated in Photo 38. Note that I was using a slitting blade on a vary short mounting directly on the lathe nose for this cut. When the two parts were separated, I tapped the inner half for the size 2-56 studs and enlarged the corresponding holes in the outer half to clear the studs. Photo 41 shows the completed group of parts and will help clarify their relationship.

34

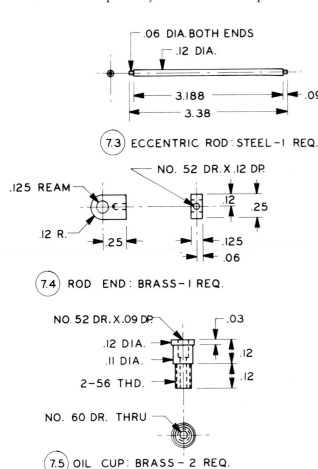

(7.3) ECCENTRIC ROD : STEEL — 1 REQ.

(7.4) ROD END : BRASS — 1 REQ.

(7.5) OIL CUP : BRASS — 2 REQ.

35

Use a vertical milling arrangement like the one I was using in Photo 39 to machine the flats where the clamping nuts bear against the outer half of the eccentric strap. After this milling cut, the rest of the external profile is best formed with files. Use common roundhead bolts to hold the two parts of the eccentric strap together during the filing and the subsequent boring operations.

36 37

38 39

40

The Shop Wisdom of Rudy Kouhoupt

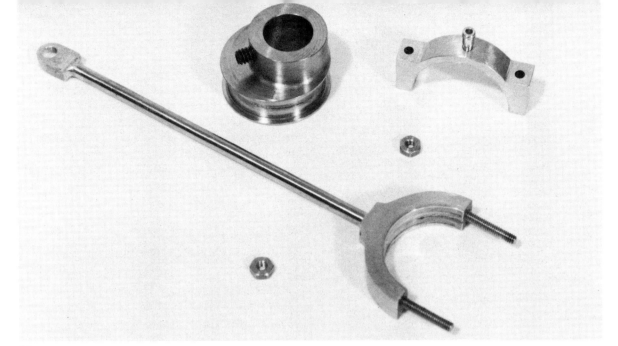

41

In order to bore the eccentric strap to fit the eccentric, I mounted it on a faceplate. Notice in Photo 40 that I had used packing blocks to prevent the boring bar from running into the faceplate. Use a wiggler to position the part on center. Center drill and open the hole as far as possible with twist drills before beginning to use the boring bar.

Cut a piece of steel rod for the Eccentric Rod (7.3). Turn down the ends to the dimensions indicated. Make the Rod End (7.4) from fairly hard brass. Slip the rod end and the eccentric strap on opposite ends of the eccentric rod, and silver solder the whole assembly.

Follow the same procedure in making the Oil Cups (7.5) as you used on the previous oil cups (2.3). Only one of the small oil cups is needed for the eccentric strap. However, another will be needed for the connecting rod, so it pays to make them both at the same time.

GUIDE ASSEMBLY (8.0)

There are quite a few small parts to be made for the Guide Assembly. No special machining setups are required. The utmost importance, however, is attached to accurate hole spacings, clearances, and fits. The complete group of parts for this assembly is laid out in Photo 42. Refer, also, to Photos 43 and 44 to obtain a clear understanding of what parts are involved and how they relate to one another.

Make the Bottom Mount (8.1) from .38" thick aluminum. It is very similar to a clevis and can be handled in the same way. Like all the other parts of this assembly, the spacing of the holes is important. Mark them out carefully. Start all holes with a small center drill. Watch that the drills don't wander on you.

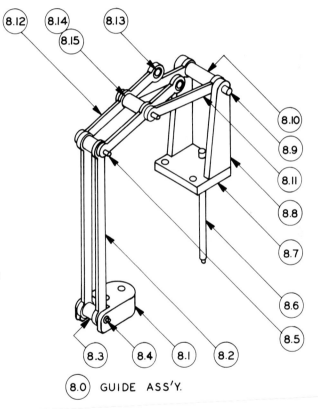

8.0 GUIDE ASS'Y.

Three sets of links are required in this assembly. All are made from .075" thick, or 14-gauge, steel. All the links are designed to operate in matched pairs. It is a good idea to make them in pairs. For example, mark out the Vibrating Links (8.2) on the steel. Saw them roughly to outline. Drill and ream one hole only in each link. Make up a close fitting bush to go through the reamed holes for alignment purposes, and clamp the pair together. Now, when you drill and ream the second hole, you will be doing matching links simultaneously, thus guaranteeing that they have identical hole spacings. Finish by filing to the outline. Repeat this procedure

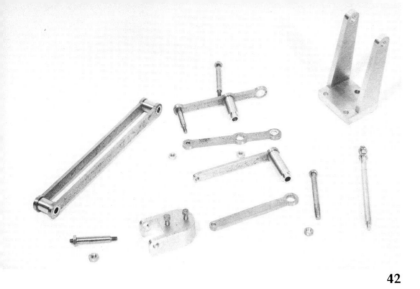

42

Bearing (8.10) and the Center Bearing (8.14).

A slightly different procedure is needed to make the End Bearings (8.13). Chuck a short piece of .188" diameter bronze rod. Center drill, drill and ream it through, after facing the end. Part off at the exact length, because bearings of this size do not take well to being re-chucked for facing cuts or other operations. It is quite easy to distort them, in fact. After pressing the end bearings into the main links, it is a good idea to pass the reamer through them again to be sure they have not tightened up a bit.

The Bottom Pin (8.4), Top Pin (8.5), Support (8.6), Radius Pin (8.9), and Center Pin (8.15) are all so similar that one description will apply to any of them. Chuck a piece of steel rod for the bottom pin, as an example. Face the end and turn down the shoulder. Cut the thread with a die mounted in the tailstock die holder. Cut to length, reverse in the chuck, and repeat on the opposite end.

When you make the Mounting Plate (8.7), be sure to locate and drill the holes accurately. This applies to the Radius Plates (8.8), as well.

to make the other two pairs of links. They are the Radius Links (8.11) and the Main Links (8.12).

Chuck a piece of .25" diameter rod to make the Spacer/Bearing (8.3). Face the end of the rod, first. Then turn the shoulder which will be a press fit in the reamed holes of the vibrating link. Part off at the correct overall length. Reverse the part in the chuck to shoulder the second end. Finally, use the tailstock chuck to center drill the end, followed by a pilot drill and reamer. Follow the same procedure for the Radius

43 44

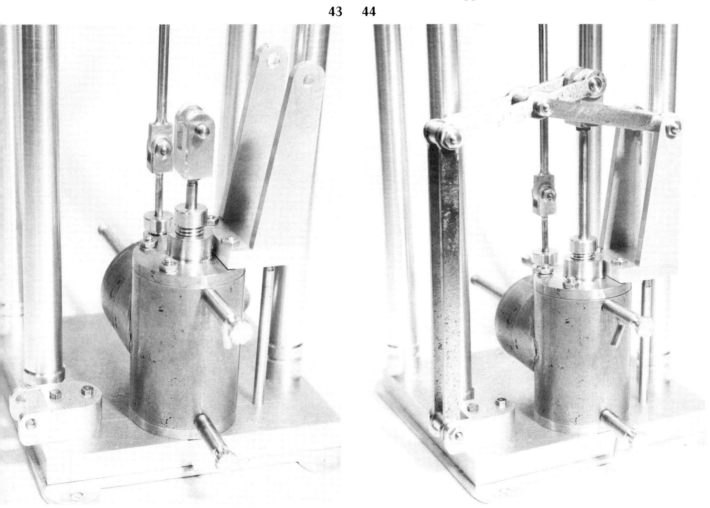

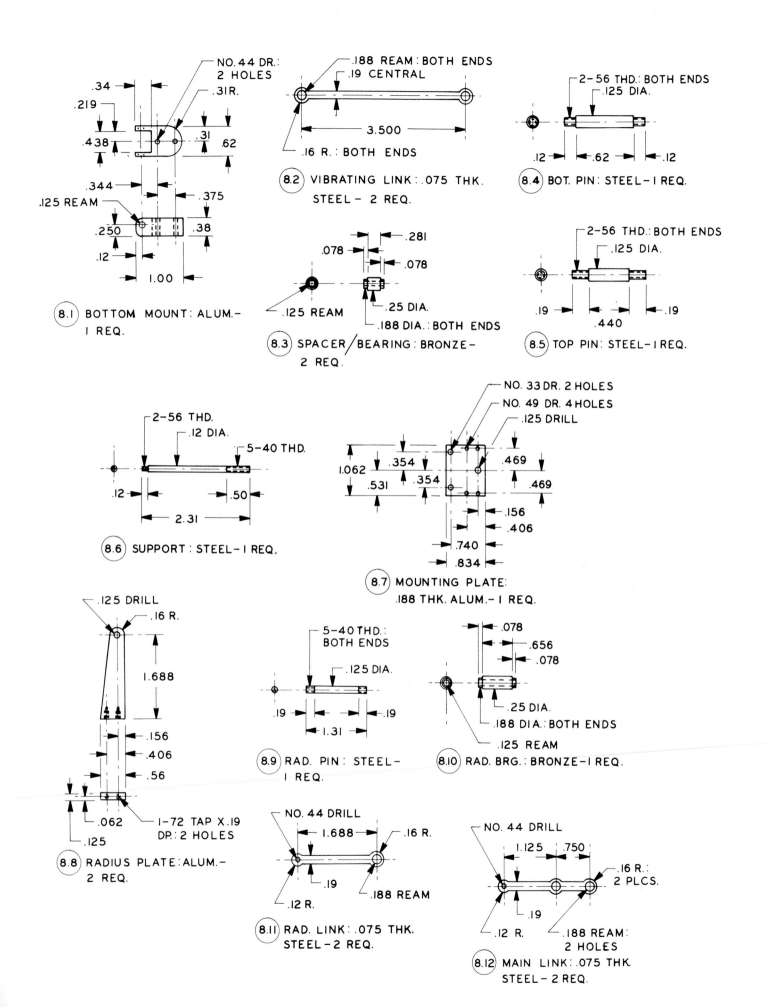

.34
.219
.438
NO. 44 DR.:
2 HOLES
.31 R.
.31
.62

.344
.375
.125 REAM
.250
.12
.38
1.00

(8.1) BOTTOM MOUNT: ALUM.–
1 REQ.

.188 REAM: BOTH ENDS
.19 CENTRAL
3.500
.16 R.: BOTH ENDS

(8.2) VIBRATING LINK: .075 THK.
STEEL – 2 REQ.

.281
.078
.078
.125 REAM
.25 DIA.
.188 DIA.: BOTH ENDS

(8.3) SPACER/BEARING: BRONZE–
2 REQ.

2–56 THD.: BOTH ENDS
.125 DIA.
.12
.62
.12

(8.4) BOT. PIN: STEEL–1 REQ.

2–56 THD.: BOTH ENDS
.125 DIA.
.19
.440
.19

(8.5) TOP PIN: STEEL–1 REQ.

2–56 THD.
.12 DIA.
5–40 THD.
.12
.50
2.31

(8.6) SUPPORT: STEEL–1 REQ.

NO. 33 DR. 2 HOLES
NO. 49 DR. 4 HOLES
.125 DRILL
1.062
.354
.354
.531
.469
.469
.156
.406
.740
.834

(8.7) MOUNTING PLATE:
.188 THK. ALUM.–1 REQ.

.125 DRILL
.16 R.
1.688
.156
.406
.56
.062
1–72 TAP X .19
DP.: 2 HOLES
.125

(8.8) RADIUS PLATE: ALUM.–
2 REQ.

5–40 THD.:
BOTH ENDS
.125 DIA.
.19
.19
1.31

(8.9) RAD. PIN: STEEL–
1 REQ.

.078
.656
.078
.25 DIA.
.188 DIA.: BOTH ENDS
.125 REAM

(8.10) RAD. BRG.: BRONZE–1 REQ.

NO. 44 DRILL
1.688
.16 R.
.19
.12 R.
.188 REAM

(8.11) RAD. LINK: .075 THK.
STEEL – 2 REQ.

NO. 44 DRILL
1.125
.750
.16 R.:
2 PLCS.
.19
.12 R.
.188 REAM:
2 HOLES

(8.12) MAIN LINK: .075 THK.
STEEL – 2 REQ.

When I made the radius plates, I drilled the .125" diameter hole first. Then I bolted the pieces together with a close-fitting bolt through that hole and machined the pair simultaneously as one piece. I used the faceplate facing cutter, as previously shown to machine the bottom surfaces flat and square. Drill and tap the 1-72 holes for the bolts to mount the radius plates on the mounting plate. Here again, I countersunk the four no. 49 holes in the mounting plate to accept flathead screws.

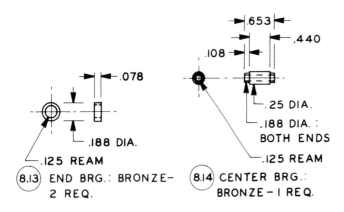

(8.13) END BRG.: BRONZE- 2 REQ.

(8.14) CENTER BRG.: BRONZE - I REQ.

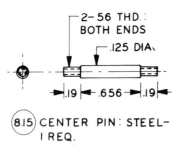

(8.15) CENTER PIN: STEEL- I REQ.

Assemble the long vibrating links by pressing in the spacer/bearings. These can remain assembled permanently, because the pins can be slipped through them in that state. The other pairs of links will have to be light press fits on their bearings to permit insertion of the shouldered pins during assembly or disassembly. Screw the support directly into its threaded hole in the base. Put a nut on the 5-40 thread, and put the mounting plate and radius plates in place. The mounting plate is secured by the two long studs of the cylinder and the support. Put another nut on the support above the mounting plate. Refer to Photo 43 which shows how this part of the assembly goes together. Note that the bottom mount has also been bolted to the base. By referring to Photo 44, you will be able to see the positions of the links and pins as well as how they are mounted in the bottom mount and radius plates. At this point, you can connect the clevis of the cylinder assembly to the guide assembly by slipping the wrist pin through. Check to be

sure that the motion is smooth throughout the entire piston stroke. A bind may indicate that the mounting plate is not perfectly horizontal. This can be adjusted slightly by adjusting the position of the nuts on the support either to raise or lower the outer end of the mounting plate. Obviously, this shifts the pivot point of the radius plates by an amplified amount. Be very cautious about making this adjustment.

CONNECTING ROD ASSEMBLY (9.0)

Photo 45 shows the group of parts that make up the Connecting Rod Assembly. The Small End (9.1) and the Large End (9.2) differ only in their dimensions. Mark the outline of each on steel of appropriate thickness. Drill and ream the bearing holes before cutting out the parts, because the larger pieces of metal are easier to secure against the forces of the cut. This makes the hole alignment a little more accurate. After reaming the holes, cut the parts out and file them to the mark. Drill the .125" diameter hole in each for insertion of the rod. Drill and tap the 2-56 hole in the large end for the oil cup.

Cut a piece of .19" diameter steel rod for making the Rod (9.3). Chuck it and turn down each end to the dimension shown in the drawing. Insert the rod into the drilled holes in the small end and the large end. Be sure the assembly is flat and that the surfaces of the ends are parallel. Silver solder the joints.

Machine the Small Bearing (9.4) by the same procedure as you did the end bearings (8.13) for the guide assembly. Machine the Large Bearing (9.5) in a similar way except that this one has the shoulder which will act as a spacer between the connecting rod and the crank. Press the bearings into their respective holes in the connecting rod. It is a good idea to put the reamers through them once again after pressing to be sure they are not undersize. Reach through the 2-56 tapped hole to drill a no. 60 hole through the side of the large bearing so the oil can flow from the oil cup (7.5) to the crankpin.

Put the connecting rod in place between the crankpin and wrist pin. Now your engine is mechanically complete as mine was when I shot Photo 46. Rotate the flywheel slowly by hand to be sure that everything moves freely with no binds or tight spots. If you detect any spots where the motion is tight or uneven, this is the time to track them down and eliminate the source of friction.

When you are satisfied that your engine is mechanically acceptable and ready for finishing,

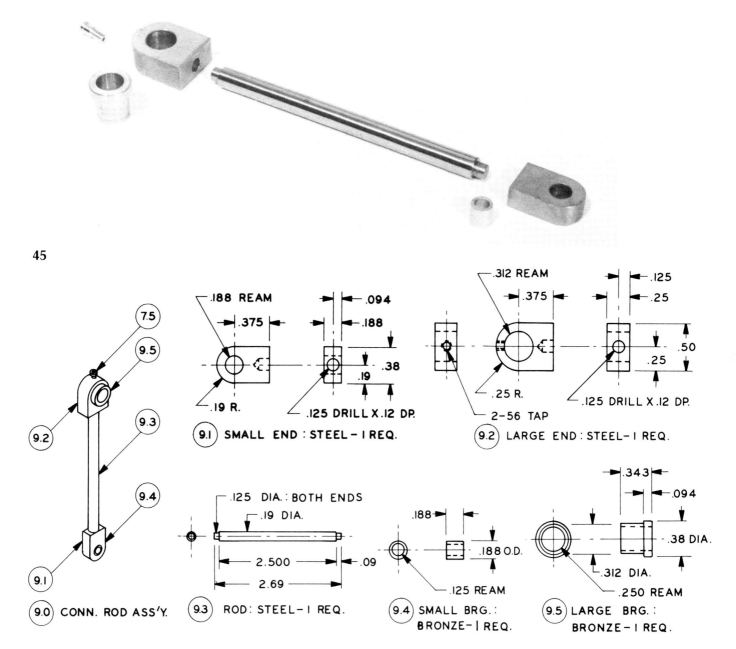

45

9.0 CONN. ROD ASS'Y.

9.1 SMALL END : STEEL – 1 REQ.
.188 REAM
.375
.19 R.
.094
.188
.38
.19
.125 DRILL X .12 DP.

9.2 LARGE END : STEEL – 1 REQ.
.312 REAM
.375
.25 R.
2-56 TAP
.125
.25
.50
.25
.125 DRILL X .12 DP.

9.3 ROD : STEEL – 1 REQ.
.125 DIA. : BOTH ENDS
.19 DIA.
2.500
2.69
.09

9.4 SMALL BRG. : BRONZE – 1 REQ.
.188
.188 O.D.
.125 REAM

9.5 LARGE BRG. : BRONZE – 1 REQ.
.343
.094
.38 DIA.
.312 DIA.
.250 REAM

remove the steam chest cover as I did for Photo 47. This will give you a chance to watch the slide valve in motion to be sure it is sitting flat with its face in contact with the surface of the port face. If it is not flat on the port face, check the valve nut and large groove in the valve back to be sure they are square. The valve should have a bit of "lift" so it can raise off the port face if condensate becomes trapped in the cylinder. Furthermore, the valve nut must be just free enough in the groove in the valve back that it does not bind and prevent the valve from settling back on the port face.

FINISHING UP

If you intend to paint the engine, this is a good time to take it all apart. Put witness marks on the bearings and other parts so they will be reassembled in their proper positions.

Before beginning the final assembly, make gaskets from thin paper. I used typing paper for the gaskets in this engine. Each gasket was soaked with lubricating oil before it was put in place. A total of four gaskets is required. They will be used under the top and bottom covers as well as under the steam chest cover and between the steam chest and port face.

Pack both stuffing boxes and the piston grooves with graphited string. I make rings for the stuffing boxes by winding several turns of packing material around a dowel of the diameter of the piston rod or valve stem. Then I cut across the winding with a sharp blade to cut off a set of rings. It takes three rings, on the average, to make a good packing under each gland. Slip

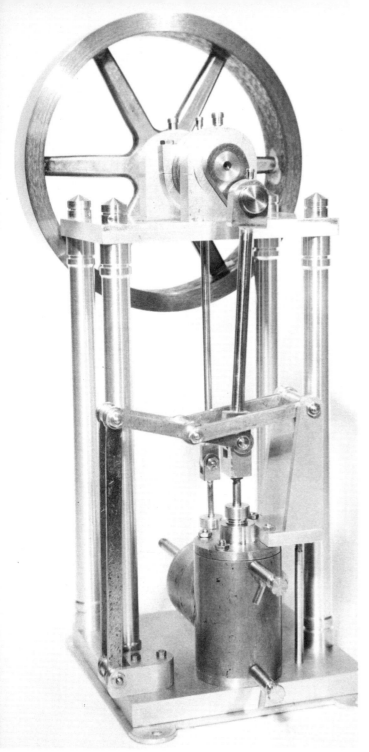

each ring down into the stuffing box compressing it lightly with the gland. Alternate the positions of the splits in the rings so they do not occur in a line. Work on a glass surface to roll the packing firmly into the grooves in the piston. Put in enough material to make a resilient packing, but don't overdo it. Too much packing simply produces friction and detracts from the running of the engine.

Apply oil to the packings and all moving parts as you put the engine back together. Once again check for tight spots as you go along. Put it all back together except for the steam chest cover

(once again back to Photo 47). Now the valve can be set.

During valve setting, *always rotate the flywheel in the direction you want the engine to run.* While this engine can be set to run in either direction, the preferred direction is for the flywheel to rotate clockwise when viewed in the position of Photo 47.

There are two adjustments that must be made to the valve. The first is to get the travel of the valve centralized over the steam ports. With the engine positioned as in Photo 47, rotate the flywheel slowly by hand while watching the valve move through a full cycle. As the valve reaches each end of its stroke, it should open the steam port fully. If it moves more toward one end than the other, loosen the setscrew and adjust the position of the valve nut on the valve stem to shift the valve in the proper direction. When you are satisfied that the valve motion is centralized over the steam ports, you are ready for the second adjustment which is the angularity between the crankpin and eccentric.

Begin the second adjustment by rotating the flywheel slowly until the piston is at bottom dead center. Secure the flywheel so it cannot rotate accidentally. Loosen the setscrew in the eccentric and rotate it around the crankshaft in the direction you want the engine to run. Watch the valve go through its motion as you move the eccentric. When the eccentric reaches the spot where the bottom port is just about to be uncovered by the valve, you have the correct angular relationship. Tighten the setscrew. Rotate the flywheel until the piston reaches top dead center. As the reaches this position, the valve should be just about to open the top steam port. If necessary, go back for a touchup to the adjustments. If you are satisfied with the valve setting, you can put the cover on the steam chest. Your finished engine will now look about as mine did in Photos 1,2, and 48. And it will be ready for running, of course!

48

Baker Fan

An altogether incredible amount of time has passed since my first stationary engine steamed its way off my drawing board. From then until the present, my fascination with designing, building, and operating model stationary steam engines has never waned. One of the activities to which a part of my time has been devoted was designing and building suitably proportioned loads for the stationary models to drive. It is much more interesting and rewarding to watch a small engine drive a load than to watch it idly and pointlessly spinning its flywheel.

One of the loads that was developed in full-size practice for breaking in and testing steam engines is the Baker fan. Anyone who has watched a big steam traction engine belted to a Baker fan knows what a dramatic show it can be. Having observed this spectacle, the first Baker fan I built was specifically for use with my model traction engines. It is shown belted to my model *Peerless* traction engine in Photo 1. For reference purposes, the scale of the traction engine is 1.25" = 1'.

Once having learned that the procedure of belting up and driving the fan added greatly to the interest of operating the traction engines, it did not take long for me to build another fan for use with my stationary engines. Photo 2 gives a close view of the fan, while Photo 3 shows it belted to the flywheel of the horizontal engine which is also detailed in this book. The

construction of the fan in Photos 2 and 3 will be presented here.

BUILDING THE FAN

The sequence in which the parts are numbered in the assembly drawing is the order in which I made them for the original. Begin by cutting a length of .44" diameter steel rod for the Shaft (Part 1). Face off both ends and center drill them for mounting between lathe centers. Turning the part from an oversize rod insures that the areas of different diameter will all be concentric with one another. After turning the shaft to the dimensions indicated, use a piece of 600 grit wet or dry paper, or something similar, to polish the .312" diameter shoulders. They are the journals that rotate in the bearings.

Either rod or flat stock is suitable for making the Collars (Part 2). If you make them from rod, cut off two slices. Chuck them in the three-jaw to face off both sides. Next, use the tailstock chuck to center drill, pilot drill and ream the central hole. Locate and tap the four holes for the bolts that will secure the Side Plates (Part 4) to the collars. Finally, drill and tap the 6-32 hole for the setscrew that will lock the collars on the shaft.

Very little work is involved in making the four Blades (Part 3). All you need do is mark them out on the steel sheet, saw to outline, and file the edges smooth. Do *not* try to cut out the sheet metal parts with snips; the

1

shearing action of the snips stretches the metal and destroys the flatness of the parts. The .036" thick steel specified is nominal 20-gauge. Galvanized steel, such as I used, actually measures .037" thick and is sold as 21-gauge. From a practical point of view, either type of steel will serve well in this application.

The four side plates (Part 4) are cut from the same stock. For clarity, I have specified dimensions on only one end of the drawing of this part. It will be obvious that the same dimensions apply to both ends. When you mark out the metal for the side plates, mark in all the center lines, punch the location of each hole, and drill all the holes. Note that the side plates will be attached to the collars in handed pairs. Therefore, it is necessary to bend two rights and two lefts. One right and one left make up each pair to be attached to one collar. Photo 4 illustrates the bent pairs, one of which has been bolted to its collar. Make the right angle bends along the center line which passes through the long axis of the parts. Not having a bending brake suitable for this job, I simply clamped the parts between 1/2" steel flats aligned with the center line and tapped the bends down by light hammer blows.

You can assemble the side plates on the collars and slip the collars into place on the shaft, as I had done in Photo 5, for you are now ready to attach the blades by means of rivets. Align the collar/side plate assemblies on the shaft as shown with a distance of 1.50" between the inner faces of the collars. Clamp each blade in position (refer to Photo 6). Measure from the shaft to get each blade parallel to it and the same distance out from it. Of course, each blade will be centered across the side plates. Drill

2

3

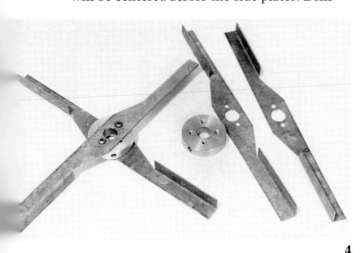

4

through the no. 52 holes in the side plates to make the matching holes in the blades. Attach the blades by putting 1/16" round head rivets

through the no. 52 holes to duplicate the assembly in Photo 6.

A slice from a rod is probably the best starting point for the Pulley (Part 5). Chuck it in the three-jaw to face off each side and make the shallow undercut. The exact depth and width of the undercut is not critical; it is there for appearance reasons alone. Use the tailstock chuck to center drill, pilot drill, and ream the central hole. Put in the tapped hole for the setscrew. Now you can mount the pulley on the shaft which is useful as a mandrel for

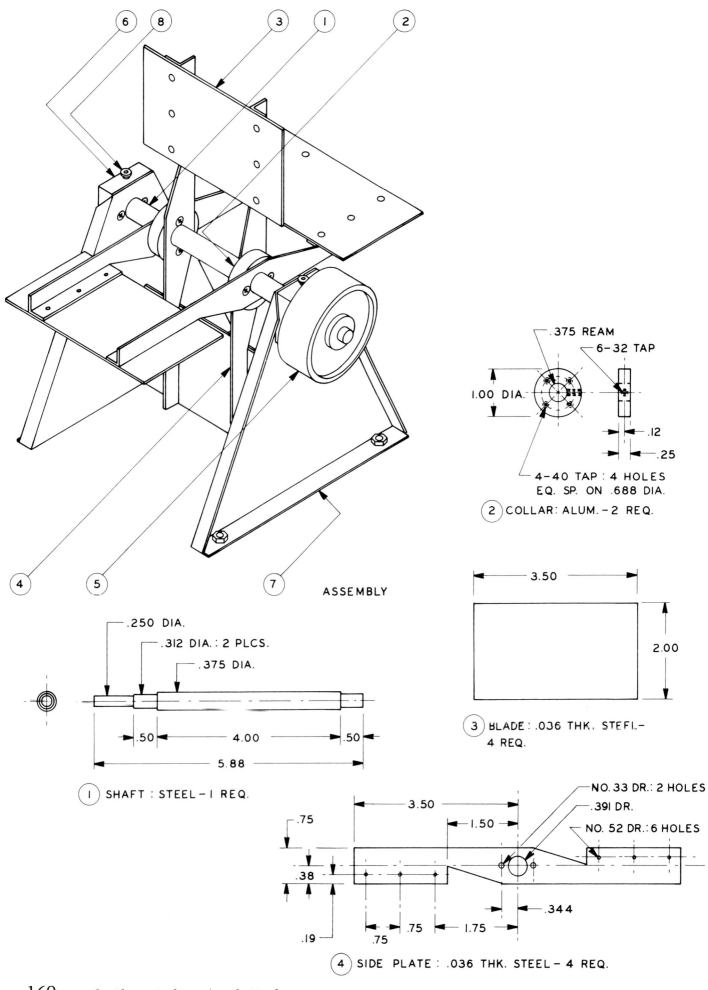

.375 REAM

6-32 TAP

1.00 DIA.

.12

.25

4-40 TAP : 4 HOLES
EQ. SP. ON .688 DIA.

2 COLLAR: ALUM. – 2 REQ.

3.50

2.00

3 BLADE : .036 THK. STEEL – 4 REQ.

.250 DIA.

.312 DIA.: 2 PLCS.

.375 DIA.

.50   4.00   .50

5.88

1 SHAFT : STEEL – 1 REQ.

ASSEMBLY

NO. 33 DR.: 2 HOLES

.391 DR.

NO. 52 DR.: 6 HOLES

3.50

1.50

.75

.38

.19

.344

.75   .75   1.75

4 SIDE PLATE : .036 THK. STEEL – 4 REQ.

turning the outside of the pulley.

Some question may arise over the shape of the pulley, since pulleys for flat belt work are traditionally crowned, or raised at the center. I did not crown the pulley for my Baker fan which is obvious in Photos 2 and 5. The surface of my pulley is cylindrical with a slight chamfer at each edge. In the small sizes of pulleys and flywheels on model engines and accessories, I have found no advantage to the crowned shape. Comparisons between pulleys with or without the crown have shown me that the small belts on my models track and stay on either type with no difficulty. This is a point individual modelers may settle according to their own preference or experience.

Use either flat stock or bar stock to make the Bearings (Part 6). After cutting them to size,

true up the edges by filing or milling. Mark out the hole locations. Drill and ream the central hole which should be a nice running fit on the .312" diameter parts of the shaft. Drill and tap the 4-40 holes for the bolts that will secure the bearings to the uprights. Also, drill and tap the 4-40 hole in the top of each bearing for the oil cup. The pilot hole should break into the reamed hole for the oil to enter, but the thread does not have to be tapped any more than .19" deep.

Make the Uprights (Part 7) from the same type of steel sheet as you used for the other sheet metal parts. As you mark the outlines, mark the bending lines, also. The bends to form the flanges are made along the chained lines parallel to the three long sides. After locating and drilling the holes, saw the parts out, and file

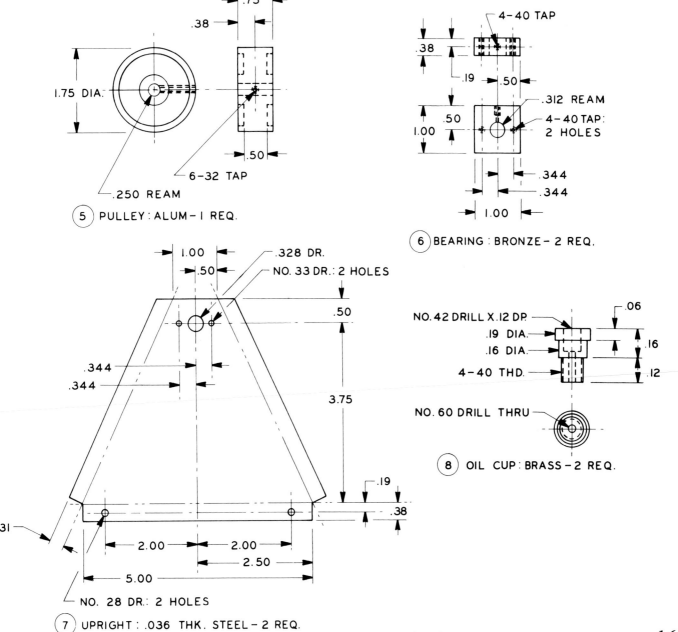

5) PULLEY: ALUM – 1 REQ.

6) BEARING: BRONZE – 2 REQ.

8) OIL CUP: BRASS – 2 REQ.

7) UPRIGHT: .036 THK. STEEL – 2 REQ.

5

6

7

the edges smooth. Make the 90° bends by clamping between blocks of steel, as you did on the side plates. Refer to Photo 7 which shows the shape of the uprights and how the bearings are mounted in them.

The last items to be made are the Oil Cups (Part 8). Chuck a piece of .19" diameter brass rod, and face it off. Turn down the .16" diameter part and the part for the 4-40 thread. Cut the thread with a die held in the tailstock die holder. Now you can part off. Use a split 4-40 nut in the three-jaw chuck to hold the oil cups in the reversed position. Working with the

tailstock chuck, center drill and drill no. 42 to a depth of .12" to form the oil reservoir. Finally, drill through with drill no. 60 for the oil to enter the bearings.

At this point, you can assemble the Baker fan complete and mount it on a simple base or stand. If necessary, bend the bottom flanges of the uprights slightly to get it standing square. Be sure that it turns freely with no binds or rubs. The purpose of driving the Baker fan is to overcome the air resistance of the blades, not to overcome mechanical friction from binds.

BELTS AND BELTING UP

Choosing a material for making the flat belts for a model can be a problem because of the requirements for flexibility, thinness, etc. I make mine from a 100% polyester hem tape I buy in Woolworth's under the name of "Wright's *Soft and Easy* Seam Binding." the last time I bought it, a three-yard package cost 75¢. The material is .47" wide and available in a wide variety of colors. The belt shown in Photo 1 is half of what comes in the package. After cutting it to length, I overlap the ends by about 1.50". Then I sew a row of very fine stitches along each side and across both cut ends to hold them down securely. In doing this, it is important that the ends be lined up carefully so the belt will not have a lateral kink in it. Beware of twists, also! Other tapes or ribbons may be just as good or better.

There are two ways the belt can be run between the flywheel of the engine and the pulley of the fan. The preferred way is to use a crossed belt as shown in Photos 1 and 3. An open belt running from flywheel top to pulley top and pulley bottom to flywheel bottom is more troublesome, because it is much more influenced by cross winds. The crossed belt also has a longer wrap on the driving surfaces which makes it less prone to slip.

There are two conditions that must be met when lining up for belt work. In the first place, the pulley and flywheel must be in a straight line with each other and tracking on centers. This can be checked by placing a straightedge across the edge of the wheels. The second requirement, that the shaft of the fan and the crankshaft of the engine be parallel, is a little harder to see directly. The straightedge across the edges of the wheels is a guide, but as running begins, some adjustment Bby hand a few revolutions which is enough to show up a lack of parallelism. A very slight shift in the angle of either the engine or the fan is enough to make a sizeable shift in the tracking pattern of the relatively long belt. Clamps or blocks may be used to keep the engine and fan from shifting in position.

I always go through the routine of getting the belt tracking before I get up steam. While belting up is a simple job, it can become hectic if you are trying to line things up, tend the fire, work the blower, watch the gauges, and start the engine all at once!

Build a Reversing, Upright Engine

Upright engines are well suited to any installation in which the floor space is limited. While their construction may take any one of a number of forms, I have selected the form in which the cylinder is mounted on double standards of plate construction for the model engine to be presented here. Not only does the plate standard form of construction provide a solid cylinder mounting, it also permits the crosshead guides to be installed in a rigid position. In overall construction, then, the model engine illustrated in Photos 1 and 2 is solid. Given accurate workmanship, it is capable of smooth running and hard work.

Having designed the engine with a fully supported crosshead, I thought it would be a good idea to incorporate a valve mechanism to permit reversing the engine. The ability to reverse adds versatility to the design and makes it more interesting to operate, as well as taking advantage of the fact that the crosshead is properly guided and braced for both directions of rotation. Specifically, reversing is accomplished by a slip eccentric driven by a slotted driver. The eccentric position is controlled by a drive pin engaging a curved slot in the eccentric driver. A drive nut secures the position of the eccentric relative to the driver. Valve gears of this sort have been used on full-size launch engines, but I don't recall having seen this exact arrangement on any model engines. The vital statistics of the engine are as follows:

Cylinder	Double action
Bore	.875"
Stroke	1.125"
Steam lap	.094"
Eccentric throw	.188"
Cutoff	75%

Some other design features of the engine are worth mentioning at this time. A review of

1   **2**

ASSEMBLY KEY

1.0 ENGINE BASE ASS'Y.
2.0 CRANKSHAFT ASS'Y.
3.0 FLYWHEEL ASS'Y.
4.0 ENGINE STANDARD ASS'Y.
5.0 CROSSHEAD & GUIDE ASS'Y.
6.0 CONN. ROD ASS'Y.
7.0 CYLINDER ASS'Y.
8.0 STEAM CHEST ASS'Y.
9.0 VALVE MOTION ASS'Y.

TOLERANCES

2 PLACE DEC. ± .01
3 PLACE DEC. ± .005

1.0 ENGINE BASE ASS'Y.

BILL OF MATERIALS									
No.	Part	Material	Quantity	Dimensions	No.	Part	Material	Quantity	Dimensions
1.1	Base	Aluminum	1	.31 × 2.62 × 3.75	7.7	Crank end cover	Aluminum	1	1.62 dia. × .44
1.2	Bearing block	Aluminum	2	.38 × 1.31 × 1.62	7.8	Gland	Brass	1	.50 dia. × .38
1.3	Bearing	Bronze	2	.62 dia. × .50	7.9	Exhaust	Tubing	1	.25 dia. × 2.00
1.4	Oil cup	Brass	2	.19 dia. × .28	7.10	Drain valve	Brass	2	.19 dia. × .75 &
2.1	Crankshaft	Steel	1	.375 dia. × 3.25					.09 OD tube × .50
2.2	Crankpin	Steel	1	.312 dia. × .75	7.11	Drain valve stem	Brass	2	.25 dia. × .56
2.3	Web	Steel	2	.188 × 1.12 × 1.69	7.12	Cyl. jacket	Shim	1	.010 × 2.00 × 4.00
3.1	Flywheel	Aluminum	1	3.50 dia. × .62	8.1	Steam chest	Aluminum	1	.50 × 1.25 × 2.00
3.2	Key	Steel	1	.062 × .125 × .50	8.2	Steam chest cover	Aluminum	1	.09 × 1.25 × 1.88
4.1	Standard	Aluminum	2	.62 × .75 × 5.75	8.3	Gland	Brass	1	.44 dia. × .38
4.2	Pad	Aluminum	2	.125 × .56 × 1.19	8.4	Bearing	Brass	1	.38 dia. × .75
4.3	Cylinder mount	Aluminum	1	.250 × 1.62 × 1.62	8.5	Inlet	Tubing	1	.19 dia. × 2.00
	Jig center	Aluminum	1	.62 × .75 × 1.00	8.6	Valve rod	Stainless	1	.125 dia. × 3.03
	Jig side	Steel	2	.036 × 2.00 × 3.50	8.7	Rod end	Brass	1	.125 × .25 × .38
5.1	Guide plate	Steel	2	.075 × .62 × 1.88	8.8	Valve face	Stainless	1	.062 × .62 × .812
5.2	Guide bar	Steel	4	.036 × .188 × 1.88	8.9	Valve back	Brass	1	.31 × .62 × .75
5.3	Crosshead	Bronze	1	.250 × .62 × .850	8.10	Setscrew	Stainless	1	.125 dia. × .125
6.1	End bearing	Bronze	1	.38 × .62 × .75	8.11	Valve nut	Brass	1	.25 × .31 × .62
6.2	Rod end	Steel	1	.075 × .25 × .75	9.1	Eccentric	Steel	1	1.00 dia. × .47
6.3	Clevis	Steel	1	.38 × .50 × .62	9.2	Ecc. driver	Aluminum	1	.25 × 1.25 × 1.25
6.4	Rod	Steel	1	.19 dia. × 2.33	9.3	Drive pin	Steel	1	.188 dia. × .72
6.5	Wristpin	Steel	1	.25 dia. × .66	9.4	Drive nut	Brass	1	.38 dia. × .31
7.1	Port face	Bronze	1	.125 × 1.25 × 1.88	9.5	Eccentric strap	Brass	1	.25 × 1.25 × 1.25
7.2	Cylinder	Aluminum	1	1.25 × 1.44 × 1.88	9.6	Clevis	Steel	1	.25 × .25 × .44
7.3	Cyl. liner	Bronze	1	1.000 dia. × 1.62	9.7	Ecc. rod	Steel	1	.12 dia. × 3.06
7.4	Piston	Brass	1	.88 dia. × .44	9.8	Pin	Steel	1	.19 dia. × .44
7.5	Piston rod	Stainless	1	.188 dia. × 3.09	9.9	Oil cup	Brass	1	.12 dia. × .25
7.6	Head end cover	Aluminum	1	1.62 dia. × .19					

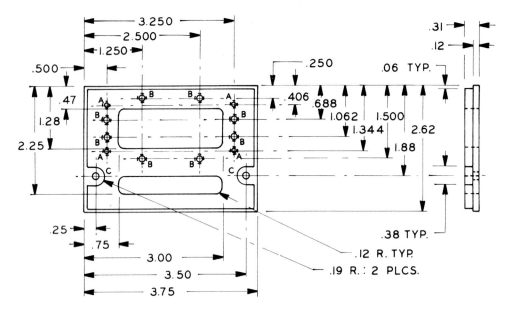

HOLE	OPERATION	NO. OF HOLES
A	NO. 44 DRILL	4
B	NO. 33 DRILL	8
C	NO. 28 DRILL	2

(1.1) BASE : ALUM. — 1 REQ.

NOTE: C'SINK A & B
HOLES FROM
UNDERSIDE

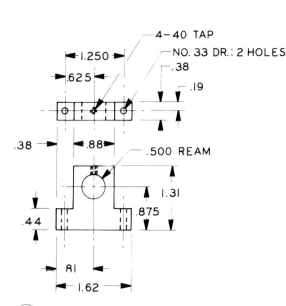

(1.2) BEARING BLOCK : ALUM.—
2 REQ.

(1.3) BEARING : BRONZE—
2 REQ.

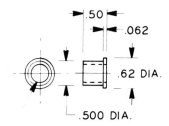

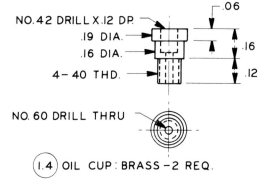

(1.4) OIL CUP : BRASS —2 REQ.

the Bill of Materials shows that I made extensive use of aluminum for many of the large structural parts of the engine, including the cylinder. Notice that I have fitted the cylinder with a bronze liner and a bronze port face against which the slide valve works. The slide valve, itself, is a composite type which has a stainless steel face silver soldered to a brass back. The valve rod is supported by a bearing at the top of the steam chest as well as by the gland and stuffing box at the bottom of the steam chest. This fact gives the valve an accurate linear motion without resorting to an external bearing and an extended valve rod.

A major assembly drawing accompanies this project. It identifies the nine subassemblies in the engine and shows their relationship to one another. The order in which the subassemblies are numbered is the order in which I built them, and it is the order in which their construction is detailed. The construction of the model engine shown in the accompanying illustrations

3

4

5

involved some very interesting machining operations. Accurate setup work was required to produce accurately fitting parts. In presenting this project, I will illustrate the setups I used by means of photographs, and I will give verbal descriptions, also. The satisfaction derived from doing the work well and producing a smooth, powerful performer is beyond words to describe. I urge all prospective builders to join in the fun, work carefully, and savor the satisfaction when the job is done; you are sure to love it!

ENGINE BASE ASSEMBLY (1.0)

Begin construction by marking the outline of the Base (1.1) on a piece of .31" thick flat stock. Saw the piece out, leaving a little material outside the mark for machining. The piece can be finished to size by either filing or milling. I chose to mill the part to size in the drill press milling setup shown in Photo 3. Note in the photo that I had used the side of an end mill to machine the outline of the part. Then I raised the end mill and used it to machine the step that forms the flange surrounding the base. While the part was set up in this position, I also milled the recessed areas that surrounded the "C" holes and form the flats for the mounting bolts. Since I had the part clamped flat on the

milling table as shown, it was necessary for me to reclamp the piece to machine the final side.

With the sides of the piece milled straight and square to one another, mark out the location of the two cutouts. The larger cutout is needed to clear the crank and connecting rod. The smaller cutout provides clearance for the eccentric strap. I removed the bulk of the metal from both cutouts by drilling the corners and sawing them roughly to outline. Then I set the piece up as shown in Photo 4 to smooth the edges off by milling. As you look at Photo 4, notice that the step was complete all the way around the base, and that you can see the flat area surrounding the "C" hole. Notice, also, that I had placed .125" thick packing strips between the base and milling table to keep the end mill clear of the table.

When the cutouts are finished, mark out the locations of all drilled holes. Use a small center punch to spot the position of each hole. Start each hole with a small center drill. Then finish each hole with the appropriate drill. It is a good idea to countersink all "A" and "B" holes from the underside to clear the heads of flathead screws. If you prefer some other head shape, leave the base flat underneath, but keep in mind that you will have to provide clearance holes in whatever surface you use for mounting the engine when it is done.

Mark the outline of the Bearing Blocks (1.2) on .38" thick flat stock. Saw them out, and machine them as a pair. I used a vertical milling setup to smooth all edges with an end mill. Refer to Photo 5 to see how I clamped the pieces together against a square clamping block on the milling table. Pay particular attention to the bottom surfaces to be sure the bearing blocks will stand straight and square when they are bolted in place on the base. In Photo 5, I was milling the step in the side of the bearing blocks. When the edges are all milled true, use the bottom surfaces as a reference to locate the holes. Drill the No. 33 holes vertically to clear the mounting bolts. Drill and tap the 4-40 hole in each block for an oil cup. Finally, drill and ream the .500" hole for the bearing in each. When you drill and ream the bearing holes, clamp the two bearing blocks tightly together with their bottom surfaces in alignment to insure that the bearing holes will be exactly in line with one another.

Only lathe work is required on the Bearings (1.3). Chuck a piece of .62" diameter bronze rod in the three-jaw chuck to take a facing cut across each end. Bring up the tailstock drill chuck to center drill, drill, and ream each bearing. Put each bearing on a mandrel between lathe centers to turn the outside to diameter. Make each bearing a light press fit in the bearing block. If you prefer, an anaerobic adhesive may be used to secure the bearings in the bearing blocks. My choice is the press fit; mine have an interference of a little less than .0005", and I pressed them in using the vise jaws. After you have pressed the bearings into the bearing blocks, drill a No. 60 hole down through the

side of the bearing through the 4-40 hole to provide a way for the oil to enter. Now, pass the reamer through the bearings again to be sure they are free of burrs raised by drilling the oil holes.

The Oil Cups (1.4) are also a lathe job. Chuck a piece of .19" diameter rod. Begin by facing it off. Turn down to form the .16" diameter part and the part for the 4-40 thread. Cut the thread by using a die held in the tailstock die holder. Part off, and reverse in the chuck, gripping by the .16" diameter shoulder. Using the tailstock drill chuck, center drill to start the hole. Form the oil reservoir by drilling with a No. 42 drill. Finally, drill through with a No. 60 drill for the oil to flow into the bearing.

Photo 6 shows the parts of the engine base assembly at this point. Notice that the bearing blocks are so placed that the flanges of the bearings will contact the flywheel on one side of the engine and the eccentric on the other. That is to say that the flanges are turned *out* to function as thrust surfaces.

6

CRANKSHAFT ASSEMBLY (2.0)

It is possible to make the Crankshaft (2.1) from a piece of a .375" diameter rod, such as drill rod. However, I prefer to start with a larger diameter piece to insure that the shoulders are concentric with the center. Refer to Photo 7 which shows my lathe set up for machining this part. With the shaft mounted in a three-jaw chuck and supported by a fixed steady rest, I took a facing cut across the end and then center drilled it. Repeating this operation with the workpiece reversed end for end, I was able to reduce the part to exact length. Then, when I mounted the part between lathe centers, I was able to turn it accurately to diameter throughout its length.

The fully turned crankshaft is shown in Photo 8. The machining operation in progress in Photo 8 is the cutting of the keyseat for the flywheel. Note that I was using a small Woodruff-type cutter to cut the keyseat. When positioning the

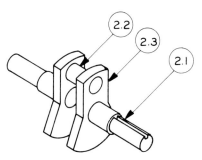

(2.0) CRANKSHAFT ASS'Y.

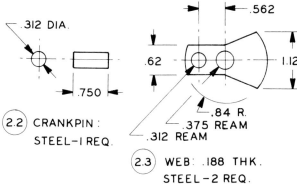

.312 DIA.

.750

(2.2) CRANKPIN:
STEEL—1 REQ.

.562

.62

1.12

.84 R.
.375 REAM
.312 REAM

(2.3) WEB: .188 THK.
STEEL—2 REQ.

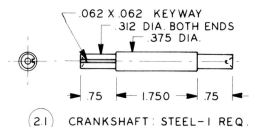

.062 X .062 KEYWAY
.312 DIA. BOTH ENDS
.375 DIA.

.75   1.750   .75

(2.1) CRANKSHAFT: STEEL—1 REQ.

7

8

9

shaft for the cut, I used an indicator to be sure the shaft was aligned parallel to the motion of the milling table. The V block is an accurate one which can be trusted to hold the work parallel to the surface of the milling table.

Drill rod may be used for the Crankpin (2.2). If you use drill rod, no machining is necessary. Once again, I started with oversize rod and turned it down to make the part. The ends do not have to be faced off or finished to exact length, since they can be finished in place in the crankshaft.

Mark out the shape of the Webs (2.3) on a suitable piece of stock. Saw them out. Since it is important both webs be identical, it is a good idea to clamp them tightly together for all other operations. Begin by filing down the sides to form the shape. Do not spend any time filing the radiused ends; these will be machined after assembly. Locate the positions of the two holes. Start them with a center drill. With the parts still tightly clamped together, drill through and ream the holes for the crankshaft and crankpin. Mark the webs to keep them in the same relative positions when you place them on the shaft. Cut a slight countersink on the *inner* surface of each web at the .375" hole and on the *outer* surface of each web at the .312" hole to assist the flow of solder when assembling the crankshaft.

Refer to Photo 9, for you are now ready to put the crankshaft together. Assemble the webs on the crankshaft with the crankpin in place, as shown. Space the webs so there is a space of .375" between their inner surfaces and a space of .500" between each outer surface and the adjacent shoulder on the crankshaft. Check to be sure the crankpin is parallel with the crankshaft. Check further to be sure the webs

The Shop Wisdom of Rudy Kouhoupt   169

are parallel to one another and square to the crankshaft. If everything is in a satisfactory position, you are ready to solder the joints using a propane torch. Silver solder may be used. However, I chose to use a stainless steel solder, which is actually pure tin, having a lower melting point. If you use silver solder, no other fastening is required. If you use the 425°F solder, as I did, it is advisable after soldering to drill a No. 52 hole through the edge of the web into the crankshaft and into the crankpin at each intersection. That is a total of four holes, two into the crankshaft and two into the crankpin. Press in short lengths of steel rod to pin the joints. I use 16-gauge brads for the pins. A few minutes of checking with a micrometer always locates a few brads that are oversize by .0005" or so, making them prefect press fits.

At this point, you can return the crankshaft to the lathe, as I had done in Photo 9, to machine down the ends of the crankpin and to turn the webs to form the radius. Finally, cut away the part of the crankshaft between the webs by means of a fine hacksaw. It is a good idea to wrap the crankpin or to insert a wooden block between the webs while sawing to prevent a sudden breakthrough of the saw from damaging it. This precaution is also valid for the next operation of filing the cut ends of the crankshaft flush and smooth with the inner faces of the webs.

10

Now you can mount the complete crankshaft assembly in the engine base assembly, as I had done in Photo 10. Check to be sure the crankshaft rotates freely in the bearings and that there is no undue pressure or drag on the webs from the ends of the bearings.

FLYWHEEL ASSEMBLY (3.0)

A slice from the end of a rod of 3.50" diameter is the perfect starting point for the Flywheel (3.1) Using a center finder, scribe a line across the center to locate the two .375" holes. Do

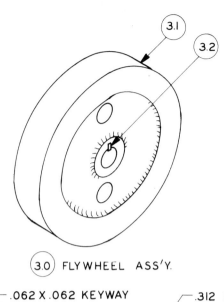

(3.0) FLYWHEEL ASS'Y.

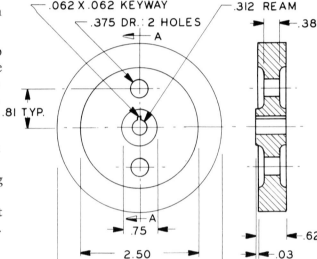

(3.1) FLYWHEEL: ALUM.– I REQ.

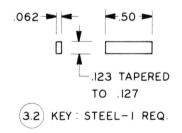

(3.2) KEY: STEEL–I REQ.

not drill them to size just yet. Center drill, pilot drill, and tap each spot 1/4-20 for bolting the part to a faceplate, as I had done in Photo 11. This permits you to take a truing cut across the rim and to do the machining of the face. After finishing the rim and face, bring up the tailstock drill chuck. Center drill, pilot drill and ream the center hole. Flip the part over to rebolt it to the faceplate. Take the facing cuts on the opposite side.

Referring to Photo 12, I had just finished facing off the second side and had all the conventional

11

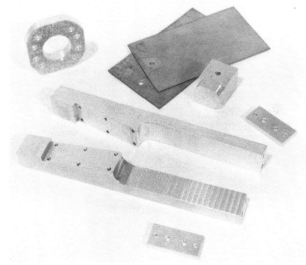

12

lathe cuts completed. The operation in progress in Photo 12 is the cutting of the keyway. Traditionally, this sort of keyway is cut with a broach. However, I cut them with the home built tool shown in the photograph. (See the article entitled "Small Keyways and Keyseats" in "The Micro Machinist section of this book.)

Once the keyway is cut and you have removed the flywheel from the faceplate, it is all right to drill out the two .375" diameter holes to clean out the threads. Slip the flywheel into place on the crankshaft, aligning the keyway with the keyseat. Make the Key (3.2) by hand filing. It will have to have a slight taper from end to end so it can be inserted into the flywheel and the crankshaft from the end of

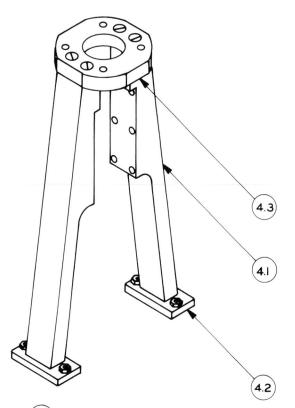

13

the crankshaft. Very light taps from a small hammer are all that is required to seat a properly fitted key and lock the flywheel in place. I finished mine so about .12" of the key projects beyond the end of the shaft to facilitate withdrawal of the key for removing the flywheel.

ENGINE STANDARD ASSEMBLY (4.0)

Before cutting any more metal, take a little time to examine Photo 13 and the isometric drawing of the Engine Standard Assembly. The photograph shows the parts of this assembly along with the parts of the assembly jig I made for putting them together. When you have a clear understanding of the parts and how they fit together, you will realize that careful work is called for in order to shape the Standards (4.1) correctly and get the bolting holes in exactly the right places. I will describe the procedure I followed in considerable detail.

Notice in the drawing of the standards that I have given all dimensions by coordinates, rather than specifying the angle. Generally speaking, more accurate work can be done by coordinate measurement. For reference purposes,

4.0 ENGINE STANDARD ASS'Y.

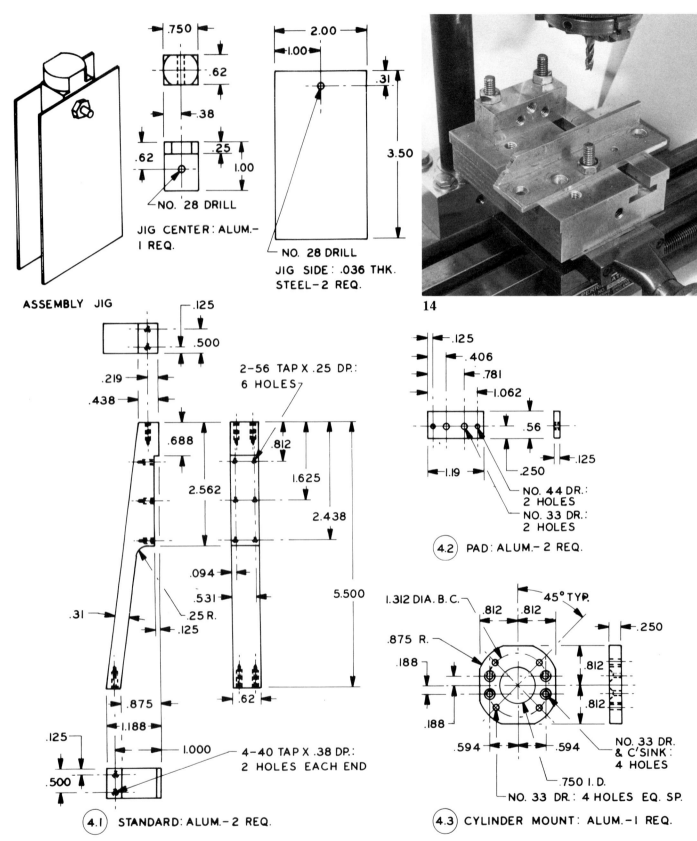

.750
.62
.38
.62
.25
1.00
NO. 28 DRILL

2.00
1.00
.31
3.50
NO. 28 DRILL
JIG SIDE: .036 THK.
STEEL-2 REQ.

JIG CENTER: ALUM.-
1 REQ.

ASSEMBLY JIG

14

.125
.500
.219
.438
2-56 TAP X .25 DP.:
6 HOLES
.688
.812
2.562
1.625
2.438
.094
.531
5.500
.31
.25 R.
.125
.875
1.188
.62
.125
1.000
4-40 TAP X .38 DP.:
2 HOLES EACH END
.500

(4.1) STANDARD: ALUM.-2 REQ.

.125
.406
.781
1.062
.56
.125
.250
1.19
NO. 44 DR.:
2 HOLES
NO. 33 DR.:
2 HOLES

(4.2) PAD: ALUM.-2 REQ.

1.312 DIA. B. C.
45° TYP.
.812 .812
.250
.875 R.
.188
.812
.812
.188
.594 .594
NO. 33 DR.
& C'SINK:
4 HOLES
.750 I. D.
NO. 33 DR.: 4 HOLES EQ. SP.

(4.3) CYLINDER MOUNT: ALUM.-1 REQ.

however, the angle that the long flat outer surface of the standard makes with a vertical line is 7° 45' 54.6".

Mark the outlines of the standards on a piece of .62" thick stock. I happened to have a rectangular piece of plate on hand that was

the right thickness, so I marked one standard on each end with the long flat outer surface of the standard parallel to the edge of the stock. My first cut was to drill a .500" diameter hole to form the blending curve on the inner surface of the standard. Then I hacksawed the parts

15 16

out of the plate and clamped them together side by side for all subsequent milling operations.

Refer now to Photo 14 which gives a view of how I arranged the milling table. Note that I had mounted an accurate square-edged clamping block on the rear of the table with an angle plate toward the front. The distance between them was exactly the thickness of the two standards clamped together. Furthermore, I had used an indicator working from the milling spindle to align the clamping block and angle plate exactly parallel to the X motion of the milling table. All of this positioning and alignment was done prior to mounting the workpieces on the table.

The first cut I took is shown in Photo 15 where I was fly cutting the long flat outer surfaces. The cutter in use is a home built tool I bolt to a faceplate. Note that the workpieces were securely fastened between the clamping block and the angle plate by gripping with a large parallel jaw clamp. It was only when the parts were securely clamped to the milling table that I would remove the individual clamp that held them to one another. Getting rid of the extra clamp gave a little more finger room and clearance around the milling spindle.

As soon as the long flat outer surfaces had been milled down, I flipped the pieces over to the position they were in for Photo 16. In this case, they were resting directly on the milling table with the long flat outer surfaces in contact with the milling table. The inner surface of the standards toward the bottom parallels the outer surface. I end milled the surface as shown in Photo 16.

17

Refer now to Photo 17 which illustrates the final position used in the milling cuts. Here the workpieces were mounted with the long outer surfaces facing down. This time, however, they had to be inclined at an angle corresponding to the angle quoted earlier. In making this setup, I did not measure the angle. Instead, I measured coordinate fashion from the accurately scribed lines on the side of the workpiece. The reference lines can be seen in the photograph. By reference to a surface gauge, I positioned the parts so the scribed lines were exactly parallel to the milling table.

18

19

20

21

bottom ends would be exactly square to the vertical inner surfaces and parallel to one another, I let the workpieces remain in position as clamped up in Photo 17. However, I lowered the milling spindle to the position shown in Photo 18 where I was milling off the top ends. When the top ends were true to the mark, I shifted the carriage along the X axis to take a similar milling cut across the bottoms. finally, I shifted back and milled away the small lip left between the blending radius and the lower end of the vertical surface.

No further milling cuts were necessary, and the standards were removed from the milling table and separated. At this point, mark out the positions of the six 2-56 tapped holes on each standard. Punch the locations. Then center drill, pilot drill, and tap the holes. Do *not* tap the 4-40 holes in the top and bottom ends just yet. Set the standards aside; we will come back to these holes.

Saw the Pads (4.2) from flat stock of suitable thickness. True the edges by either milling or filing. Mark out the four holes on each pad and drill them. When the pads are mounted on the base, size 2-56 bolts will pass through the No. 44 holes to hold the pads in place. Size 4-40 bolts will pass through the base and the No. 33 holes in the pads into the tapped holes in the bottom of the standards. In positioning the pads on the base, turn the pads so the .250" dimension positioning the holes in the pads will be toward the cutout in the base.

When you mark out the Cylinder Mount (4.3), it is a good idea to start by locating the center

When I was sure the parts were in the correct position, I used an end mill to mill the uppermost flat vertical surface, the one having a length of .688" in the drawing. Then I lowered the milling cutter by .125" to mill the inset surface, which is just being completed in Photo 17. Note that there is a small clamp holding the standards together in addition to the large clamp holding them between the clamping block and the angle plate on the milling table.

With the two vertical surfaces milled flat, attention was turned to machining the top and bottom ends. To insure that the top and of the piece on the metal with a shallow punch mark. By working with a divider from the central mark, it is possible to lay the part out quite accurately. Saw the part out roughly to outline. Center punch the location of the eight No. 33 holes. Start them with a center drill, drill them to size, and countersink the four holes indicated. The plain No. 33 holes will clear the studs in the lower end of the cylinder. The other holes are countersunk for the bolts that will pass through the cylinder mount into the top ends of the standards. The flat edges of the part can now be trued up by milling.

Position the cylinder mount in the four-jaw chuck, as in Photo 19. Use a wiggler or other center finder in the punch mark at the center to get the part running true in the chuck. Bring up the tailstock drill chuck to center drill and drill through. Drill out to a diameter of about .50". Then you can put on a boring bar, as I had done in Photo 19 to bring the hole to exact diameter. Take pains to get the hole in exactly the right spot and to the exact diameter. This hole is critical for accurate assembly of the engine standard assembly as well as for positioning the cylinder, later on. When the hole is complete, you can grip the part in the three-jaw chuck with the jaws gripping from the inside of the hole. Put on a knife tool to turn down and form the radius on the corners.

Take a piece of the same stock from which you made the standards to make the jig center. Mill the sides flat to a width of .750". This is a critical dimension, as it will determine the spacing between the standards. Chuck the piece in the four-jaw chuck running on center. Face it off square and turn down a .25" length to form the curved surfaces. The diameter of this part is also critical; make it a close fit in the central hole of the cylinder mount. Drill the No. 28 hole to clear a 6-32 bolt.

Cut the jig sides from a piece of flat stock, and file them smooth. Locate and drill the holes to clear a 6-32 bolt. Now you can bolt the jig sides to the jig center to complete the jig as shown in the isometric drawing.

Refer to Photo 20. Note that I had slipped the standards into the assembly jig. The top end of each standard must be positioned in line with the shoulder of the jig center. Also, the uppermost vertical surface of each standard must be firmly in contact with the sides of the jig center in the .750" direction. If you have machined the angles into the standards accurately and have everything positioned correctly, the distance between the inner

surfaces of the standards at the bottom will be 2.500". Clamp the standards into the assembly jig, place the cylinder mount over the curved part of the assembly jig, and spot drill through the countersunk holes of the cylinder mount into the top ends of the standards. Leave the standards clamped in the jig while you drill and tap the 4-40 holes in the top ends of the standards. With the holes drilled and tapped, bolts can be used to fasten the standards to the cylinder mount as in Photo 21. The assembly jig is no longer needed.

The final operation that has to be taken care of is to locate and tap the bolt holes in the bottom ends of the standards. Notice in Photo 21 that I had clamped a rectangular steel bar across the base. In clamping the bar, I had measured its position so its far side, as viewed in the photo, would coincide with the desired location of the near side of the standards. Thus, it was a simple matter to clamp the standards and cylinder mount in their proper location, as I had done in Photo 21. Once it is properly clamped up, turn the assembly over to spot through the holes in the base into the bottom ends of the standards. Drill and tap the holes. You can now put it all together with bolts passing through the base, pads, and into the standards.

CROSSHEAD AND GUIDE ASSEMBLY (5.0)

Little machine work is required on this subassembly. Mark out the Guide Plates (5.1), and saw them out. Once again, it is a good idea to clamp them together for

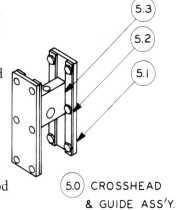

filing the edges to dimension and for drilling the holes. Position the holes carefully, because they will have to match the 2-56 holes tapped in the standards. Follow the same general procedure for making the Guide Bars (5.2).

The guide plates and guide bars can now be bolted in place in the standards. Photo 22 gives an indication of how the parts look and how they fit into the standards. When I was designing the engine, I had intended to bolt the guide plates and guide bars in with hex head bolts and drew them that way. Not wishing to take the time to make the hex heads at this stage of construction, I used socket head screws in

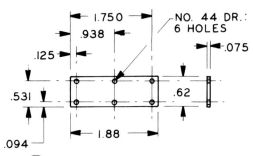

1.750
.938
.125
.531
.62
.075
.094
1.88

NO. 44 DR.:
6 HOLES

(5.1) GUIDE PLATE: STEEL-2 REQ.

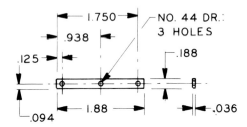

1.750
.938
.125
.188
.094
1.88
.036

NO. 44 DR.:
3 HOLES

(5.2) GUIDE BAR: STEEL-4 REQ.

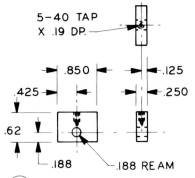

5-40 TAP
X .19 DP.

.850
.425
.125
.250
.62
.188
.188 REAM

(5.3) CROSSHEAD :
BRONZE-1 REQ.

A simple rectangle of bronze is all that is needed for the Crosshead (5.3). Mill the edges to make them flat and square. The .850" dimension is critical. Fit it to the space between the guide plates to produce a close, sliding fit throughout the full length of the guide plates. If necessary, you can enlarge the holes in the guide bars slightly in order to obtain a bit of lateral adjustment for the crosshead to move between the guide bars. Locate the vertical 5-40 tapped hole exactly on the midline of the crosshead so it will line up with the piston rod. Put in the reamed hole for the wrist pin to arrive at the stage shown in Photo 23.

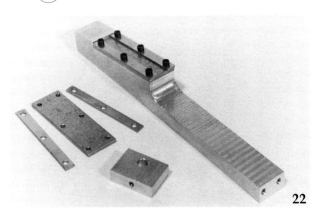

22

24

CONNECTING ROD ASSEMBLY (6.0)

Photo 24 shows the group of small parts that goes together to make up the connecting rod. Start on the End Bearing (6.1) by chucking a short length of .75" square bronze in the four-jaw chuck to face off both sides, leaving it with a thickness of .375". Locate and drill the two No. 44 drilled holes that will clear the bolts used in assembling it. Use a slitting blade to cut the bearing into its two halves by cutting along the horizontal midline, as shown. Bolt the two halves back together with size 2-56 bolts. Mount it in the four-jaw chuck, as I had done in Photo 25. Use a wiggler or other center finder to get the part running true on its center point. Bring up the tailstock chuck to center drill, pilot drill, and ream the central hole. Use a lathe tool to take a partial facing cut. This operation is to form the thrust ring on the side of the bearing. Reverse the bearing in the chuck to machine the thrust ring on the opposite side.

23

order to get on with it. Then I grew to like the appearance of the socket heads, so they are still in the finished engine!

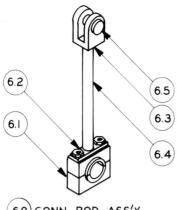

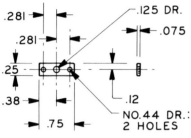

6.0 CONN. ROD ASS'Y.

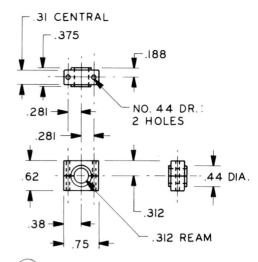

.31 CENTRAL
.375
.188

NO. 44 DR.:
2 HOLES

.281
.281
.62
.44 DIA.
.38
.312
.75
.312 REAM

6.1 END BEARING: BRONZE – 1 REQ.

.281
.281
.125 DR.
.075
.25
.38
.12
NO. 44 DR.:
2 HOLES
.75

6.2 ROD END: STEEL – 1 REQ.

25

Cut the Rod End (6.2) from a small piece of steel. File it to shape. Locate and drill the three holes. The No. 44 holes will accept the bolts passing through the bearing.

The rod will be silver soldered into the central hole. Make the Clevis (6.3) from a small piece of steel. Mark the location of the reamed hole in order to use this point as a reference for marking out the dimensions. Drill and ream the hole for the wrist pin. Then drill the hole from the end. File the part to outline. Now you are ready to set up a slitting operation to cut away the metal from the center of the clevis. That is the operation shown in Photo 26.

Chuck a short length of .19" diameter steel rod to make the Rod (6.4). Take a facing cut across the end. Then use a knife tool to reduce the diameter of the end, in accordance with the drawing. Reverse the rod in the chuck and

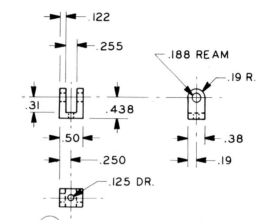

.122
.255
.188 REAM
.19 R.
.31
.438
.50
.38
.250
.19
.125 DR.

6.3 CLEVIS: STEEL – 1 REQ.

.125 DIA. BOTH ENDS
.19 DIA.
.06
2.172
.09

6.4 ROD: STEEL – 1 REQ.

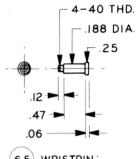

4-40 THD.
.188 DIA.
.25
.12
.47
.06

6.5 WRISTPIN: STEEL – 1 REQ.

26

repeat the steps. Pay particular attention to the 2.172" length so your connecting rod will come out with the correct spacing between the reamed hole of the clevis and the reamed

hole in the end bearing. Put the .09" long end of the rod into the clevis and the other end into the rod end. Use a propane torch to silver solder both ends at one heating. Clean up the connecting rod to remove the flux and oxide formed by the heating.

Turn the Wrist Pin (6.5) from a short length of .25" diameter steel rod. Use a knife tool to turn down the .188" diameter

27

journal. Make it a close fit in the reamed hole in the crosshead and finish it with a nice polish using a bit of fine emery cloth. Turn down the shoulder for the thread. Use a die held in the tailstock die holder to cut the thread. Part off to complete the wrist pin.

You will now be at the stage shown in Photo 27, if you put the connecting rod in place. Turn the flywheel over by hand. Be sure there are no binds in the end bearing or the crosshead; everything must move smoothly throughout the full rotation of the crankshaft.

CYLINDER ASSEMBLY (7.0)

Quite a few parts must be made to complete the Cylinder Assembly. They are all grouped together in Photo 28. Examine the photograph and the isometric assembly drawing to gain an understanding of what is involved.

Make the Port Face (7.1) first, as it will be useful in subsequent work. Mark out the outline on a piece of .125" thick bronze. Saw it out, and mill the edges to get them straight and square. If you are unable to obtain bronze for making the port face, hard brass may be used as a suitable substitute, since the face of the valve will be made from stainless steel which works out well against either metal.

Next, mark out the locations of the eight No. 33 holes. Center punch them, start with a small center drill, and drill each hole to size. Now you are ready to mark out the locations of the steam and exhaust ports. Accuracy in locating and cutting the ports is called for, since it relates directly to steam distribution and free exhaust when the engine is running.

Photo 29 indicates the way I set the port face up to mill the ports. Note that the port face is supported on packing blocks well above the milling table. This protects the surface of the table as well as providing a clear area into which the chips may drop. Align the long edges of the port face with the X motion of the milling table. The cutter in use in Photo 29 is a Dremel No. 194 which gives a good cut under these circumstances and leaves a smooth surface. When you have finished cutting the ports, lap both surfaces of the port face flat by rubbing on 600 grit wet or dry paper supported on a plate glass surface.

Machining the Cylinder (7.2) requires an interesting sequence of steps. The clearances are close in places. Work slowly and thoughtfully to avoid any breakthroughs or distortions. As commented earlier, I used aluminum for this part, knowing that I would fit a bronze cylinder liner. It makes a good job. Anyone who has misgivings about the use of aluminum may substitute brass. From my experience with both metals, I would have to conclude that they are equivalent for this use.

The cylinder for my engine was cut from a piece of 1.25" thick aluminum plate. This left the steam passage face and the drain valve face rough from the saw cut. My first machining operation, therefore, was to fly cut each of these faces to make them parallel to each other and square to the sides. The ends may be left rough until after the bore has been put in.

With the steam passage face smoothed out, mark out on it the location of the edges of the steam passages. Then mark out the location of the 1/4-28 tapped hole for the exhaust. Mark out the center lines on the ends which indicate the bore center line. Finally, mark out the two 4-40 tapped holes for the drain valves. Center punch the spot for the 1/4-28 tapped hole. Start the hole with a center drill. Then pilot drill the hole and tap the thread in it. Don't run the pilot drill too deep, because there is a chance of breaking into the area where the bore will be. After milling the exhaust passage, you will be able to see if this hole needs to be deepened slightly. Refer to Photo 30. In it, you

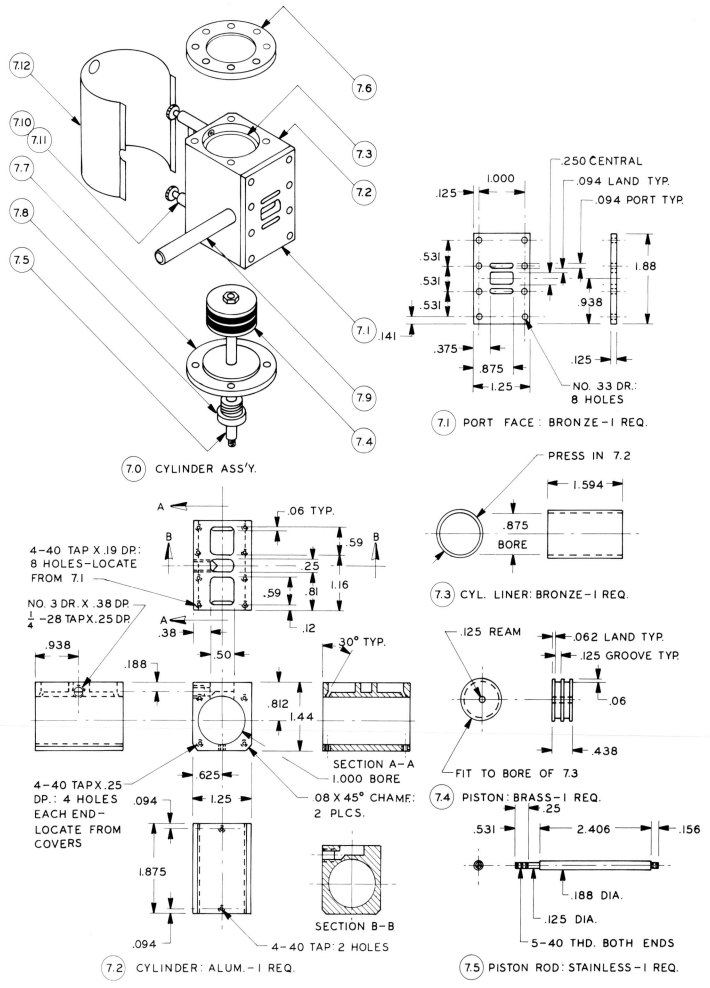

7.12

7.10

7.11

7.7

7.8

7.5

7.6

7.3

7.2

7.1

7.9

7.4

7.0 CYLINDER ASS'Y.

.250 CENTRAL
.094 LAND TYP.
.094 PORT TYP.

1.000
.125
.531
.531
.531
.141
.375
.875
1.25
1.88
.938
.125

NO. 33 DR.:
8 HOLES

7.1 PORT FACE: BRONZE-1 REQ.

PRESS IN 7.2
1.594
.875
BORE

7.3 CYL. LINER: BRONZE-1 REQ.

A
B
.06 TYP.
.59
.25
1.16
.59
.81
.12
.38
.50
A
B

4-40 TAP X .19 DP.:
8 HOLES-LOCATE
FROM 7.1

NO. 3 DR. X .38 DP.
1/4 -28 TAP X .25 DP.

.938
.188

30° TYP.
.812
1.44
1.000 BORE
.08 X 45° CHAMF.
2 PLCS.

SECTION A-A

4-40 TAP X .25
DP.: 4 HOLES
EACH END-
LOCATE FROM
COVERS

.625
1.25
.094
1.875
.094

4-40 TAP: 2 HOLES

SECTION B-B

7.2 CYLINDER: ALUM.-1 REQ.

.125 REAM
.062 LAND TYP.
.125 GROOVE TYP.
.06
.438

FIT TO BORE OF 7.3

7.4 PISTON: BRASS-1 REQ.

.531
.25
2.406
.156
.188 DIA.
.125 DIA.
5-40 THD. BOTH ENDS

7.5 PISTON ROD: STAINLESS-1 REQ.

The Shop Wisdom of Rudy Kouhoupt   179

29   30

can see the tapped exhaust hole which connects with the milled exhaust passage. In the photograph, I was using a 3/16" end mill to cut the passages.

The next two operations on the cylinder are both lathe work. Since the steam passage face of the cylinder must be aligned parallel to the bore, I flipped the cylinder over and clamped the steam passage face flat on the lathe cross slide for the boring operation in progress in Photo 31. Having marked the bore center lines on the ends, packings of thin metal plates were stacked between the cross slide and the

steam passage face to bring the bore center line up to the level where it coincided with the lathe center height. Also, I had indicated the cylinder block from the side to be sure the sides were parallel to the lathe axis and the longitudinal travel of the carriage. When the cross slide had been shifted to put the bore center line on the lathe axis, I locked up the cross slide gib to be sure it could not shift.

When your cylinder is properly positioned on the lathe cross slide, chuck a center drill in the lathe chuck to start the bore. Use twist drills to remove as much metal from the bore as

31   32

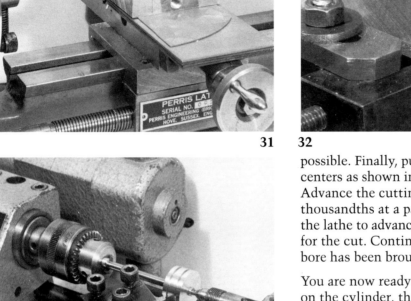

possible. Finally, put a boring bar between lathe centers as shown in Photo 31 to finish the bore. Advance the cutting point in the bar a few thousandths at a pass, using the power feed of the lathe to advance the carriage and workpiece for the cut. Continue in this way until the bore has been brought up to its full diameter.

You are now ready for the final lathe operation on the cylinder, that of facing off the ends. Turn a mandrel between lathe centers to make it a push fit in the cylinder bore. Push the cylinder onto the mandrel, return the mandrel to its position in the lathe, and take light facing cuts across each end until the cylinder is reduced to its finished length.

33   34

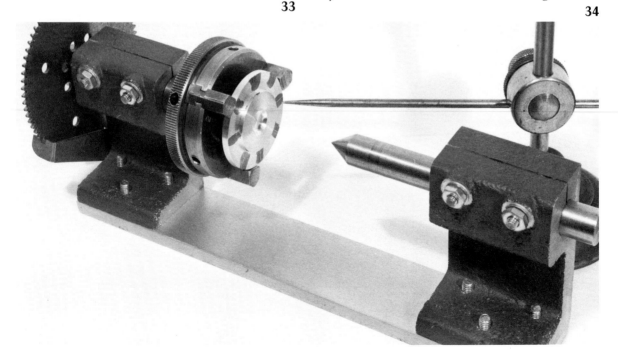

At this point, the steam passages which were end milled in the steam passage face will not be connected with the bore. A fine bit of end milling is called for to make the connections at each end of the cylinder. Since the connections go through at an angle of 30°, I set the cylinder up at a 30° angle, as shown in Photo 32, to cut the connecting passages with a Dremel No. 113 cutter. This cutter is only about .050" in diameter; cut slowly and carefully, because it is delicate.

Use the previously completed port face as a drilling jig to locate the eight 4-40 tapped holes in the steam passage face of the cylinder. Drill and tap the holes at this time. Drill and tap the two 4-40 holes for the drain valves, also. Chamfer the two corners of the drain valve

face of the cylinder. The chamfer forms a blend with the radius of the round cylinder end covers. You will not be able to put the four 4-40 tapped holes into the ends until the end covers are made.

A commercial bronze bushing of 1.000" OD and .875" ID could be used for the Cylinder Liner (7.3). However, a word of caution is in order for anyone wishing to use one. Be sure that your bronze bushing is *solid* bronze as opposed to the sintered bronze oil impregnated type. The reason for this precaution is that the sintered bronze is porous and will not hold steam pressure. Mine was machined from a piece of solid bronze bearing stock. Set up a suitable length of bearing stock on the lathe carriage for boring, as you did for the cylinder. Go through the same procedure to open the

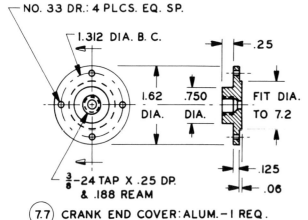

7.6 HEAD END COVER: ALUM.—I REQ.

7.7 CRANK END COVER: ALUM.—I REQ.

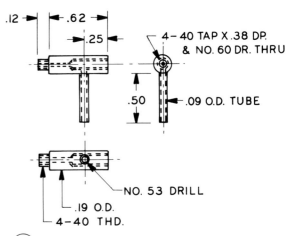

7.10 DRAIN VALVE : BRASS—2 REQ.

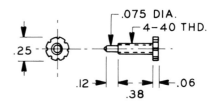

7.11 DRAIN VALVE STEM: BRASS—2 REQ.

7.8 GLAND: BRASS—I REQ.

7.9 EXHAUST: COPPER TUBE—I REQ.

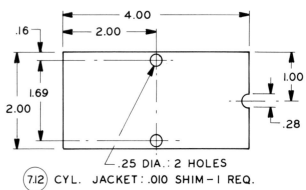

7.12 CYL. JACKET: .010 SHIM—I REQ.

35 36

bore to .875". On the final advance of the cutting tool, traverse the cylinder liner over the tool several passes at the same tool setting. This will leave the bore glassy smooth and true with no need for honing or polishing. Make up another mandrel between lathe centers to fit the cylinder liner bore. Push the cylinder liner on the mandrel to machine the ends to length and to turn down the outside for a press fit in the cylinder.

When I turned my cylinder liner down, I planned to use a shrink fit to hold it in the cylinder. Going by the rule of thumb for such work, I allowed .001" of interference; that is, the OD of the cylinder liner was finished .001" larger than the ID of the cylinder. I heated the cylinder in boiling water and chilled the cylinder liner. They started to go together just fine. But when the cylinder liner was about two-thirds of the way in, there had already been enough change of temperature for the parts to change dimension, and they stuck. Having anticipated that this could happen, I had a turned plug ready to slip into place to protect the end of the cylinder liner, and I quickly pressed the liner home to its centered position in the cylinder. It is a lovely, tight fit. However, it would have been just as good to allow a lighter interference of about .0003"-.0005" and press it in place directly without being concerned about the shrink or expansion of the parts.

The Piston (7.4) and the Piston Rod (7.5) are so closely related that they must be made virtually as a single unit. For the piston, chuck a short piece of brass rod in the three-jaw chuck. Take

a facing cut across it. Reverse it in the chuck, and take a facing cut across the opposite side, reducing it to the proper thickness. Bring up the tailstock drill chuck to center drill, pilot drill, and ream the central hole. Now chuck a length of .188" diameter stainless rod. Face each end to bring it to length. Center drill the end which will go through the piston. Use a knife tool to turn down each end to the dimension shown. Cut the thread on each end by means of a 5-40 die held in the tailstock die holder. The short threaded end will screw into the crosshead. Put the piston on the other end and lock it in place with a 5-40 nut.

Mount the piston rod in a true running chuck with the piston end supported by the tailstock center in the center drilled spot. My setup is shown in Photo 33. This setup insures the concentricity of the piston on the piston rod and gives good support while machining the packing grooves in the piston. Use a tool shaped like a parting tool to machine the packing grooves. Run the lathe at a very low speed while cutting the grooves to avoid chatter. After cutting the grooves, put on a very sharp tool having a slight radius at the tip to turn down the outside of the piston to fit the bore of the cylinder liner.

Either flat stock or rod is suitable for making the Head End Cover (7.6) and the Crank End Cover (7.7). Mine were turned from slices of rod. For the head end cover, chuck a slice of rod in the three-jaw, letting it project from the jaws enough to permit turning the outer edge to diameter. Then take a facing cut across the cover. Also, cut the slight undercut in the outer surface at this time. Reverse the part in the chuck. Face it off to its total thickness of .19". Use a knife tool to face down from the edge to form the register which will fit in the cylinder. Note that the registers of both covers will fit the bore of the cylinder (7.2), not the cylinder liner. Don't forget to make the .06" deep undercut at the center. It is needed to clear the nut which secures the piston on the piston rod.

With the cover still gripped in the three-jaw chuck, I transferred the chuck to the indexing attachment shown in Photo 34. Using a surface gauge, I scribed the eight equally space radial marks to show the centers of the stud holes. In this photograph, you can see the undercut that clears the nut on the piston rod at the

37

center of the register. Half of the stud holes in the cover are drilled No. 33 to clear the 4-40 studs in the end of the cylinder. The other half are tapped 4-40. Put short pieces of threaded

rod in the tapped holes with nuts on top to give the appearance that there are eight studs holding the cover.

The procedure for machining the crank end cover is a bit different. Chuck a slice of rod in the three-jaw chuck, and take a facing cut to get started. Then use a knife tool to face down to form the .750" diameter stuffing box. Machine the .750" diameter very carefully, making it a very close fit in the central hole in the cylinder mount. Besides serving as the stuffing box, this part aligns the cylinder assembly on the vertical axis of the engine. This fact dictates that extra care be lavished on it to guarantee the accuracy of centering and the concentricity of the stuffing box with the piston rod hole and with the register which will fit into the end of the cylinder.

Notice in Photo 35 that I had already machined the stuffing box. Bring up the tailstock drill chuck to center drill the part. Pilot drill all the way through for the reamed hole. Pilot drill for the threaded part. Now, use the tailstock drill chuck to start the tap straight into the stuffing box as I was doing in Photo 35. After cutting the thread to its full depth in the stuffing box, use the tailstock drill chuck to hold a .188" reamer, and ream the piston rod hole.

You can now reverse the part to work on the register side. If your three-jaw chuck has had as long and active a career as mine, it cannot be depended upon to hold the stuffing box exactly on center. To get around this difficulty, I chucked a piece of steel tubing to make a chuck adapter which can be seen in Photo 36. I took a facing cut across the end and then bored it out to make a close fit over the stuffing box. I marked the jaw locations for returning it to its original position in the chuck and split the side with a thin saw cut. The saw cut shows in Photo 36 in which the cover is accurately positioned for the machining of the register. Machine the register as you did on the head end cover.

Remove the cylinder mount from your partially assembled engine. Put the stuffing box in the central hole of the cylinder mount. You now can use the cylinder mount as a drilling jig to spot through the four No. 33 holes for the studs. After drilling the holes in the crank end cover, you can place each cover on the cylinder to spot through the holes in the cylinder ends. Drill and tap the cylinder for the studs to finish the cylinder.

To make the Gland (7.8), chuck a piece of .50" diameter brass rod. Face off both ends, and then turn down the part for the thread. Cut the thread by using a die in the tailstock die holder. Bring up the tailstock drill chuck to center drill, pilot drill, and ream the central hole. In detailing other projects I have stated my preference for roundheaded glands. I drill five or six No. 52 holes to a depth of .06" equally spaced around the head. For tightening, I insert the end of a short steel rod into the holes as a tightening bar.

If you have a particular installation in mind for your engine, you may wish to make the Exhaust (7.9) to suit. If not, the 2.00" length specified should prove adequate. Cut the tubing to length. File the ends smooth. Slip a piece of close fitting steel rod inside to prevent it from being crushed when you grip it in the three-jaw chuck. Use a 1/4-28 die in the tailstock die holder to cut the thread on the end. Remove the piece of steel rod before screwing it into the cylinder.

Drain valves are such a convenience in starting any steam engine that they are well worth the effort involved in making them. Chuck a piece of .19" diameter rod for the body of the Drain Valve (7.10). Face off the end. Turn down for the thread. Cut the thread with a die held in the tailstock die holder. Reverse the part in the chuck. After facing the second end, bring up the tail-stock drill chuck to center drill, pilot drill and tap the thread. Drill through with a No. 60 drill to give the condensate a way out of the cylinder. Drill through the side with a No. 42 drill as shown, and solder a .50" length of .09" diam-eter brass tube in the hole to form the side arm. Run a No. 53 drill down through the tube to be sure you have not soldered the end shut.

You will need a Drain Valve Stem (7.11) for each drain valve. Turn down a piece of .25" diameter brass rod while holding it in the three-jaw chuck. Cut the 4-40 thread using a die held in the tailstock die holder. Then turn down the tip to form the .075" diameter part as shown in the drawing. A few strokes with a fine file while it is running in the lathe will form a conical tip. After parting off, file a series of light notches around the head to provide a finger grip for opening and closing the valve.

Roll the Cylinder Jacket (7.12) from a piece of .010" thick shim stock. I used brass, but aluminum or stainless steel would be suitable, also. The two .25" diameter holes may be cut either by drilling with a properly sharpened drill or by punching with a sharp punch. My preference is for the punch. After rolling the jacket to fit snugly around the cylinder covers, you will have to straighten out a short flange

along each vertical edge to fit against the flat sides of the cylinder for about .19". When you get it about right and slip it in place, you will be able to see exactly where to notch the one vertical edge to clear the exhaust.

Mount the cylinder assembly in its place on the cylinder mount as I had done in Photo 37. Screws of temporary studs are adequate for checking the assembly at this point. Turn the flywheel over to be sure there are no rubs or binds. If there are any tight spots, they are likely to be where the piston rod passes through the gland and crank end cover or between the piston and the cylinder liner. If everything moves freely, as it should, you can go ahead with putting in lengths of 4-40 threaded stainless rod for studs in the cylinder ends. Don't forget that the studs at the bottom of the cylinder must pass through both the cover and the cylinder mount, so they will have to be longer than the studs at the top. Wait until you get the steam chest and its cover fitted before putting in the eight studs that will hold these parts in place.

STEAM CHEST ASSEMBLY (8.0)

All of the parts of the Steam Chest Assembly are grouped together in Photo 38. Start by marking the outline and the central cavity of the Steam Chest (8.1) on a piece of .50" thick aluminum. Mill the outer edges straight and square after sawing the part out. The central cavity can be cut out by either drilling and filing or by end milling. I cut the metal away with a 3/16" end mill. While the drawing shows the cavity to be square cornered, I left the .09" radius formed by the end mill in the corners, as you will notice in Photos 38 and 41. The cavity is long enough that this small amount of radius does not interfere with the movement of the valve.

Mark the location of the three tapped holes. Center punch each location, pilot drill, and tap each with the appropriate thread. Pay particular attention to the locations of the 1/4-28 and the 5/16-24 tapped holes; they are for the bearing and gland respectively. The valve rod will pass through the gland and bearing, making their alignment important. Clamp the steam chest and port face together in their working position. Spot through the eight No. 33 holes in the port face to locate the stud clearance holes in the steam chest. Drill the eight holes through to finish the steam chest.

The Steam Chest Cover (8.2) is a very simple job. Saw it out and true the edges by filing or milling. Use the port face once again as a drilling jig to locate the eight stud clearance holes. Having made the gland for the crank end cover, follow the same procedure for the Steam Chest Gland (8.3). The only difference between them is in their dimensions.

Chuck a piece of .38" diameter brass rod in the three-jaw to make the Bearing (8.4). Use a tool with a radiused tip to turn down the .25" diameter part. The radius at the tip of the tool will leave the blending radius between the .25" and .38" diameter parts. Radius the tip of the bearing by filing to contour while running

the lathe at a fairly high speed. Reverse the part in the chuck, gripping it by the .25" diameter part. Use a knife tool to turn down the part for the thread. Cut the thread with a die held in the tailstock die holder. Bring up the tailstock drill chuck to center drill the end. Then drill the bearing hole into which the valve rod will fit.

Follow the same procedure for making the Inlet (8.5) as you did for making the exhaust. The Valve Rod (8.6) is so similar to other parts that little description is needed. Check its fit through the gland, stuffing box, and bearing. It

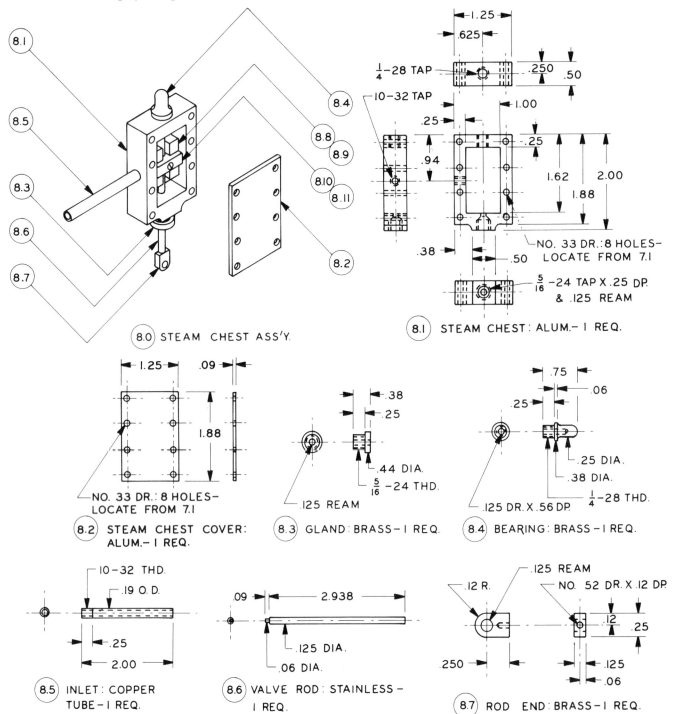

8.0 STEAM CHEST ASS'Y.

8.1 STEAM CHEST: ALUM.— 1 REQ.

8.2 STEAM CHEST COVER: ALUM.— 1 REQ.

8.3 GLAND: BRASS—1 REQ.

8.4 BEARING: BRASS—1 REQ.

8.5 INLET: COPPER TUBE—1 REQ.

8.6 VALVE ROD: STAINLESS— 1 REQ.

8.7 ROD END: BRASS—1 REQ.

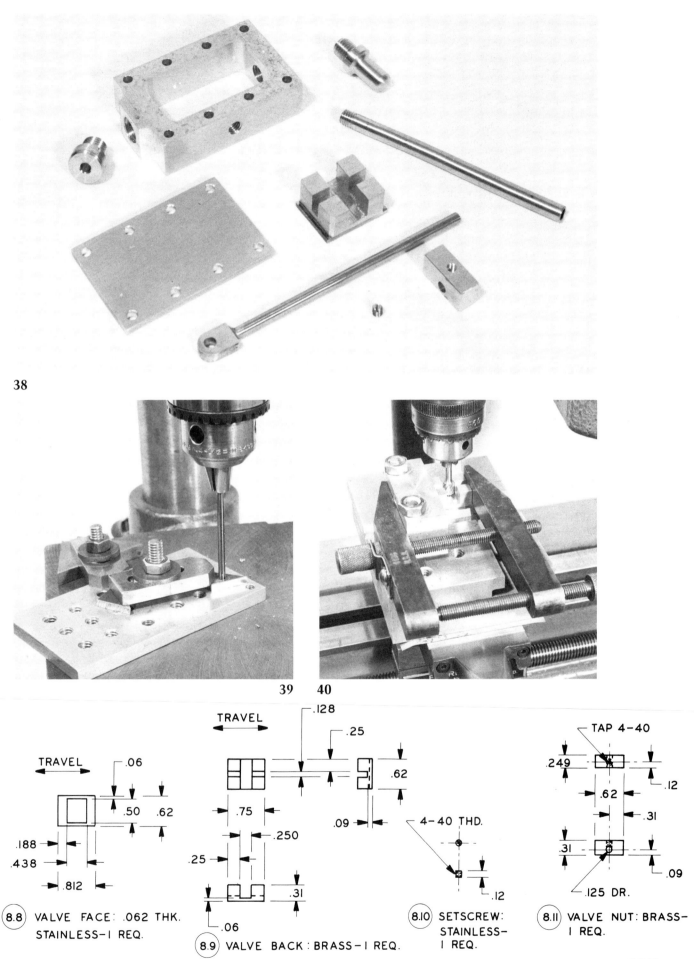

38

39   40

TRAVEL

.128

.25

.62

.09

TRAVEL

.06

.50   .62

.75

.250

.25

.31

.06

4-40 THD.

.12

TAP 4-40

.249

.62

.12

.31

.31

.09

.125 DR.

.188

.438

.812

8.8 VALVE FACE: .062 THK.
STAINLESS-1 REQ.

8.9 VALVE BACK: BRASS-1 REQ.

8.10 SETSCREW:
STAINLESS-
1 REQ.

8.11 VALVE NUT: BRASS-
1 REQ.

is a good idea to file a flat spot about .50" long and about .01" deep on the side of the rod at the tip, where it enters the bearing. The flat relieves the vacuum formed at the tip as the rod moves downward in its stroke in the bearing.

Mark out the Rod End (8.7) on a small bit of brass. Center drill, pilot drill, and ream the .125" diameter hole. The clamping arrangement I use to handle these small bits is shown in Photo 39. This clamping arrangement holds the parts very securely, which makes for accuracy and safety. File the part to shape, and drill the No. 52 hole. Insert the tip of the valve rod into the No. 52 hole. Now you can silver solder the two parts together.

Careful measuring and filing are what is required to make the Valve Face (8.8). Mark the complete outline of the valve face on a piece of stainless. It is easier to handle the part while it is still in the large piece as far as clamping or holding it in the vise. Therefore, drill through to start the exhaust cavity and file it out to the mark before sawing the part out. After you finish filing the exhaust cavity, saw the part out and file the outer edges to dimension.

Cut a rectangular block of brass for the Valve Back (8.9). True up all the edges by filing or milling. Place the valve back centrally on the valve face for silver soldering. The "travel" direction indicated on the drawings of these two parts refers to the direction of valve travel as the engine is running. After silver soldering the valve parts together, use a milling setup to machine the slots in the valve back as I was doing in Photo 40. Note in the photograph that I had already milled the narrower slot using a Dremel No. 194 cutter. After cutting the narrower slot, I rotated the valve 90° to the position shown to mill the wider slot using a Dremel No. 196 cutter. Lap the stainless face of the valve flat on 600 grit wet or dry paper supported on a plate glass surface.

A stainless No. 4-40 Setscrew (8.10) is needed to lock the valve nut in place on the valve rod. I cut a short piece of threaded rod, filed it off smooth on the end, and made a fine hacksaw kerf for the screwdriver slot. The Valve Nut (8.11) is a small rectangle of brass which you can shape by milling. Drill a .125" hole for the valve rod, and tap the intersecting hole for the setscrew. Fit the .249" dimension of the valve nut into the .250" slot in the valve back. The valve nut should fit the slot in such a way that the valve can lift and seat freely, but it must not be a sloppy fit. The idea is for the valve to be able to lift off the port face and

41

reseat without losing appreciable motion in the travel direction.

With all the parts of the steam chest assembly ready to be put together, you can put the eight stainless studs in the steam passage face of the cylinder. Photo 41 shows this assembly on my engine with the steam chest cover omitted to show the interior detail. Be sure that the valve rod moves freely through the gland and bearing. Check that the valve can lift from the port face slightly and that it drops back against the port face easily.

VALVE MOTION ASSEMBLY (9.0)
The Eccentric (9.1) shown in the group of parts in Photo 42 is the heart of the valve motion. To make the eccentric, set up a length of 1.00" diameter steel rod as I had done in Photo 43. Note that I had one end supported in the three-jaw chuck and the other end running in a fixed steady rest. Begin by taking a facing cut across the end of the rod. Then use a parting tool to cut the groove. I had just finished cutting the groove to full width and depth when I shot Photo 43. The facing cut leaves a circular tool pattern on the end of the rod which accurately indicates the center. With your surface gauge set at exact center height, scribe a fine line across the end before removing the rod from the lathe. Saw the part off. Rechuck it in the three-jaw chuck to face off the saw cut side.

Measure from the center, indicated by the tool marks, along the scribed line to locate the centers of the .312" reamed hole and the 4-40 tapped hole which are equally spaced on either side of the center along the scribed line. Center punch each spot. Then pilot drill and ream

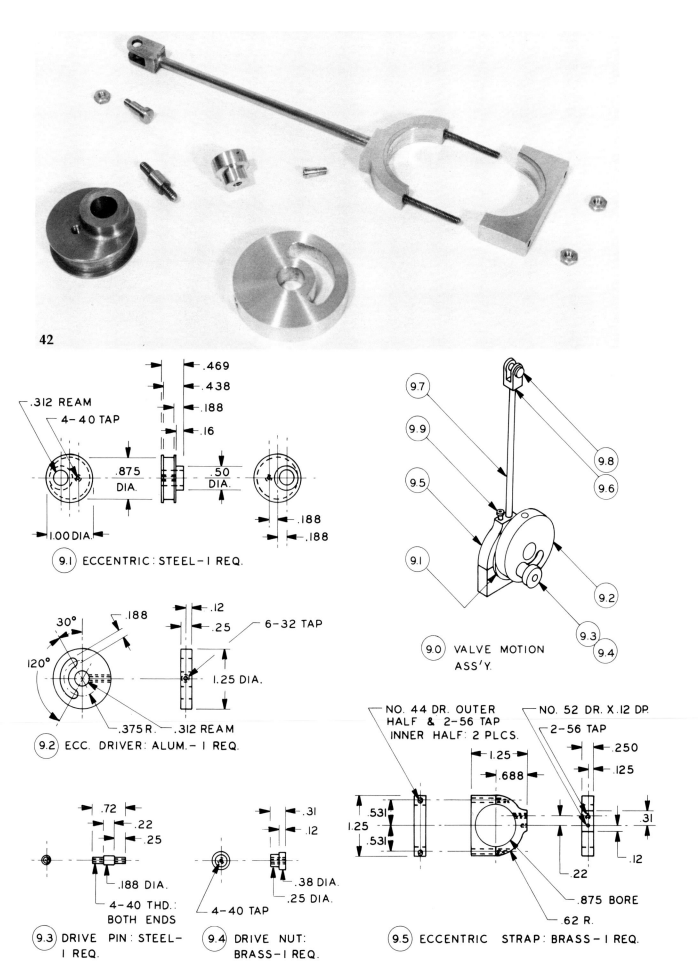

42

.469
.438
.188
.16

.312 REAM
4-40 TAP

.875 DIA.

.50 DIA.

1.00 DIA.

.188
.188

9.1 ECCENTRIC: STEEL-1 REQ.

30°
.188
120°

.12
.25
6-32 TAP

1.25 DIA.

.375 R.   .312 REAM

9.2 ECC. DRIVER: ALUM.- 1 REQ.

.72
.22
.25

.188 DIA.

4-40 THD.:
BOTH ENDS

9.3 DRIVE PIN: STEEL-
1 REQ.

.31
.12

.38 DIA.
.25 DIA.

4-40 TAP

9.4 DRIVE NUT:
BRASS-1 REQ.

9.7
9.9
9.5
9.1

9.8
9.6

9.2

9.3
9.4

9.0 VALVE MOTION
ASS'Y.

NO. 44 DR. OUTER
HALF & 2-56 TAP
INNER HALF: 2 PLCS.

NO. 52 DR. X .12 DP.
2-56 TAP

1.25
.688

.250
.125

.531
1.25
.531

.31

.22

.12

.875 BORE
.62 R.

9.5 ECCENTRIC STRAP: BRASS-1 REQ.

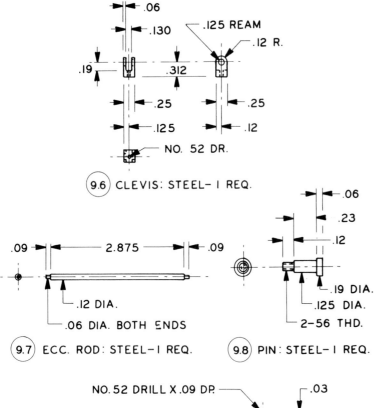

.06
.130
.125 REAM
.12 R.
.19
.312
.25
.25
.125
.12
NO. 52 DR.

(9.6) CLEVIS: STEEL— 1 REQ.

.09
2.875
.09
.12 DIA.
.06 DIA. BOTH ENDS

(9.7) ECC. ROD: STEEL—1 REQ.

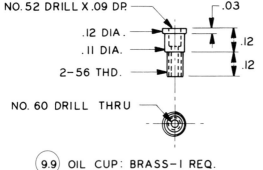

.06
.23
.12
.19 DIA.
.125 DIA.
2-56 THD.

(9.8) PIN: STEEL—1 REQ.

NO. 52 DRILL X .09 DP.
.12 DIA.
.11 DIA.
2-56 THD.
.03
.12
.12

NO. 60 DRILL THRU

(9.9) OIL CUP: BRASS—1 REQ.

43

and tap as indicated on the drawing. Mount the eccentric on a short mandrel in the lathe to machine it down to form the hub surrounding the reamed hole. Note in Photo 44 that I was using a mandrel having a threaded end. Since the eccentric has no setscrew, I machined the mandrel with a shoulder against which the nut and a spacer locked the eccentric for the machining cuts.

Everything about the Eccentric Driver (9.2) relates to the center point, as far as marking out is concerned. Locate and center punch the center point on a square piece of .25" thick flat stock. Use your dividers to lay out the outline of the part, the curved center line of the curved slot, and the edges of the curved slot. Make a light punch mark where the horizontal center line shown in the drawing crosses the curved center line in the slot. Set your dividers exactly for the radius of the curved center line. With one point of the divider in the punch mark, the other point of the divider will cross the curved center line at the exact spot on either side of the horizontal center line which defines the 120° angle. On the horizontal center line, where it goes over the edge, mark the location for the 6-32 tapped hole. Center drill and pilot drill the center hole. Center drill, pilot drill, and tap the 6-32 hole. Now go back and ream the center hole. Drill a .188" diameter hole at each spot where the curved center line of the slot intersects the 120° center lines. These holes accurately define the ends of the slots. Chain drill a row of .156" diameter holes along the curved center line between the .188" diameter holes. File away the rest of the metal to form the curved slot. Place the part on a mandrel between lathe centers to turn down the periphery to size. I used the same mandrel as the one shown for machining the eccentric.

The Drive Pin (9.3) is a simple lathe job. Chuck a piece of .188" diameter steel rod. Face each end to length. Turn down and thread each end in turn using a die in the tailstock die holder. The Drive Nut (9.4) is also a simple job. Chuck a piece of .38" diameter brass rod, and face each end to length. Turn down to form the shoulder. Bring up the tailstock drill chuck to center drill, pilot drill, and tap.

When you mark out the shape of the Eccentric Strap (9.5) on a piece of brass flat stock, mark the locations of the four holes on the edge. Begin work by center punching and drilling the long holes for the bolts which will hold the two halves of the eccentric strap together. Since you know where the strap will be split, you can drill No. 44 to the split line and No.

44

45

46

50 below the split line as the pilot holes for the 2-56 thread. This is a good time to drill the No. 52 hole for the eccentric rod and the No. 50 hole for the 2-56 thread in the opposite edge. Drill the No. 50 hole deep enough to break into the bore so that oil from the oil cup can enter the strap.

This is the time to split the strap into its two halves, as I was doing in Photo 45. The part was securely clamped to the cross slide to permit cutting with a slitting blade. Notice in this photograph that I had allowed for the wasting of the metal by the width of the slitting blade between the two halves when I did the marking out. After slitting, tap the three No. 50 drilled holes with a 2-56 tap.

Now you can bolt the two halves of the eccentric strap back together for mounting in the four-jaw chuck as mine was in Photo 46. Use a wiggler or other center finder to position the part in the chuck with the center mark of the bore running true. Bring up the tailstock

47

drill chuck to center drill and open the hole as much as possible with twist drills. Finish the bore to size using a boring bar. Bore the strap so it will be a free but close running fit on the eccentric. Remove the eccentric strap from the chuck to file the contoured shape.

The machining operations involved in making the Clevis (9.6), Eccentric Rod (9.7), Pin (9.8), and Oil Cup (9.9) are all identical to previously machined parts, so no further description is required. When you get them done, slip one end of the eccentric rod into the inner half of the eccentric strap and the other end into the rod end for silver soldering. Then proceed to assemble the parts on your engine as I had done in Photo 47.

GETTING IT ALL TOGETHER!

With all the parts made and roughly assembled, you can get a pretty good feel for the engine. Once again run through the routine of turning the flywheel over slowly to be sure there are no rough spots. When everything is moving smoothly, you are ready to time the valve.

The curved slot in the eccentric driver, if accurately cut, will automatically fix the angular relationship between the eccentric and the crankpin. In this engine, the eccentric leads the crank by exactly 120°. You will realize from this that when the setscrew in the eccentric driver is in line with the crankpin, as mine is in Photos 2, 47, and 48, the eccentric will be in the right angular

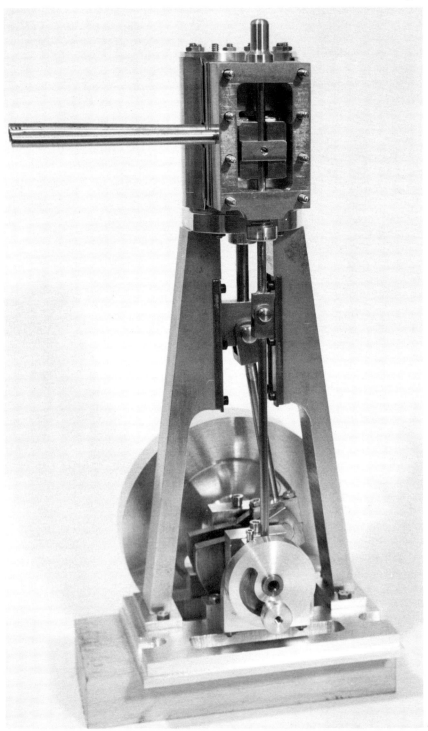

48

position for either direction of rotation. By slipping the eccentric around the crankshaft and locking the drive pin and drive nut at the end of the slot, the direction of rotation may be controlled. In Photo 2, my engine was set for counterclockwise running (judged from the eccentric end of the crankshaft), while in Photos 47 and 48 it was set for clockwise running. Don't tighten the setscrew in the eccentric driver too tight at this time.

Take off the steam chest cover, as I had done in Photo 48, so you can watch the valve go through its stroke. Turn the flywheel slowly by hand in the correct direction of running to take the valve through a full stroke up and down over the ports. The valve must be centered in its movement so the top and bottom steam ports are uncovered equally at the ends of the valve stroke. Notice in Photo 48 that the valve is correctly set, since the top port is fully uncovered at the bottom of the stroke. The adjustment of the valve position is made by loosening the setscrew in the valve nut and changing the position of the valve nut on the valve rod.

When you get the valve motion properly centered, swing the flywheel over slowly by hand in the correct direction of rotation until the piston is at its top dead center position. At this point, the top steam port should be just ready to open. Continue on in the direction of rotation to the bottom dead center position where the bottom port should be just ready to open. If the ports are opening too soon or too late, it means that you have the eccentric driver off a little. Loosen its setscrew to shift it just a degree or two. When you are satisfied, loosen the drive nut to slip the eccentric to the other end of the slot. Turning the flywheel in the opposite direction, repeat the checking procedure.

When you are sure you have everything in a satisfactory position, tighten the setscrew in the eccentric driver enough to leave a small mark on the crankshaft. Remove the eccentric driver so you can file a small flat seat in the crankshaft for its setscrew.

Now is the time to take the engine all apart for painting, striping, polishing, or whatever other decoration you wish to do on it. While the paint is drying, cut a set of gaskets for the cylinder. I use oil-impregnated typewriter paper for gaskets. You will want gaskets for each cylinder end cover, as well as under the port face, under the steam chest, under the steam chest cover, and under the bearing at the top of the steam chest.

As you reassemble the engine, put in the graphited string packings in the piston grooves and both stuffing boxes. Roll the packing into the piston grooves working on a glass surface. Strive to get the piston packings resilient, but don't overpack them. Overpacking simply causes too much friction. For the stuffing boxes, I like to put in little rings of packing. I wind several turns of the packing string on a dowel of the same diameter as the rod that goes through the gland and stuffing box. As I take a cut across the winding with a sharp knife, I cut off a set of packing rings. About three rings should be slipped around the rod and pressed into each stuffing box with the splits in the rings set opposite one another. Give all moving parts a light coating of oil, not forgetting to put some on the packings. Don't overtighten the glands, because that could be a source of needless friction, also. Wind a bit of *Teflon* pipe jointing around the threads on the inlet and exhaust before screwing them in. Place a small gasket under each drain valve as you screw it in. Give the valve motion one last check before putting on and tightening the steam chest cover.

Your engine is now finished as mine was in Photos 1 and 2, and it is all ready for running on either steam or compressed air.

A Fore and Aft Compound

Several correspondents have expressed an interest in building a compound steam engine. This interest encouraged the design and construction of the trim little fore and aft compound in Photos 1 and 2. Everything in the engine is fabricated or carved from stock metal forms, completely eliminating the need for any castings.

First thoughts about this project led me to design the engine as a non-reversing type. When the drawings had been finished and the construction work was about a third done, a friend of mine went out to a steam show in the Poconos with me. At the end of our day at the show, we sat over dinner talking about the new engine. Afterward, Eddie looked at the drawings and what was already done on the engine. He is a fine machinist who has built quite a few engines from my designs. After examining everything, he expressed a desire to build one but said he felt it should have a reversing mechanism. There was still plenty of work to do before getting to the valve motion, so I agreed to consider it while working to that point. As you can see from the photos, a reversing mechanism was designed for the engine. It increases the

amount of work in the project a bit, but it adds much to the pleasure of building and running the engine. The prototype engine is, in fact, a very sweet performer. As a shelf model, it is a complete modelmaker's project in its own right. Installed in an open river launch, it will satisfy the most fastidious observer with regard to both appearance and performance.

A few words about the nature of compound engines may prove helpful to anyone who is not too familiar with them. Compounds have two cylinders of different sizes. The smaller cylinder is the high pressure, or HP cylinder, to which steam is admitted at high pressure from the boiler. As you look at Photo 1, the HP cylinder is to the right. Steam enters the steam chest through the small pipe that projects out the right side. After the steam has undergone partial expansion in the HP cylinder, it is exhausted into the receiver, which is the curved pipe running horizontally along the side of the cylinder block. When the steam undergoes partial expansion in the HP cylinder, its pressure naturally drops, resulting in a lower pressure in the receiver. From the receiver, the steam passes into the low pressure, or LP cylinder –

1   **2**

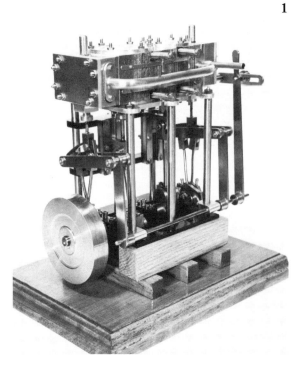   

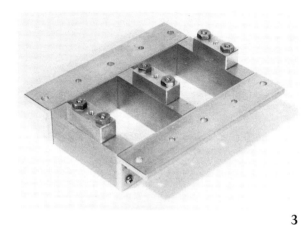

3　**4**

the larger cylinder to the left in Photo 1. In the LP cylinder, the steam undergoes further expansion and is finally exhausted out the exhaust

pipe, which projects to the right in Photo 2. Photo 1 shows the compound engine from the front, while Photo 2 shows it from the rear.

BILL OF MATERIALS

No.	Part	Material	Quantity	Dimensions (all inches)
1.1	Bed rail	aluminum	2	.125 × .75 × .75 × 3.50″ angle
1.2	Bearing	brass	3	.38 × .75 × 1.75″
1.3	Bearing cap	brass	3	.31 × .38 × .88″
1.4	Oil cup	brass	3	.19″ dia. × .28″
1.5	Column	steel	6	.25″ dia. × 4.12″
1.6	Entablature	aluminum	1	.125 × 3.00 × 3.62″
2.1	Crankshaft	steel	1	.375″ dia. × 5.75″
2.2	Crank web	steel	4	.125 × .50 × 1.00″
2.3	Crankpin	steel	2	.312″ dia. × .62″
3.1	Flywheel	brass	1	2.50″ dia. × .50″
3.2	Key	steel	1	.062 × .125 × .50″
4.1	Guide support	aluminum	2	.19 × .75 × 3.75″
4.2	Guide plate	steel	2	.125 × .75 × 1.62″
4.3	Spacer	steel	4	.125 × .188 × 1.62″
4.4	Guide strip	steel	4	.062 × .25 × 1.62″
5.1	Slipper	brass	2	.125 × .375 × .62″
5.2	Upright	brass	2	.25 × .50 × .66″
6.1	Clevis	steel	2	.25 × .50 × .56″
6.2	Rod	steel	2	.19″ dia. × 1.75″
6.3	Bearing	bronze	2	.375 × .62 × .62″
6.4	Wristpin	steel	2	.19″ dia. × .66″
7.1	HP port face	bronze	1	.125 × 1.25 × 1.50″
7.2	LP port face	bronze	1	.125 × 1.25 × 2.00″
7.3	Cylinder block	aluminum	1	1.25 × 2.00 × 3.75″
7.4	HP cylinder liner	bronze	1	1.125″ dia. × 1.250″
7.5	LP cylinder liner	bronze	1	1.500″ dia. × 1.250″
7.6	HP piston	brass	1	.875″ dia. × .25″
7.7	LP piston	brass	1	1.250″ dia. × .25″
7.8	Piston rod	stainless	2	.125″ dia. × 2.19″
7.9	Gland	brass	2	.44″ dia. × .44″
7.10	HP head end cover	aluminum	1	1.62″ dia. × .125″
7.11	LP head end cover	aluminum	1	2.00″ dia. × .125″
7.12	HP crank end cover	aluminum	1	1.62″ dia. × .375″
7.13	LP crank end cover	aluminum	1	2.00″ dia. × .375″
7.14	Exhaust	brass	1	.31″ OD tube × 1.00″ and .062 × .44 × 1.00″
7.15	Drain valve	brass	4	.19″ dia. × .75″ and .09″ OD tube × .38″

No.	Part	Material	Quantity	Dimensions (all inches)
7.16	Drain valve stem	brass	4	.25″ dia. × .56″
8.1	HP steam chest cover	aluminum	1	.09 × 1.25 × 1.50″
8.2	LP steam chest cover	aluminum	1	.09 × 1.25 × 2.00″
8.3	HP steam chest	aluminum	1	.50 × 1.50 × 1.50″
8.4	LP steam chest	aluminum	1	.50 × 1.50 × 2.00″
8.5	Gland	brass	2	.38″ dia. × .38″
8.6	Bearing	brass	2	.25″ dia. × .62″
8.7	Inlet	copper	1	.19″ OD tube × 1.50″
8.8	Valve rod	stainless	2	.094″ dia. × 2.50″
8.9	Clevis	steel	6	.25 × .25 × .50″
8.10	Motion pin	steel	6	.19″ dia. × .31″
8.11	HP valve face	stainless	1	.062 × .562 × .62″
8.12	LP valve face	stainless	1	.062 × .562 × .81″
8.13	HP valve back	brass	1	.31 × .50 × .62″
8.14	LP valve back	brass	1	.31 × .50 × .75″
8.15	Valve nut	brass	2	.25 × .31 × .62″
8.16	Setscrew	stainless	2	4-40 × .125″
8.17	Receiver	composite	1	.25″ OD copper tube × 6.00″ and .062 × .38 × 2.00″ brass
9.1	Reversing bearing	aluminum	2	.25 × .50 × .62″
9.2	Reversing shaft	steel	1	.125″ dia. × 5.62″
9.3	Reversing arm	steel	2	.125 × .38 × 2.44″ and .38″ dia. × .25″
9.4	Trunnion	steel	4	.25″ dia. × .62″
9.5	Reversing lever	steel	1	.08 × .38 × 4.88″ and .38″ dia. × .31″
9.6	Post	steel	1	.25″ dia. × .44″
9.7	Slide	brass	1	.062 × .31 × 1.88″
9.8	Thumbscrew	steel	1	.44″ dia. × .56″
10.1	Eccentric	steel	4	1.00″ dia. × .375″
10.2	Eccentric strap	brass	4	.125 × 1.25 × 1.25″
10.3	Eccentric rod	steel	4	.094″ dia. × 1.44″
10.4	Die block	bronze	2	.125 × .25 × .25″
10.5	Expansion link	steel	2	.125 × .75 × 1.62″
10.6	Drag link	steel	4	.075 × .31 × 2.62″
10.7	Drag link bushing	bronze	8	.188″ dia. × .075″
10.8	Expansion link bushing	bronze	4	.188″ dia. × .125″
10.9	Oil cup	brass	4	.125″ dia. × .25″

The specifications of the fore and aft compound engine presented here are as follows:

Cylinder arrangement Fore and aft compound
HP cylinder bore: .875"
LP cylinder bore: 1.250"
Piston stroke: .812" (both cylinders)
Reversing valve gear: Stephenson's link motion
Weight: 5 pounds

Refer to the major assembly drawing: the engine is broken down into ten subassemblies, numbered in the sequence in which they were built and will be appearing. The material requirements are really quite modest. Gather what materials you need and get the chips flying! Every reader who builds this engine is in for many happy hours of challenging shop work followed by dependable, steamy operation.

FRAME ASSEMBLY (1.0)

When you cut the Bed Rails (1.1) from a piece of aluminum angle stock, it is a good idea to check the squareness of the angle. If it is out a little, you will have no difficulty in taking a light cut with a fly cutter to skim one surface. True the ends to bring the two bed rails to the desired length. Locate and drill the holes shown in the detail drawing.

You will notice in Photo 3, showing the bed rails assembled to the Bearings (1.2), that there are two extra holes drilled in each bed rail between the No. 28 holes. These are not detailed in the drawing, because they are intended for bolting the finished engine to the beams on the base. You may drill holes in a location that suits your intended mounting, or you may locate them on the center line of the No. 28 holes and midway between them, as they are on the prototype.

After cutting the bearings (1.2) from a piece of suitable stock, square the ends by milling the pieces to length. Locate the positions of the holes. Then, drill and tap them to sizes shown. Next, cut the Bearings Caps (1.3) to size and square off the ends. Drill the No. 33 holes

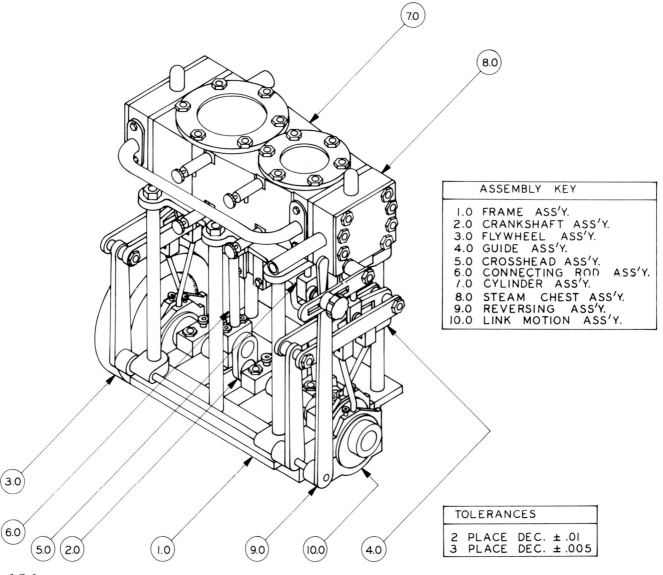

ASSEMBLY KEY

1.0 FRAME ASS'Y.
2.0 CRANKSHAFT ASS'Y.
3.0 FLYWHEEL ASS'Y.
4.0 GUIDE ASS'Y.
5.0 CROSSHEAD ASS'Y.
6.0 CONNECTING ROD ASS'Y.
7.0 CYLINDER ASS'Y.
8.0 STEAM CHEST ASS'Y.
9.0 REVERSING ASS'Y.
10.0 LINK MOTION ASS'Y.

TOLERANCES

2 PLACE DEC. ± .01
3 PLACE DEC. ± .005

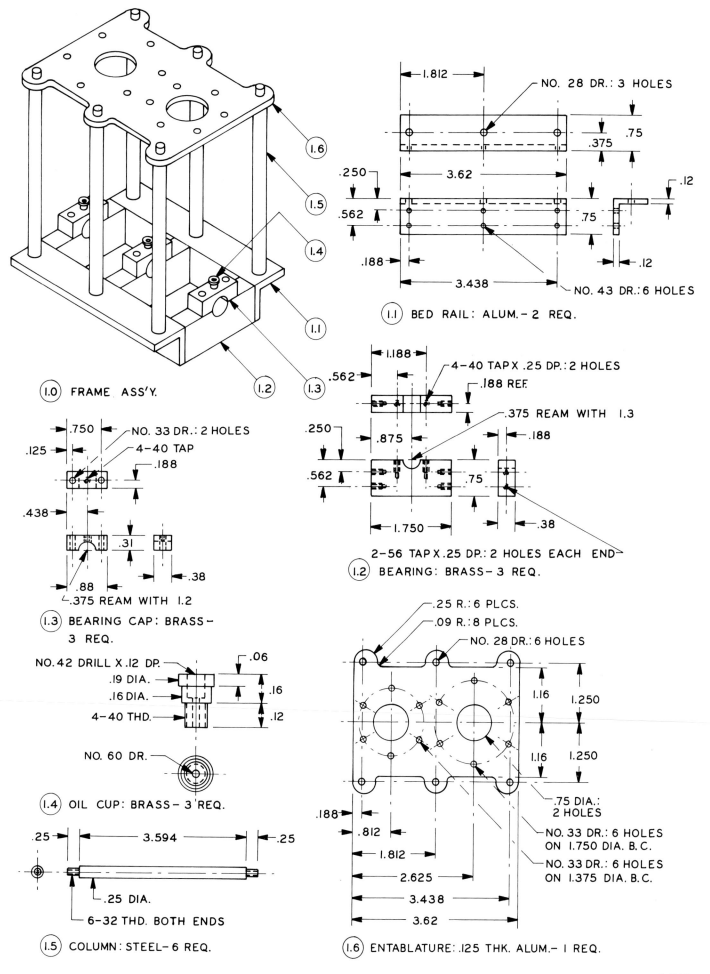

1.0 FRAME ASS'Y.

1.1 BED RAIL: ALUM.– 2 REQ.

NO. 28 DR.: 3 HOLES
NO. 43 DR.: 6 HOLES
1.812 .375 .75 .12
3.62 .250 .562 .188 3.438 .12

1.2 BEARING: BRASS– 3 REQ.

1.188 4-40 TAP X .25 DP.: 2 HOLES
.562 .188 REF.
.375 REAM WITH 1.3
.250 .875 .188
.562 .75
1.750 .38
2-56 TAP X .25 DP.: 2 HOLES EACH END

1.3 BEARING CAP: BRASS– 3 REQ.

.750 NO. 33 DR.: 2 HOLES
4-40 TAP
.125 .188
.438
.31
.88 .375 REAM WITH 1.2
.38

1.4 OIL CUP: BRASS– 3 REQ.

NO. 42 DRILL X .12 DP.
.19 DIA.
.16 DIA.
4-40 THD.
.06 .16 .12
NO. 60 DR.

1.5 COLUMN: STEEL– 6 REQ.

.25 3.594 .25
.25 DIA.
6-32 THD. BOTH ENDS

1.6 ENTABLATURE: .125 THK. ALUM.– 1 REQ.

.25 R.: 6 PLCS.
.09 R.: 8 PLCS.
NO. 28 DR.: 6 HOLES
1.16 1.250
1.16 1.250
.75 DIA.: 2 HOLES
NO. 33 DR.: 6 HOLES ON 1.750 DIA. B.C.
NO. 33 DR.: 6 HOLES ON 1.375 DIA. B.C.
.188
.812
1.812
2.625
3.438
3.62

5 **6**

which will clear the mounting studs in the bearings. Then drill and tap the 4-40 hole for the Oil Cup (1.4).

Now you can put the bed rails, bearings, and bearing caps together as they are in Photo 3 for reaming out the bearings and bearing caps to accept the crankshaft. Refer to Photo 4 which shows a setup that guarantees that the three bearings are reamed exactly in line. Note that the assembly was mounted on the lathe carriage with packings to support it at the correct height for the center line of the bearings to coincide with the axis of the lathe. The hole through the bearings was drilled out undersize and finished to exact size with the long shank reamer shown in the photo.

Turn the oil cups (1.4) from brass rod. Chuck the rod in the three-jaw chuck. After taking a facing cut across the end of the rod, use a knife tool to reduce the diameter for the body and for the threaded part. Cut the thread using a die held in the tailstock die holder. Use a parting tool to cut the part off to length. Screw the part into a threaded adapter held in the chuck. Center drill the end of the part to start the hole. Drill in the end to form the oil cup, then drill the No. 60 hole the rest of the way through for the oil to enter the bearing.

Mount a piece of steel rod in the three-jaw chuck. Cut the Columns (1.5) to length by parting off six pieces. Use of a parting tool leaves the ends flat and square with no further facing necessary. Chuck each column in turn to turn down both ends for the thread. Refer to Photos 5 and 6 for a moment. Photo 5 shows the lathe with a rod projecting from the hole in the spindle. This is a depth rod arrangement used to position each column, in turn, in the same position in the lathe chuck. By positioning the parts in turn against the depth rod, it was

a simple matter to machine them all to the identical length of 3.594" between shoulders.

In order to cut the thread, the arrangement shown in Photo 6 was used. After removing the belt from the lathe, the manual handle was mounted on the outer end of the lathe spindle. By pulling the spindle over manually with the handle, the threads were cut with a die held in the tailstock die holder. Threads cut this way in the lathe are started straight on the axis of the workpiece. The leverage provided by the handle makes it easy to pull the spindle over with one hand while advancing the tailstock with the other.

Saw the Entablature (1.6) roughly to size. Finish the ends to exact length by filing or milling. Locate the center line of the part, being careful that it is square to your reference end. Locate the centers of the two large holes which will coincide with the axes of the cylinders. Working from the centers of the large holes, locate the centers of the six No. 33 holes around each where the studs will pass through from the cylinder block and crank end covers. Finally, locate the positions of the No. 28 holes, and mark out the outlines of the sides. Note in Photo 7 that the edges of the entablature were being milled to form the shape between the column bosses on the sides. Use a small center drill to start each hole, and drill it to the indicated size. Since the capacity to drill .75" diameter holes was not available, the two large holes were drilled out to .50" diameter and finished to size with a round file.

At this point, you can put the entire frame assembly together to be at the stage shown in Photo 8. Note that Phillips head screws were used to attach the bed rails to the bearings. The heads of these screws do not show in the finished engine. Everywhere else, studs cut

7

8

from threaded stainless rod were employed with undersize nuts for a neat scale appearance.

CRANKSHAFT ASSEMBLY (2.0)

All of the parts that go into the construction of the crankshaft are shown grouped together in Photo 9 as well as being detailed in the drawings. Cut a length of steel rod for the Crankshaft (2.1). You may use drill rod that is accurately sized by simply turning down the .312" diameter step that fits into the flywheel. However, you may prefer to start with oversize rod and center drill the ends for turning between centers. It takes a little longer to do it this

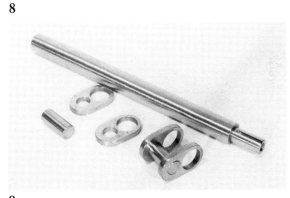

9

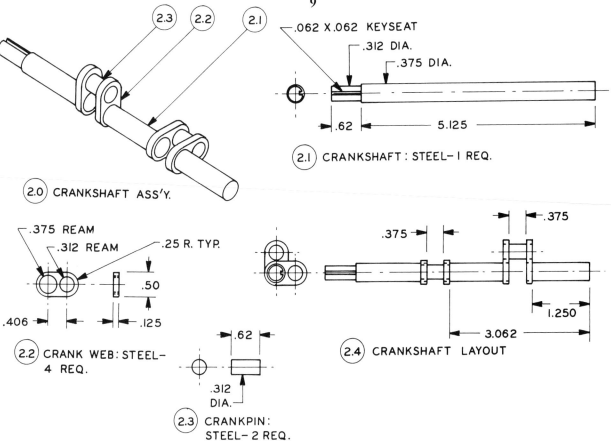

(2.0) CRANKSHAFT ASS'Y.

.062 X.062 KEYSEAT
.312 DIA.
.375 DIA.
.62
5.125
(2.1) CRANKSHAFT : STEEL– I REQ.

.375 REAM
.312 REAM
.25 R. TYP.
.50
.406
.125
(2.2) CRANK WEB: STEEL– 4 REQ.

.62
.312 DIA.
(2.3) CRANKPIN: STEEL– 2 REQ.

.375
.375
1.250
3.062
(2.4) CRANKSHAFT LAYOUT

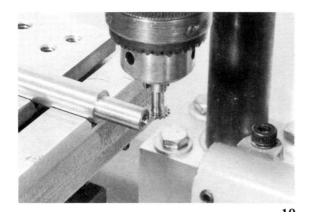

10

11

12

the lathe if you use oversize rod, or they may be cut from drill rod if you prefer. It is a good idea to cut the crankpins a little longer than needed; this helps in setting up for the silver soldering, and the extra length can be filed away after the silver soldering.

Refer now to Drawing 2.4, the Layout of the crankshaft. Note that the cranks are at an angle of 90° to one another. Slip the crank webs onto the crankshaft and insert the crankpins, spacing the parts according to the dimensions on the drawing. The angular orientation of the keyseat is unimportant. When you are sure that everything is positioned correctly with the cranks in the right spots, at 90° to one another, and with the crankpins parallel to the crankshaft, you are ready to silver solder the assembly. Apply flux to the joints where the webs contact the crankshaft and crankpins. Heat the whole crankshaft as evenly as possible, apply the silver solder to each joint watching for good penetration, and then cool it down slowly. To obtain even heating on the crankshaft of the prototype, the whole assembly was placed across the gas burner on the kitchen stove to heat it. When the temperature was pretty well up on the whole crankshaft, a small propane torch supplied the extra heat to bring each crank to full heat to melt the silver solder. This way, there was little tendency for local overheating that could have caused distortion through warping.

After cooling the crankshaft down slowly, polish away the oxides on the surface by using very fine emery cloth. You will have to cut away the parts of the crankshaft between webs of each crank. If you do the job with a hacksaw, be sure to wrap each crankpin with some thin sheet metal; you can be sure you will scar the crankpins when the saw breaks through if you don't! Photo 11 shows a setup that works well for doing this job using a slitting blade to cut away the metal while the crankshaft was clamped to the milling table. Whichever way you do it, file the crankshaft ends flush with the inside surfaces of the crank webs and the crankpin ends flush with the outside surfaces so your crankshaft winds up like the one in Photo 12.

FLYWHEEL ASSEMBLY (3.0)

Engines intended for marine purposes are traditionally fitted with a Flywheel (3.1) that is compact and dense. Chuck a slice of 2.50" diameter brass rod. Take a facing cut to smooth the face. Working from the tailstock drill chuck, center drill, pilot drill, and ream the central hole. The keyway can be cut in the flywheel

way, but it guarantees axial concentricity of the flywheel seat with the shaft. Whichever way you turn the shaft, set it up to mill the keyseat, as shown in Photo 10.

Cut the blanks for the Crank Webs (2.2) from suitable stock. Mark out the hole positions on one blank. Punch and center drill to start the holes. At this point, it is best to clamp all the crank webs together for the drilling and reaming operation. By drilling and reaming the crank webs simultaneously, you will be sure that all the webs have the same spacing between the holes. Before loosening the clamp, put a witness mark on the edge of each crank web in order to keep them paired off in the same relative position in which they were reamed. File the crank webs to outline. Then put a slight chamfer on the edge of each hole to improve the penetration of the silver solder when you put it all together.

The Crankpins (2.3) are a simple job to turn in

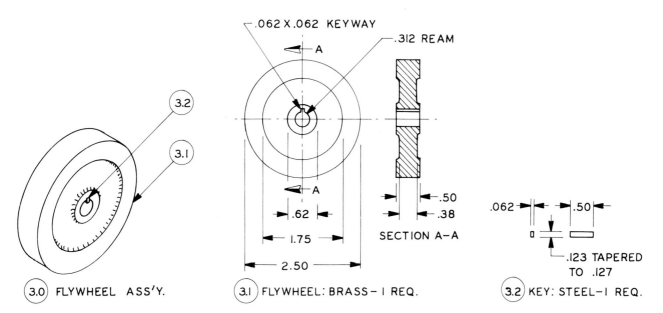

.062 X .062 KEYWAY
.312 REAM

SECTION A–A

.50
.38

.062 .50
.123 TAPERED TO .127

(3.0) FLYWHEEL ASS'Y.

(3.1) FLYWHEEL: BRASS–1 REQ.

(3.2) KEY: STEEL–1 REQ.

by means of a broach, if you have one. Or you may cut the keyway with a home built tool similar to that in Photo 13. Use a round nose tool to make the undercut in the face of the wheel. Reverse the flywheel in the chuck to repeat the operation of facing and undercutting the second side. Mount the flywheel on a

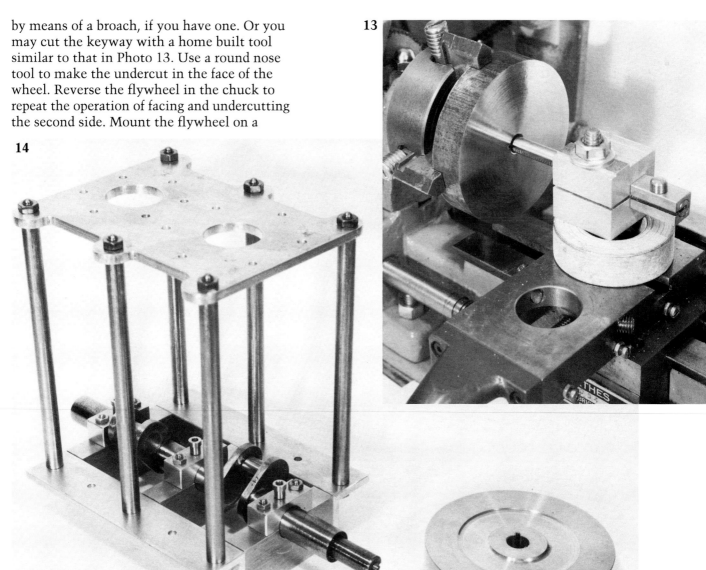

short mandrel to take a light cut across the outside diameter.

No machining is required to make the Key (3.2). File the key to the dimensions making it a slip fit about two-thirds of the way into the keyway/keyseat when the flywheel is in place on the crankshaft. The tapered shape of the key allows it to be seated by a gentle tap from a small bronze hammer, thus locking the flywheel securely in place on the crankshaft. Note in Photo 14 that a slight radius filed on one end of the key made it snug fit into the curved area where the Woodruff-type cutter had cut the keyseat in the crankshaft.

GUIDE ASSEMBLY (4.0)

Begin making the Guide Supports (4.1) by cutting out two rectangles of aluminum measuring .75 x 3.75 x .19" thick. Mark out the locations of all the holes and the outline

15

of the parts. Do all the drilling and tapping before finishing the parts to outline. Notice that the four size 2-56 tapped holes are spaced to align the other parts with the cylinder bores. With the drilling and tapping completed, finish the parts by filing or milling to outline.

The Guide Plates (4.2), Spacers (4.3), and Guide Strips (4.4) are all simple pieces of rectangular steel. Cut them to size by sawing and filing. Their relationship to one another and to the guide supports is clearly shown in Photo 15 and the isometric drawing. You will notice an

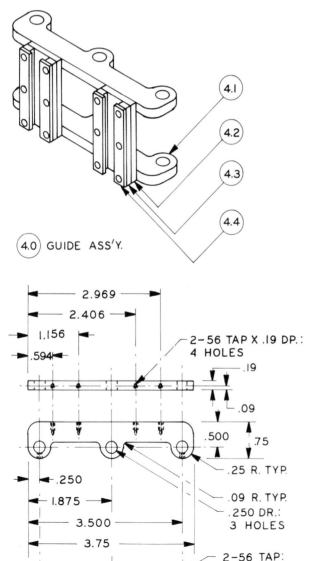

4.0 GUIDE ASS'Y.

4.1 GUIDE SUPPORT: ALUM.- 2 REQ.

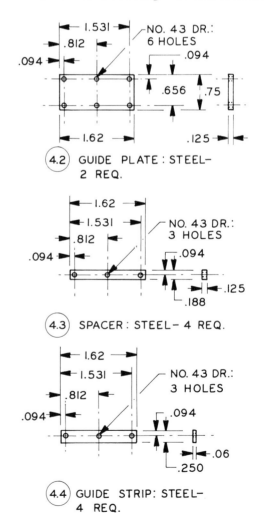

4.2 GUIDE PLATE: STEEL- 2 REQ.

4.3 SPACER: STEEL- 4 REQ.

4.4 GUIDE STRIP: STEEL- 4 REQ.

16 **17**

extra piece of metal in Photo 15, the dark one in front of the partially assembled group of parts. It is a drilling jig made up from a scrap of .075" thick steel. It is the same length as the guide plates, spacers, and guide strips with the holes located and drilled .094" from the near edge. In use, it was clamped in place on the other engine parts for spotting through the holes to locate them. This saved a lot of measuring on the parts and avoided the possibility of accumulating spacing errors that might have caused the assembly to be tight or poor fitting.

Photo 16 shows the general position of the guide assembly. Perhaps this is a good place to point out that Photo 16 shows the *form* of the engine. That is, the near end of the assembly shown in the picture is the high pressure end, and the far end is the low pressure end. Orient the guide supports in a position that centers the other parts on the center lines of the .75" diameter holes in the entablature for alignment with the cylinders. Note that the distance between the underside of the entablature and the top surface of the upper guide supports is .531".

CROSSHEAD ASSEMBLY (5.0)

With the guide assembly in place, it is appropriate to make and fit the crossheads next. The crossheads are plain little things, but they must be made accurately. Saw out two pieces of brass a little oversize for the Slippers (5.1). Cut two more pieces for the Uprights (5.2), but finish these to the dimensions shown in the detail drawing. Silver solder the uprights to the

slippers, as indicated in the assembly drawing. Now you can clamp the crosshead assemblies to an angle plate or other supporting structure for milling the edges of the slippers as in Photo 17. Note that the crosshead in the photo is clamped by the upright to assure that the edges of the slipper are milled true with reference to the flat sides of the upright. Mill the slipper so the upright will center between the guide strips with the crossheads moving smoothly in the guide assembly. Now you can locate and put the holes in the uprights. The wrist pins will fit into the reamed holes, and the piston rods will screw into the tapped holes in the flat top surfaces. Photo 18 gives you another view of the crossheads and shows how they fit into the guide assembly.

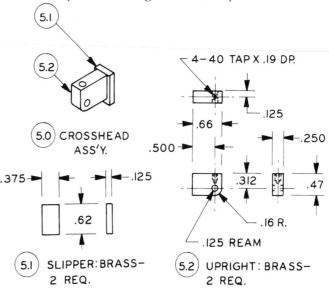

18

CONNECTING ROD ASSEMBLY (6.0)

Begin on the connecting rods by marking out the Clevis (6.1) on the end of a length of steel bar stock. Since it is necessary to make one for each connecting rod, it is convenient to mark out one on each end of the metal. Drill and ream the .125" diameter hole. Then use a file to shape the radius on the top end. Clamp the bar stock on the milling table as shown in Photo 19 to cut away the metal leaving the fork shape. Now you can cut the clevis from the bar, file the bottom to shape, and put the .125" drilled hole in from the underside.

Turn the Rods (6.2) from .19" diameter steel rod. Reduce each end of the rod to .125" diameter. Leave one end plain to fit into the clevis, and cut a 5-40 thread on the opposite end to screw it into the Bearing (6.3).

Make the bearings (6.3) before silver soldering the rods into the clevises. You will see in Photo 20 how to mark out and machine the bearings from the end of a .75" square bronze bar. Drill the No. 44 bolt clearance holes through the bar. Then set up with the slitting blade to make the cut shown to separate the two halves of the bearings while they are still in the bar. After completing the slitting cut, saw the bearing halves free from the bar, knowing that they can be accurately bolted together by putting 2-56

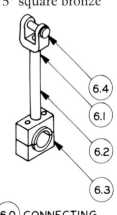

(6.0) CONNECTING ROD ASS'Y.

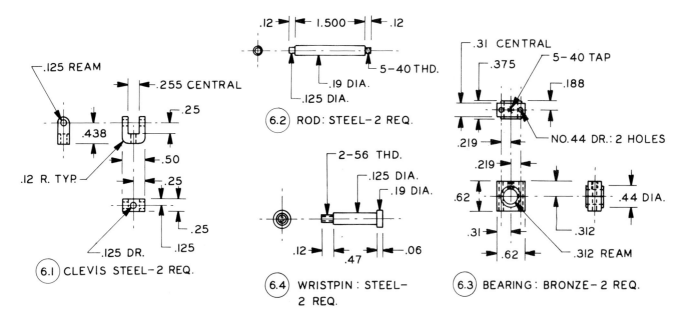

.125 REAM

.255 CENTRAL

.25

.438

.50

.25

.12 R. TYP.

.25

.125 DR.

.125

.25

6.1 CLEVIS STEEL–2 REQ.

.12 ← 1.500 → .12

5–40 THD.

.19 DIA.

.125 DIA.

6.2 ROD: STEEL–2 REQ.

2–56 THD.

.125 DIA.

.19 DIA.

.12

.47

.06

6.4 WRISTPIN: STEEL–2 REQ.

.31 CENTRAL

.375

5–40 TAP

.188

.219

NO. 44 DR.: 2 HOLES

.219

.62

.44 DIA.

.31

.312

.62

.312 REAM

6.3 BEARING: BRONZE–2 REQ.

---

bolts through the drilled holes. With the halves bolted together, chuck the bearings in the four-jaw chuck, center the part by adjusting the chuck jaws, and drill and ream the .312" diameter central hole. Now you can drill and tap the 5-40 hole where the rod screws into the bearing.

You will notice there is an annular thrust surface surrounding the .312" reamed hole on each side of the bearing. Turn the thrust surfaces by mounting the bearing on a stub mandrel like the one in Photo 21. The stub was turned in place in the lathe in the fixture shown in the three-jaw chuck. The thread on the stub was not needed for this job; it was there from a previous one. The stub was turned to a diameter which was a line-for-line fit in the reamed hole making a secure mounting when the part was tightened on it as in Photo 22. Use a round nose tool to cut away the metal leaving the annular surface around the reamed hole. Turn the part around on the stub to repeat the operation on the opposite side of the bearing.

Screw the rod tightly into the tapped hole in the bearing. Put the clevis on the plain end of the rod turning it to get the reamed hole in the clevis parallel to the reamed hole in the bearing. Now you can silver solder the joint between the rod and clevis to reach the point where the prototype engine was in Photo 23, after turning the Wrist Pins (6.4). The turning of the wrist pins is similar to the columns, making further description unnecessary.

Put the connecting rods in place on the crankshaft. Be sure the crankshaft is rotating freely and the connecting rods move smoothly

19

20

21

22

23

on the crankpins. If all is well, slip the crossheads into the guides, and pass the wrist pins in to connect each clevis to its crosshead. Turn the crankshaft over slowly by hand to be sure that everything moves smoothly, freely, and without binds. It is a good idea to check the freedom of motion at each stage of assembly. This procedure simplifies things and prevents problems from piling up later on.

CYLINDER ASSEMBLY (7.0)

As you view Photo 24 and the drawings of the Cylinder Assembly, you may conclude there are a lot of parts to make. This is true, of course, because there are two cylinders to be accommodated. Many parts are identical, requiring duplication. Others differ only in size. In any event, machining the various parts is a very interesting job, since a variety of operations is involved.

24

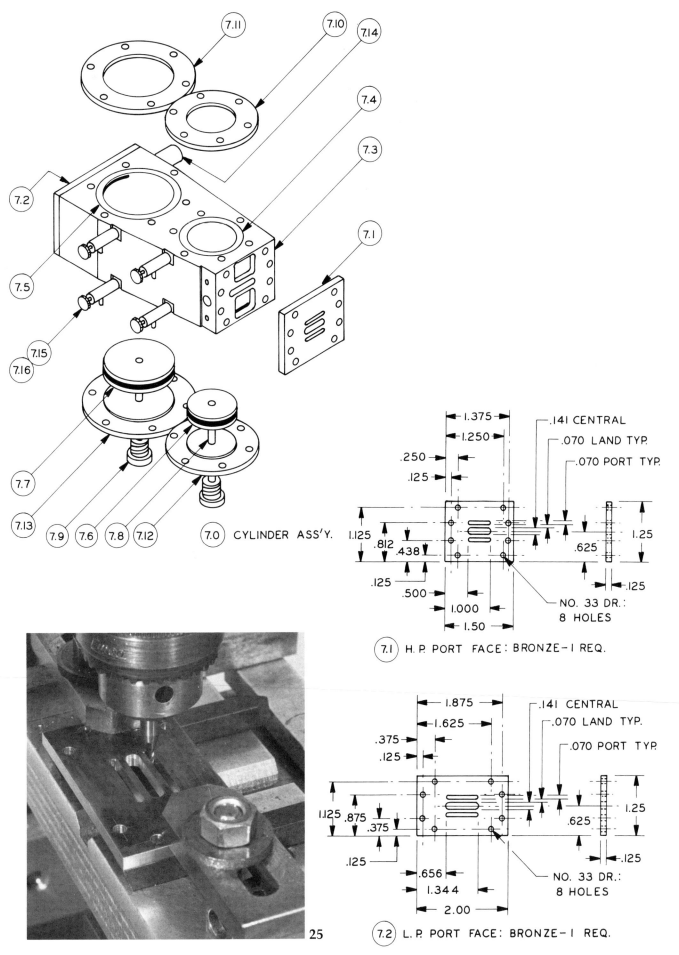

7.11   7.10   7.14

7.14

7.4

7.3

7.2

7.1

7.5

7.15

7.16

7.7

7.13   7.9   7.6   7.8   7.12   7.0 CYLINDER ASS'Y.

25

7.1 H. P. PORT FACE: BRONZE—1 REQ.

|——1.375——| .141 CENTRAL
|——1.250——| .070 LAND TYP.
.250   .070 PORT TYP.
.125

1.125   .812   .438   1.25
.125   .625
.500   .125
1.000   NO. 33 DR.:
1.50   8 HOLES

7.2 L. P. PORT FACE: BRONZE—1 REQ.

|——1.875——| .141 CENTRAL
|——1.625——| .070 LAND TYP.
.375   .070 PORT TYP.
.125

1.125   .875   1.25
.375   .625
.125   .125
.656   NO. 33 DR.:
1.344   8 HOLES
2.00

Saw out the HP Port Face (7.1) and LP Port Face (7.2) allowing a little oversize for truing the edges by either milling or filing. Milling is the preferred method for obtaining edges that are straight and square. Mark out the locations of the stud clearance holes and the ports. Notice that the hole spacings are different in the two parts. Work carefully in setting them out, since clearances are close in the Cylinder Block (7.3). If you make any sizable errors in placing the holes, there is a possibility of getting breakthroughs into the steam passages or other undesirable events later on.

Punch the hole locations with a sharp punch, start the holes with a small center drill, and drill them through with a No. 33 drill. Small end mills are needed for milling out the steam and exhaust ports. A setup for doing the job is shown in Photo 25. Since end mills, especially in the smaller sizes, normally cut a bit oversize, it is good practice to start the cut by milling down the center of each port using an undersize cutter. Then you can traverse the work a few thousandths of an inch to get the edges right.

Use a 1/16" end mill for the .070" wide steam ports and a 1/8" end mill for the .140" wide exhaust ports. Set the port faces aside for now; they will be needed as drilling jigs to locate the stud holes in other parts later on.

The cylinder block (7.3) is obviously the most complex single part in this engine. Work slowly and carefully, because quite a bit of time will go into it. The clearances *are* close.

Make the cylinder block from a rectangular piece of aluminum. In the original engine, it started as a 2.00 x 3.75" rectangle cut from a piece of 1.25" thick plate. The first operations that are required are to true up the sides and ends to get them flat and square. Photo 26 indicates a lathe set up for fly cutting these surfaces. You will note in the photo that the sides had already been done and that an end was being finished. Bring the width of your block down to 2.00", and reduce the length to 3.625" as shown in the drawing. Do *not* cut the tapered shape just yet; you will find subsequent operations will be easier to set up if the block is left rectangular.

Refer now to Photo 27. It demonstrates the use of the lathe faceplate as an aid in clamping the cylinder block on one side in a straight and

SECTION B-B

SECTION A-A

7.3 CYLINDER BLOCK: ALUM-1 REQ.

.875 BORE

◄─ 1.250 ─►

FIT O.D. TO 7.3

(7.4) H.P. CYL. LINER:
BRONZE– 1 REQ.

1.250 BORE

◄─ 1.250 ─►

FIT O.D. TO 7.3

(7.5) L.P. CYL. LINER:
BRONZE– 1 REQ.

FIT O.D. TO 7.4

4–40 TAP

◄─►.25

.09 CENT. X .09 DP.

(7.6) H.P. PISTON: BRASS–
1 REQ.

FIT O.D. TO 7.5

4–40 TAP

◄─►.25

.09 CENT. X .09 DP.

(7.7) L.P. PISTON: BRASS–
1 REQ.

◄.16► ◄── 1.750 ──► ◄.25►

.125 DIA.

4–40 THD. BOTH ENDS

(7.8) PISTON ROD: STAINLESS–
2 REQ.

.44
.31

.125 REAM

$\frac{5}{16}$ –24 THD.

.44 DIA.

(7.9) GLAND: BRASS–
2 REQ.

NO. 33 DR.: 6 HOLES ON
1.375 DIA. B.C.

◄─►.03

1.62
DIA.

FIT DIA.
TO 7.4

.094

◄─►.03

(7.10) H.P. HEAD END COVER:
ALUM.– 1 REQ.

NO. 33 DR.: 6 HOLES ON
1.750 DIA. B.C.

◄─►.03

2.00
DIA.

FIT DIA.
TO 7.5

.094

◄─►.03

(7.11) L.P. HEAD END COVER:
ALUM.– 1 REQ.

SECTION C– C

.141 CENTRAL
.070 LAND TYP.
.453 TYP.
.031 TYP.

◄─ 1.00 ─►

B

1.250

.06 TYP.   .625

.38
.66
1.34
◄──── 2.00 ────►

4–40 TAP X .25 DP.: 8
HOLES–LOCATE
FROM 7.2

26

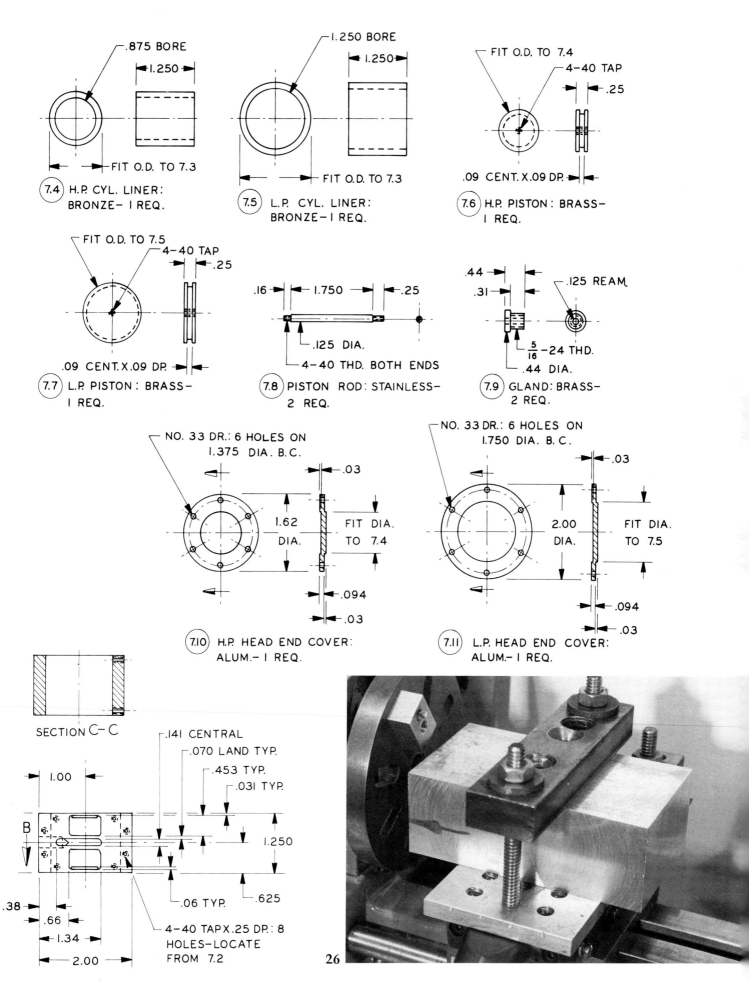

The Shop Wisdom of Rudy Kouhoupt 209

27

28

29

30

square position on the cross slide for truing up the bottom surface. Note in Photo 28 that a very light cut was being taken with a fly cutter. Make this cut as light as possible to obtain a truly flat surface without reducing the thickness of the block appreciably.

With the block still clamped in position on the cross slide, measure out to locate the centers of the cylinder bores. The center height of the Perris lathe happens to coincide exactly with the longitudinal center line of the cylinder block through the bores. If you lathe is larger, use packing under the block to get it up to the correct height before fly cutting the bottom surface. Use a center drill to start each bore. Then use the largest twist drill you can to remove as much metal as possible from each bore. Finally, use a single point boring bar mounted between lathe centers to open

the bores fully. Photo 29 shows the cylinder block with the high pressure bore finished and the boring tool just about to finish the low pressure bore.

Set the cylinder block aside for a while now; this is a good place to make up and insert the cylinder liners. Both the HP Cylinder Liner

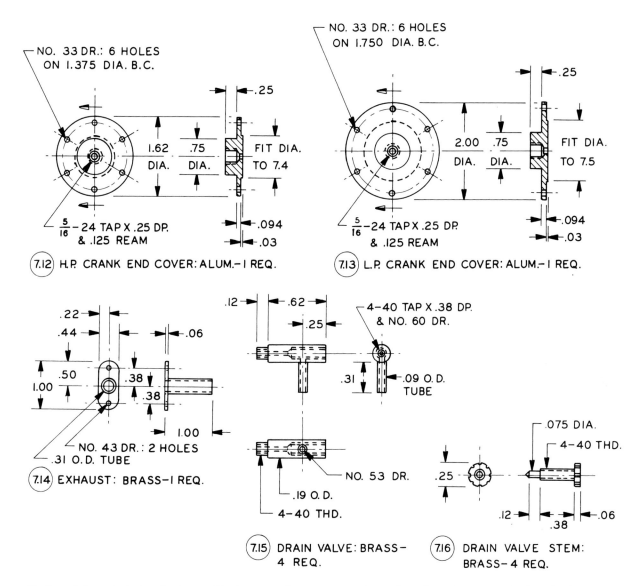

NO. 33 DR.: 6 HOLES
ON 1.375 DIA. B.C.

.25

1.62 DIA. .75 DIA. FIT DIA. TO 7.4

5/16 – 24 TAP X .25 DP. & .125 REAM

.094
.03

7.12 H.P. CRANK END COVER: ALUM.–1 REQ.

NO. 33 DR.: 6 HOLES
ON 1.750 DIA. B.C.

.25

2.00 DIA. .75 DIA. FIT DIA. TO 7.5

5/16 – 24 TAP X .25 DP. & .125 REAM

.094
.03

7.13 L.P. CRANK END COVER: ALUM.–1 REQ.

.22
.44
.06
.50
1.00
.38
.38
1.00

NO. 43 DR.: 2 HOLES
.31 O.D. TUBE

7.14 EXHAUST: BRASS–1 REQ.

.12 .62
.25
4–40 TAP X .38 DP. & NO. 60 DR.
.31
.09 O.D. TUBE

NO. 53 DR.
.19 O.D.
4–40 THD.

7.15 DRAIN VALVE: BRASS– 4 REQ.

.075 DIA.
4–40 THD.
.25
.12
.38
.06

7.16 DRAIN VALVE STEM: BRASS– 4 REQ.

(7.4) and the LP Cylinder Liner (7.5) are made from bronze bearing stock. Do *not* use sintered bronze, because it will not hold pressure. The clamping of the bronze stock for boring must be done carefully. Since the bronze is relatively soft, uneven clamping pressure may cause distortion of the part as metal is removed in the boring cut. Photo 30 shows a convenient way of clamping the work. A solid block of oak clamped on the lathe cross slide was bored out a close fit for the piece of bearing stock. By doing it this way, the cavity holding the stock was accurately aligned with the lathe axis which automatically started the bore of the cylinder liner on center. Note that the workpiece was surrounded by oak which gripped it evenly with no chance of distortion. If you follow this procedure, you can now drill and bore the cylinder liner to finish size, as you did with finishing the bores in the cylinder block.

After you finish boring the cylinder liners, mount each one on a mandrel between lathe centers. Use a tool shaped like a parting tool

to reduce their length to match the thickness of the cylinder block. Now you will have to fit the outside diameters of the liners to the bores in the block. In the prototype, the liners are a press fit in the cylinder block with an interference of just under .0005". When you press the cylinder liners into the bores, be careful to start them straight, so they will go in directly on axis.

Now you can cut away the excess metal from the sides of the cylinder block to give the tapered shape toward the HP end. Cut the bulk of the metal off with a hacksaw. Then you can finish the sides with a fly cutter in a setup similar to that shown in Photo 26.

Mark out the steam and exhaust passages on the ends of the cylinder block. Refer to Photo 31 which indicates a setup for end milling the passages with a 1/8" end mill. Be careful as your cut approaches the top and bottom surfaces of the block; the lip of metal remaining there is only .031" thick. After finishing the milling of the HP end shown in Photo 31, the block was turned over to perform a similar

31   **32**

33   **34**

operation on the LP end. The connecting passages that go from the steam passages into the cylinder bores near the ends are only .06" wide. Use a No. 54 drill to drill a row of holes across the width of these passages right through the wall of the cylinder liner into the bore. Mill out the rest of the metal between the drill holes using a Dremel No. 113 cutter which has a diameter of .054". The shank of the cutters, as supplied, is too large to permit cutting the connecting passages full depth. Take a look at Photo 32. The cutter resting on top of the angle plate is the way you buy them. The cutter in the chuck has been altered by grinding away enough of the shank to reduce its diameter to .050" for enough length to permit it to cut fully

into the bore of the cylinder liner. It is a small cutter and a delicate job; don't try to set any speed records on getting it done!

Mark out the l4.5s of the .188" drilled hole that connects with the HP exhaust passage and the .250" drilled hole that connects with the LP exhaust passage. Drill the holes, being certain that the milled exhaust passages connect fully with the drilled holes. Drill and tap the 2-56 holes alongside the exhaust holes. Drill and tap the 4-40 holes where the drain valves screw into the cylinder block. You will most likely leave burrs inside the cylinder liners where the drills break through for the tapped holes and the milling cutter breaks through in

35

a parting tool to machine the packing groove. A packing groove was being cut in Photo 33.

Chuck a short length of brass rod to make the Glands (7.9). Take a facing cut across the end. Turn it down, and cut the thread with a die held in the tailstock die holder. Center drill, drill, and ream the central hole, working from the tailstock chuck. Cut the piece off with a parting tool.

Cut off two slices of aluminum rod to make the HP Head End Cover (7.10) and the LP Head End Cover (7.11). Grip them in the three-jaw chuck to take a facing cut with a round nose tool. Change to a knife tool to machine the small register which is to be a close fit into the top end of the cylinder liner. If your chuck is true running, grip each cover by the register to face off the opposite side. Turn down the edge of the cover to the desired diameter. Use a round nose tool to make the undercut in the top surface of each cover.

Cut off two more slices of aluminum rod for the HP Crank End Cover (7.12) and the LP Crank End Cover (7.13). Chuck them in the three-jaw chuck to face them off. Use a round nose tool to turn down to form the stuffing box which is visible in Photo 34. Now you are ready to center drill, pilot drill, and tap the stuffing box. The last operation, working from the tailstock drill chuck, is to ream the central hole for the piston rod.

Reverse the cover in the chuck, gripping it by the stuffing box. Be certain that the central hole is running dead true. Take a facing cut with a round nose tool. Put on a knife tool to machine the register that is to be a very close fit into the crank end of the cylinder liner. Pay close attention to the bolting flanges of these covers so they are both .094" thick. These flanges will separate the cylinder block from the entablature on final assembly. Therefore, they must both be of the same thickness.

Now you are ready to mark out the locations of the six No. 33 stud clearance holes in each cover. This can be done with a dividing head if you have one. If not, there is no reason you cannot do it with a divider. Set your divider to the radius of the bolting circles to lay them out. Since six holes are required with equal spacing, the distance between the holes on the circle is equal to the radius of the circle. Punch the center of each hole. Center drill each spot and finish with a No. 33 drill. Clamp the covers in place on the cylinder block to spot through the holes, thus locating the stud positions.

cutting the connecting passages. Remove all the burrs carefully so they will not interfere with the pistons and packings later on. Clamp the port faces to the ends of the cylinder block to spot through for the stud holes. Drill and tap the ends for the studs which will secure the steam chests.

The cylinder block is nearly finished at this point. Set it aside while you work on a few other things, and we will come back to it.

Cut off two slices of round brass rod for the HP Piston (7.6) and the LP Piston (7.7). Chuck the pieces to take a facing cut across each side, reducing the slices to a thickness of .25" in the process. Use the tailstock drill chuck to center drill, drill, and tap the central hole.

Cut two pieces of stainless steel rod for the Piston Rods (7.8). Turn the ends down in the lathe. Cut the thread on the ends as you did in making the connecting rods. Screw a faced off piston blank onto each piston rod. The end of the piston rod with the long thread screws into the piston. When you get further along in the assembly, the short thread will screw into the crosshead. Grip each piston/piston rod assembly in a collet or true-running chuck to center drill the piston end of the piston rod. Now you can mount each assembly in a lathe setup as in Photo 33. Support one end of the piston rod in a true-running chuck while the center drilled end is supported on the tailstock center. Use a very keen tool with a slight radius to turn each piston down until it is a close slip fit in its cylinder liner. Put on a tool shaped like

36

cut through the rest of the hole. Drill a hole through the side of the valve for the side arm. Solder a bit of tubing in the hole. Put a No. 53 drill down through the center of the tube to be sure it is not clogged with solder.

The last parts to be made in this part of the assembly are the Drain Valve Stems (7.16). Turn them from brass rod, cutting the thread as you have done on similar parts. The point on the tip may be shaped by setting the top slide at an angle or by using a fine cut file, as you prefer. After parting off, use a needle file to cut a series of notches around the edge of the handle to improve the finger grip.

At this point, everything was together for Photo 36. It was a distinct pleasure to turn the flywheel over slowly by hand and feel the pistons move through their complete stroke without binding or sticking, despite the absence of packings or studs to hold the cylinder assembly down on the entablature.

STEAM CHEST ASSEMBLY (8.0)

The HP Steam Chest Cover (8.1) and the LP Steam Chest Cover (8.2) are very similar to the port faces from the previous assembly. Cut them from aluminum. True up the edges by filing or milling. Clamp each cover to the corresponding port face to spot through the stud holes with a No. 33 drill.

Cut the HP Steam Chest (8.3) and the LP Steam Chest (8.4) from aluminum plate. True

Drill and tap the 24 holes in the cylinder block for the studs used to secure the covers. Refer now to Photo 35 which illustrates the final machining operation on the cylinder block. This is the operation of milling the flat spotfaces that form the seats for the drain valves. Note, also, in the same setup, the flat area around the HP exhaust had been milled to form a flat seating to which to bolt the receiver flange.

Mark out the bolting flange of the Exhaust (7.14) on a sheet of brass. Locate and drill the three holes. Cut off a short piece of either copper or brass tubing. Attach the tubing in the central hole in the flange by silver soldering.

Chuck a piece of brass rod for the Drain Valves (7.15). Face the end, turn it down, and cut the thread with a die in the tailstock die holder. Part off to the desired length. Reverse the part in the chuck. After center drilling, drilling, and tapping the central hole, put a No. 60 drill in the tailstock chuck to

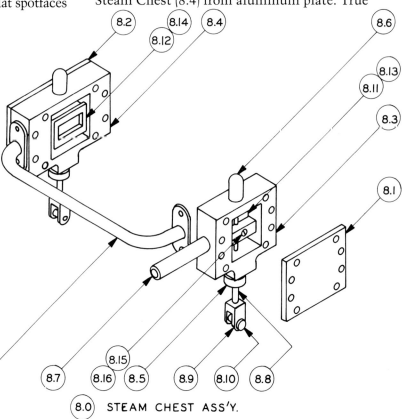

8.0 STEAM CHEST ASS'Y.

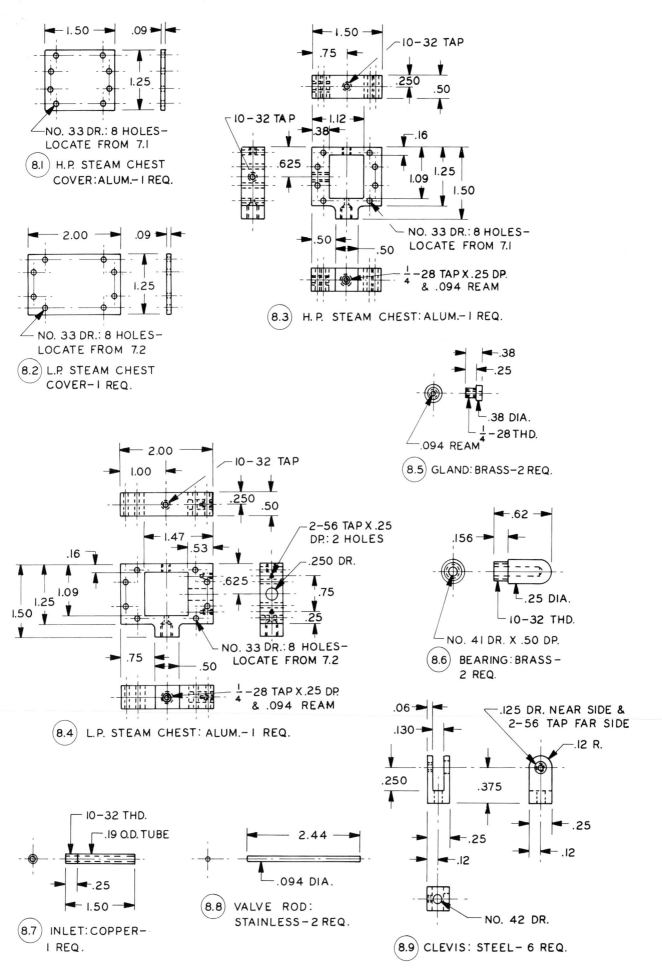

├─ 1.50 ─┤ .09 ├─┤

NO. 33 DR.: 8 HOLES-
LOCATE FROM 7.1

(8.1) H.P. STEAM CHEST
COVER: ALUM.—1 REQ.

├─ 2.00 ─┤ .09 ├─┤

1.25

NO. 33 DR.: 8 HOLES-
LOCATE FROM 7.2

(8.2) L.P. STEAM CHEST
COVER—1 REQ.

10-32 TAP
├─ 1.50 ─┤
.75
.250
.50

10-32 TAP
├─ 1.12 ─┤
.38
.625
.16
1.09 1.25
1.50

NO. 33 DR.: 8 HOLES-
LOCATE FROM 7.1

.50
.50

¼−28 TAP X .25 DP.
& .094 REAM

(8.3) H.P. STEAM CHEST: ALUM.—1 REQ.

.38
.25
.38 DIA.
¼−28 THD.
.094 REAM

(8.5) GLAND: BRASS—2 REQ.

├─ 2.00 ─┤
├─ 1.00 ─┤   10-32 TAP
.250 .50

2-56 TAP X .25
DP.: 2 HOLES
.250 DR.
├─ 1.47 ─┤
.53
.625
.75
.16
1.09
1.25
1.50
.25
NO. 33 DR.: 8 HOLES-
LOCATE FROM 7.2
.75
.50
¼−28 TAP X .25 DP.
& .094 REAM

(8.4) L.P. STEAM CHEST: ALUM.—1 REQ.

.62
.156
.25 DIA.
10-32 THD.
NO. 41 DR. X .50 DP.

(8.6) BEARING: BRASS—
2 REQ.

.125 DR. NEAR SIDE &
2-56 TAP FAR SIDE
.06
.130
.12 R.
.250 .375
.25 .25
.12 .12

10-32 THD.
.19 O.D. TUBE
.25
1.50

(8.7) INLET: COPPER—
1 REQ.

├─ 2.44 ─┤
.094 DIA.

(8.8) VALVE ROD:
STAINLESS—2 REQ.

NO. 42 DR.

(8.9) CLEVIS: STEEL—6 REQ.

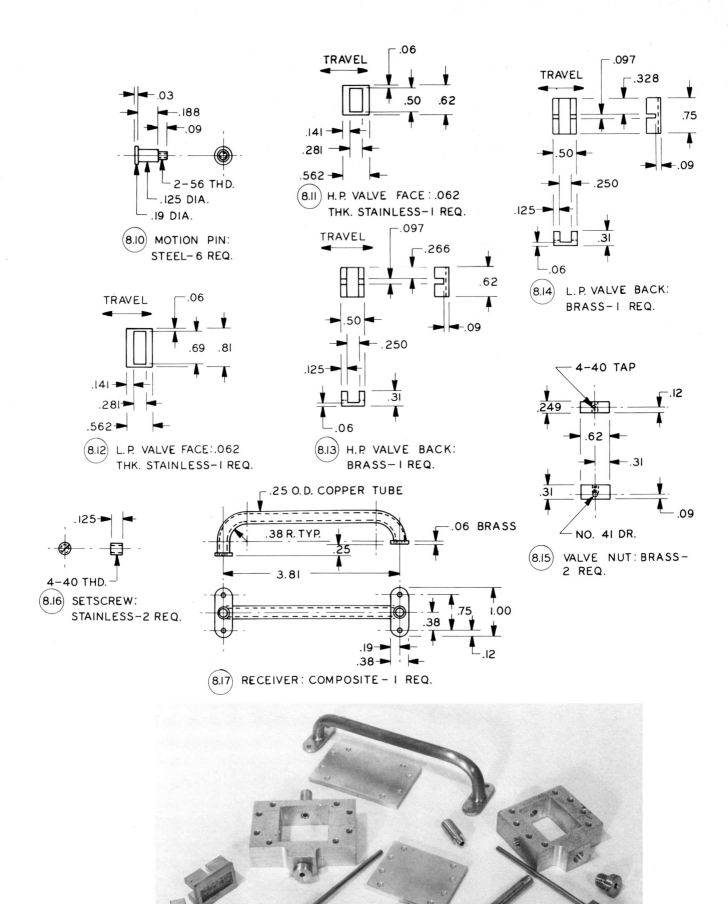

.03
.188
.09
2-56 THD.
.125 DIA.
.19 DIA.

8.10 MOTION PIN: STEEL-6 REQ.

TRAVEL
.06
.50
.62
.141
.281
.562

8.11 H.P. VALVE FACE: .062 THK. STAINLESS-1 REQ.

TRAVEL
.097
.328
.75
.50
.250
.125
.31
.06

8.14 L.P. VALVE BACK: BRASS-1 REQ.

TRAVEL
.06
.69
.81
.141
.281
.562

8.12 L.P. VALVE FACE: .062 THK. STAINLESS-1 REQ.

TRAVEL
.097
.266
.62
.50
.250
.125
.31
.09
.06

8.13 H.P. VALVE BACK: BRASS-1 REQ.

4-40 TAP
.12
.249
.62
.31
.31
.09
NO. 41 DR.

8.15 VALVE NUT: BRASS-2 REQ.

.125
4-40 THD.

8.16 SETSCREW: STAINLESS-2 REQ.

.25 O.D. COPPER TUBE
.38 R. TYP.
.06 BRASS
.25
3.81
.75
1.00
.38
.19
.38
.12

8.17 RECEIVER: COMPOSITE - 1 REQ.

37

all the edges by milling. As you mill away the metal to form the stuffing box, your end mill will automatically form the radius where the stuffing box joins the bottom of the steam chest. Drill the bulk of the metal out of the large central cavities that clear the valves. File away the rest of the metal to finish the cavities.

Clamp each steam chest to its corresponding port face to spot through and drill the No. 33 stud holes. Mark out the location of the hole in the stuffing box on each steam chest as well as the 10-32 tapped hole in the top surface. Do this job carefully; the valve rod works through the reamed hole inside the stuffing box and the Bearing (8.6) that screws into the 10-32 tapped hole. You can see the need for careful alignment here by checking the parts in Photos 37 and 39. The LP steam chest cover was left off in Photo 39 so you could see into the LP steam chest to see the valve rod and associated parts. Drill and tap the top hole and stuffing box. Pilot drill through the stuffing box and finish the hole for the piston rod with a .094" reamer.

Drill and tap the 10-32 hole in the side of the HP steam chest where the pipe will be screwed in for steam admission. Drill the .250" diameter hole through the side of the LP steam chest. Drill and tap the 2-56 holes. The holes in the LP steam chest accommodate the receiver which can be seen clearly in Photo 39.

Make the Glands (8.5) from brass rod following the same procedure you used to make the glands for the previous assembly. Chuck a piece of .25" diameter brass rod to make the Bearings (8.6). Take a facing cut across the rod. Reduce the diameter of the end with a knife tool to cut the thread as you have done on similar parts. Center drill the end before drilling the No. 41 hole that will support one end of the valve rod. After parting off, reverse the bearings in the chuck to form the radius on the end. There are a lot of complex ways of turning such a radius; hand-cutting with a file is simple and to the point!

When you cut the 10-32 thread on the Inlet (8.7), you will have to insert a close fitting rod inside the copper tube to prevent it from collapsing. With the rod inside the tube, grip the length of tube in the three-jaw chuck. Use a die held in the tailstock die holder to cut the thread. Pull the lathe spindle over slowly by hand as you advance the tailstock with the other hand. Copper has a tendency to tear. Use cutting oil to keep the cut clean. Remove any burrs with a fine needle file.

38

39

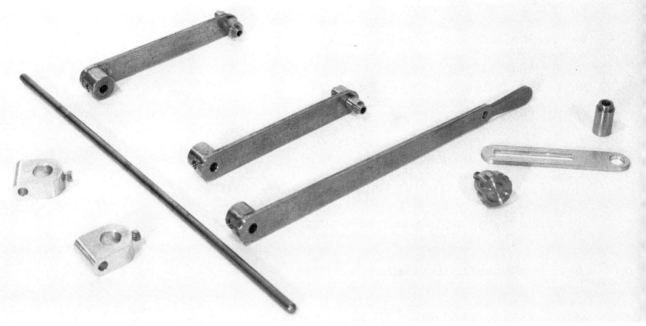

40

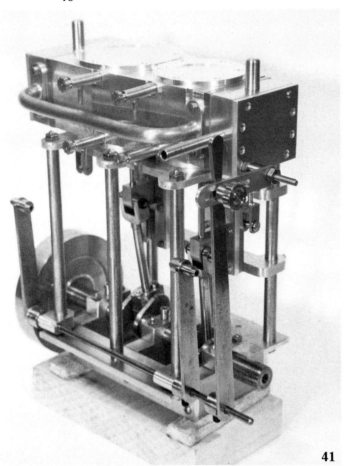

41

No machining is required on the Valve Rods (8.8); they are plain lengths of stainless rod. You will note that the drawing indicates that six Clevises (8.9) are required. Obviously, only two will be used in the steam chest assembly. The other four are for the link motion assembly, but it is convenient to make them all at once.

Follow the same basic procedure as you did in making the connecting rod clevises. Insert the tip of one valve rod into the No. 42 drilled hole in each one of the clevises for the assembly. Silver solder the parts together. The tip of the valve rod should be just flush with the inner surface of the hole in the clevis to obtain the correct overall length. The Motion Pins (8.10) are another case of working ahead with duplicate parts. Two will be used in the valve rods, while the other four will be set aside for the link motion assembly. Machine the pins in the same general way that you made the wrist pins and similar parts.

When you mark out the HP Valve Face (8.11) and the LP Valve Face (8.12), pay particular attention to the accuracy of the .141", .281", and .562" dimensions. These dimensions will influence the accuracy of admission and exhaust events, since they are in the travel direction of the valves. Cut the central holes in the valve faces while they are still in the sheets, because they are easier to grip in the vise that way. Drill through the central cutouts to remove enough metal to get into them with needle files. Then you can file to the mark. When you are satisfied with the dimensions of the central holes, saw the parts out, and file the outsides to dimension.

It is necessary to silver solder the HP Valve Back (8.13) and the LP Valve Back (8.14) to their corresponding valve faces. Therefore, it is better to mill the grooves in the valve backs *after* doing the silver soldering. Cut plain rectangles of brass to the size indicated in the detail drawings, and silver solder them to the valve faces. Now you can end mill the grooves in the valve backs as shown in Photo 38. After finishing the broad groove shown in the photo, rotate the valve 90° in the milling setup to mill the narrow groove at right angles to it. When you finish the milling cuts, lap the working surfaces of the valve faces dead flat by rubbing them on 600 grit wet or dry paper laid on a flat plate glass surface.

The Valve Nuts (8.15) are also plain rectangles of brass. Drill the No. 41 hole to fit the valve rod. Drill and tap the 4-40 hole for the setscrew (8.16) that secures the valve rod in the hole. Fit the .249" dimension into the wide slot in the valve back. It will have to be a free moving fit in the slot without shake. This will permit the valve to lift slightly from the port face to expel condensate, should any form while the engine is running. Cut a short piece of 4-40 stainless threaded rod for the Setscrew (8.16). Dress the ends so they are smooth and free of burrs. Use a very fine hacksaw blade to cut a screwdriver slot across one end.

Before you try to bend the copper tube to make the Receiver (8.17), you will have to anneal the copper to soften in. Heat the copper to a dull red heat, then set it aside in a safe, fireproof place to cool slowly. Even though you have softened the copper by annealing it, you will have to support the sides of the tube to prevent it from spreading out and collapsing from the bending. Use a little "bender" for this. The "bender" is a piece of 1.25" diameter round stock turned in the lathe to have a bobbin shape. It has a .25" wide groove machined in it to a depth of .25". Place the annealed copper in the groove and bend it around using finger pressure only. The bottom of the groove forms the correct radius for the bend while the sides of the groove prevent the tube from spreading out and collapsing. Make the tube part oversize to begin with. Cut the ends off after forming the bends, since you will not be able to make the bends so close to the ends. The .25" offset between the ends is needed to allow for the difference in width between the HP and the LP ends of the cylinder block. Cut the bolting flanges from brass stock. Drill the holes in them, file them to shape, and silver solder them to the copper tube to finish the receiver. Before putting the parts together to reach the stage of Photo 39, lap the working faces of the HP and LP port faces flat on the 600 grit wet or dry paper as you did with the valve faces. This is to insure that the valves seal against the port faces as tightly as possible.

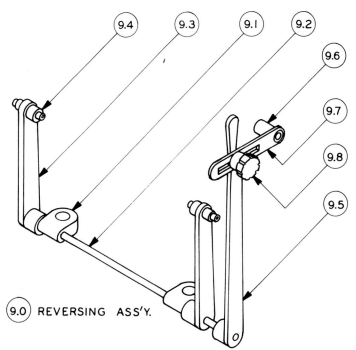

(9.0) REVERSING ASS'Y.

REVERSING ASSEMBLY (9.0)

Mark out the Reversing Bearings (9.1) on a piece of .25 x .50" aluminum bar. It is easier to drill and ream the .125" and .250" holes before cutting the parts out. After completing the holes and cutting the parts from the bar, drill and tap the 2-56 hole for the setscrew that will secure the bearings to the columns of the engine. Cut a length of steel rod for the Reversing Shaft (9.2). No machining is necessary on this part, but you may wish to radius the ends for a neat appearance. This shows up in Photo 40, which shows the group of parts, and in Photo 41 where the parts had been assembled on the engine.

The Reversing Arms (9.3) are made from two pieces of steel silver soldered together. The arms will work as a matched pair. Therefore, it is a good idea to clamp them together to drill the pilot holes through the ends simultaneously to guarantee identical spacing of the holes in both arms. Face off two short pieces of steel rod for the bosses, and silver solder one to each arm as shown. Drill through the smaller pilot hole in the arm right through the boss. Ream both holes, and drill and tap the 6-32 hole for a setscrew. As you will note, the setscrews on the prototype enter through the underside of the bosses. They were shifted to the side in the drawing, because the experience of assembling it indicated that it might be easier to reach the setscrews on the side. However, they *look* better on the bottoms. The choice is yours to make.

Turn the Trunnions (9.4) from steel rod. Only two are required for this assembly, but you will need two more for the next assembly. It

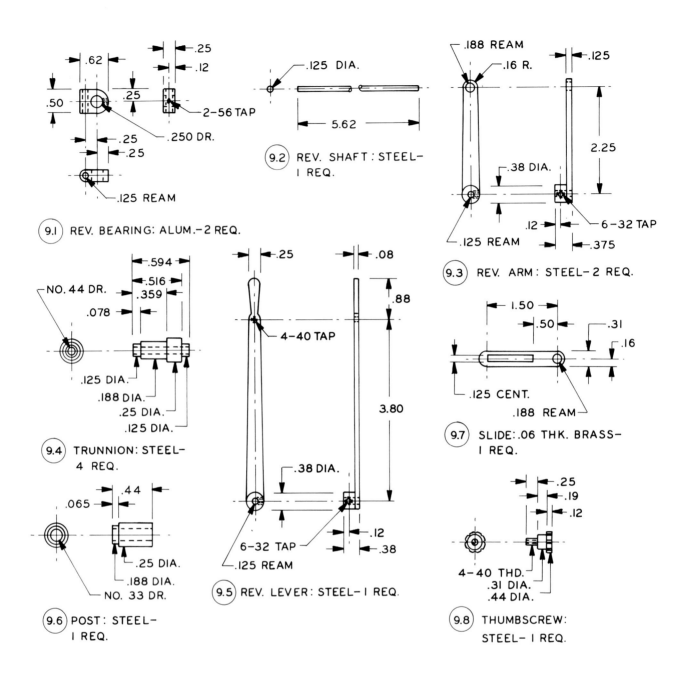

.62 .25 .12

.50 .25

2-56 TAP

.250 DR.

.25 .25

.125 REAM

(9.1) REV. BEARING: ALUM.-2 REQ.

.125 DIA.

5.62

(9.2) REV. SHAFT : STEEL—1 REQ.

.188 REAM .16 R. .125

2.25

.38 DIA.

6-32 TAP

.12 .375

.125 REAM

(9.3) REV. ARM: STEEL—2 REQ.

NO. 44 DR.

.594 .516 .359

.078

.25 .08

.88

4-40 TAP

3.80

.38 DIA.

.125 DIA.
.188 DIA.
.25 DIA.
.125 DIA.

(9.4) TRUNNION: STEEL—4 REQ.

1.50 .50 .31 .16

.125 CENT.

.188 REAM

(9.7) SLIDE: .06 THK. BRASS—1 REQ.

.065 .44

.25 DIA.
.188 DIA.
NO. 33 DR.

(9.6) POST: STEEL—1 REQ.

6-32 TAP

.12 .38

.125 REAM

(9.5) REV. LEVER: STEEL—1 REQ.

.25 .19 .12

4-40 THD.
.31 DIA.
.44 DIA.

(9.8) THUMBSCREW: STEEL—1 REQ.

42

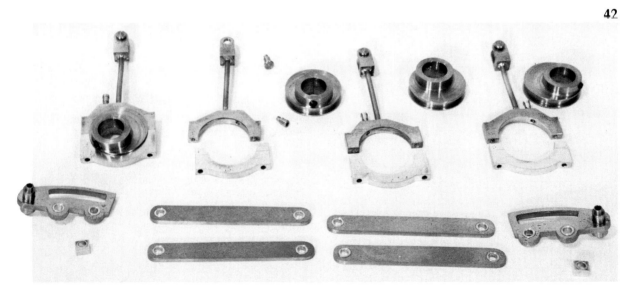

pays to make them all at once. Use a sharp knife tool to turn down the .125" and .188" diameter parts. After parting off, reverse the part in the chuck, gripping it by the .188" diameter shoulder to turn down the .125" diameter part on the opposite end. Center drill the end and drill it through, working from the tailstock drill chuck. Now you can press fit one trunnion into each reversing arm. If your .188" diameter shoulder is loose in the reamed hole, you will have to silver solder it. The Post (9.6) is a small lathe job that is quite similar to the trunnions; handle the turning and drilling as you did on them.

In form, the Reversing Lever (9.5) is much like the reversing arms. It has a boss silver soldered to the bottom end. Make it in the same way you made the reversing arms. Lay out the Slide (9.7) on brass strip. Drill several holes in the rectangular cutout. Then you can use needle files to finish the rectangular hole. After drilling and reaming the round hole, cut the piece to length, and file the radius on the ends.

Chuck a piece of .44" diameter steel rod to make the Thumbscrew (9.8). Turn it down and cut the thread as you have done on similar parts. If you have a knurling tool, you may wish to cut a light knurl on the head. As an alternative, transfer it to a dividing attachment to mill eight shallow V-grooves that give more than ample finger grip.

LINK MOTION ASSEMBLY (10.0)

The clevises, motion pins, and trunnions you've already made give you a bit of a head start on this final assembly, the parts of which are all laid out in Photo 42. To make the Eccentrics (10.1), mount a length of steel rod

43

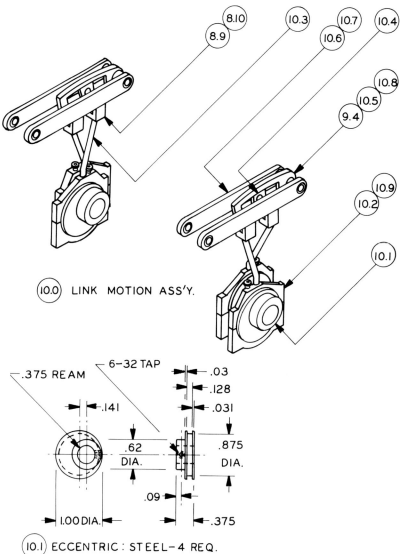

(10.0) LINK MOTION ASS'Y.

(10.1) ECCENTRIC : STEEL–4 REQ.

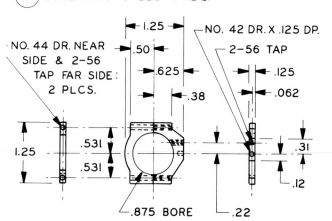

(10.2) ECC. STRAP : BRASS–4 REQ.

in the lathe with one end supported in a chuck and the outer end running in a three-point steady rest. Face off the end with a round nose tool. Use a knife tool to turn down a long enough piece for all four eccentrics. Change to a tool shaped like a parting tool to cut the groove in the first eccentric at the end of the rod. Work accurately on the width and depth of the groove as well as the .031" width of the

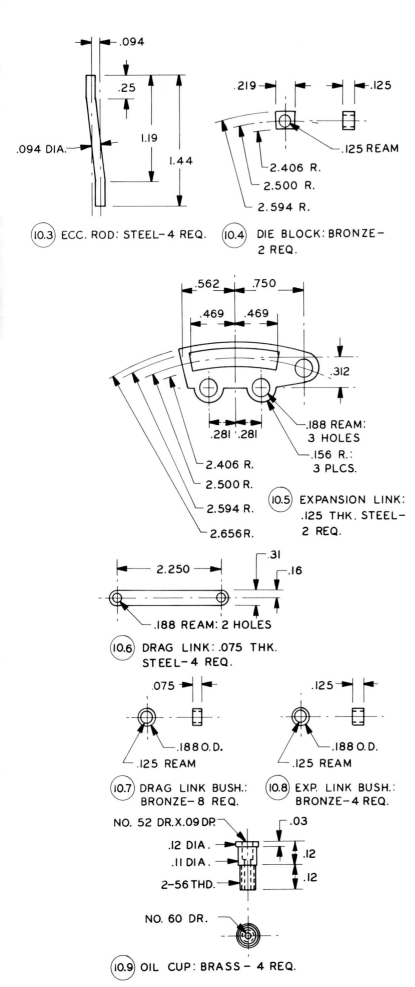

.094

.25

1.19

1.44

.094 DIA.

(10.3) ECC. ROD: STEEL– 4 REQ.

.219 ·|← →|←.125

.125 REAM

2.406 R.

2.500 R.

2.594 R.

(10.4) DIE BLOCK: BRONZE–
2 REQ.

.562   .750

.469   .469

.312

.281 .281

.188 REAM:
3 HOLES

.156 R.:
3 PLCS.

2.406 R.

2.500 R.

2.594 R.

2.656R.

(10.5) EXPANSION LINK:
.125 THK. STEEL–
2 REQ.

.31

.16

2.250

.188 REAM: 2 HOLES

(10.6) DRAG LINK: .075 THK.
STEEL– 4 REQ.

.075 →|←

.188 O.D.
.125 REAM

.125 →|←

.188 O.D.
.125 REAM

(10.7) DRAG LINK BUSH.:
BRONZE– 8 REQ.

(10.8) EXP. LINK BUSH.:
BRONZE– 4 REQ.

NO. 52 DR.X.09 DP.

.12 DIA.

.11 DIA.

2-56 THD.

.03

.12

.12

NO. 60 DR.

(10.9) OIL CUP: BRASS – 4 REQ.

flange. Part off the first piece. Then repeat the procedure of accurate grooving and parting off until you have the four partially completed eccentrics. Now you must put in the reamed hole. Since the eccentrics must work together in pairs, it is important to place the holes precisely so they will all have the same "throw," or amount of eccentricity. This is best accomplished by making up some sort of fixture that will hold each eccentric in turn in a known position for the drilling and reaming of the hole. Photo 43 shows a home-built micrometer faceplate on the head of the lathe for doing this job. The construction of this attachment is described in the "Micro Machinist" section of this book. Whether you use this type of tool, some other faceplate positioning device, or indicate the eccentrics into position in a four-jaw chuck, you will cut the holes the same way. Use a center drill in the tailstock drill chuck to start the hole. Drill the hole out as much as possible with twist drills. Then finish the hole with either a reamer or a single point boring bar like the one in the photo. When you finish the holes, transfer the eccentrics to a mandrel between centers to turn down the shoulder that is concentric with the hole. Drill and tap the 6-32 hole for the setscrew.

It is necessary for the Eccentric Straps (10.2) to be split in two for mounting them on the eccentrics, as you will notice in Photo 42. It is best to mark them out as solid pieces cut in two by means of a slitting blade. If you do it that way, remember to allow the thickness of the slitting blade in the layout. After marking out the metal, pilot drill the two holes that are .531" from the center line. Slit the piece in two with the slitting blade. Tap the 2-56 thread in one part, and drill the other part out with a No. 44 drill as indicated in the drawing. Now you can bolt the two parts together again. Make a setup in the four-jaw chuck as shown in Photo 44, with the intersection of the center lines running on the lathe axis. Use a center drill to start the hole, and drill it out as large as possible with twist drills. Finish boring the hole to a good running fit on the eccentrics by using a short boring bar. Drill the No. 42 hole for the eccentric rod, and drill and tap the 2-56 hole for the oil cup. Finish the part to outline by filing.

No machining is required on the Eccentric Rods (10.3), as they are just short lengths of steel rod. Cut them to length. Bend in the .094" offset which compensates for the width of the eccentric flange plus a half of the width of the eccentric groove. The offset permits the eccentric strap to center in the groove while the clevis centers on the expansion link. Make a simple bending fixture by drilling a No. 41 hole through a piece of .25" thick steel. With the fixture flat on the bench, stick one end of the rod into the hole and bend the other end over slightly. The thickness of the fixture will take care of getting the bend in the right place. Reverse the rod end for end in the fixture to put in the second bend.

Insert one end of the eccentric rod into the drilled hole in an eccentric strap and the other end into a Clevis (8.9). the center-to-center distance from the hole in the eccentric strap to the hole in the clevis is 2.250". Since it is important that the eccentric rods all have this dimension accurately, make an assembly jig consisting of an aluminum plate with a pin in it to pass through the hole in the clevis and a straight strip against which the split edge at the center of the upper half of the eccentric strap can make contact. Space the pin 2.250" from the edge of the straight strip. Clamp the half of the eccentric strap against the straightedge and slip the hole in the clevis over the pin with the rod in place between the clevis and strap. Support the clevis on a bit of packing under it to give the .094" offset between the center line through the eccentric strap and the center line of the clevis. Silver solder both ends to secure the rod in the clevis and the eccentric strap.

You will notice from the photos of the finished engine and from Photo 45 that on each end of the engine, the outer eccentric rod bends back to the expansion link while the inner eccentric rod bends forward to the expansion link. Also, the eccentric straps are oriented to have the oil cups turned *out* for easier access. In Photo 42, the eccentric rods are grouped in working pairs to help you visualize the orientation of the clevises with respect to the eccentric straps and the complete rods with respect to one another in pairs.

Which comes first, the die block or the expansion link? They must fit together nicely, which makes it a bit like the old chicken and egg dilemma. Both have curved surfaces that have to match each other. The curves could be conveniently milled using a rotary table or other rotary fixture. The primitive process of filing them by hand was adopted in building the prototype engine! Mark out the Die Blocks (10.4) on a piece of bronze stock, drawing the curves from a common point with a divider. Drill and ream the central hole. Saw the parts out and finish them to shape with files.

44

45

Mark out the Expansion Links (10.5) on a piece of steel. Again, draw the curves from a common point with a divider. Punch the locations of the three reamed holes. Start the holes with a center drill, drill them out, and finish them with a reamer. Drill a row of undersize holes along the curved center line in the slot. Use needle files to remove the rest of the metal from the slot. As you get close to the outline, begin to use the die blocks as test gauges of the width of the slot. File the slot out until the die block is a close sliding fit from end to end. Be careful of burrs, as they can cause all sorts of mischief on close fitting parts. When you are satisfied with the way the expansion links and die blocks fit together, cut the expansion links out, and file the outside surfaces to the mark. At this point, you can press one of the Trunnions (9.4) into each expansion link in the reamed hole at the end of the curved slot. The situation here is the same as it was with the reversing arms; if the trunnions are not a good press fit, you can secure them in the holes by silver soldering.

The Drag Links (10.6) connect the trunnions in the reversing arms with the trunnions in the expansion links. Therefore, the holes in them must all be spaced the same distance apart. Clamp them all together after marking out the first one so you can center drill, drill, and ream the end holes all at once. Finish them by filing the edges and the radius on the ends.

You will need the Drag Link Bushings (10.7) and the Expansion Link Bushings (10.8) to press into the reamed holes in these parts. They differ only in length, making it a simple matter to turn them all out at once. Chuck a piece of bronze rod. Turn it down to be a good press fit in the .188" diameter reamed holes. Take a facing cut across the end of the rod. Center drill the end. Then run in a No. 13 drill to a depth of .25", or thereabouts. Part off the bushing at the correct length. Continue drilling and parting off until you have the full set of bushings. After you press them into the reamed holes in the drag links and expansion links, you can put the .125" reamer through to finish them to size in place. Make the Oil Cups (10.9) as you made the larger ones for the bearing caps.

FINISHING UP AND TIMING THE VALVES

By now you have all the parts made. If you have been assembling as you go along, your engine will look about like Photo 45. The prototype was already standing on a pair of oak beams that were fitted to the bed rails with inletting to clear the nuts on the column ends and the bolt heads securing the bearings. If you are not sure of how to assemble the link motion parts, we will go into this in more detail after clearing up some other things. The next job is to cut the studs from 4-40 threaded stainless steel rod. Note that the twelve studs that hold the crank end covers in place must be .125" longer than the twelve studs that hold the head end covers, because they have to pass through the thickness of the entablature, also. The eight studs that hold the LP steam

chest assembly and seven studs for the HP steam chest assembly are all the same length. However, you will need one that is .50" longer for the HP steam chest assembly so it can pass through the post which is part of the link motion assembly. Photos 1, 2, and 46 show the finished engine from various angles to show up these details.

You will have to take the upper works of the engine apart to pack the pistons and stuffing boxes as well as to put in various gaskets. This is the right time to do any painting, polishing, or other finishing operations that you wish to incorporate into the engine. Many engines built for marine use have had the cylinders jacketed for heat retention. Those having teak or mahogany strips showing in the outer layer look very natty. To give the prototype a finished appearance, a red mahogany board was cut to obtain lagging strips that are about .045" thick and .75" wide. They were fitted to the sides of the cylinder block with cutouts to clear the drain valves. In Photos 1, 2, and 46, you can see the .03 x .125" brass strips that hold the wood in place. Clearance holes were drilled in the brass strips after bending them to fit the cylinder sides. Then, matching 00-90 holes were drilled and tapped into the cylinder block for the little hex head bolts that secure the strips. Check the spacings to be sure they are clear of the passages, studs, etc.

Use graphited string for packing the pistons and stuffing boxes. Strip the strands down to about 1/16" diameter. Wind the string into the grooves on the pistons compacting it into the grooves by rolling the pistons on a plate glass surface. Put in enough string to make the packings resilient, but don't overdo it. Too much packing simply makes for friction that makes the engine hard running and robs it of power. Wind several turns of the packing string around wooden dowels of the same diameter as the piston rods and valve rods. Holding the string tight, cut across the windings with a sharp knife or single-edge razor blade to produce a series of packing rings. Slip three or four rings around each piston rod and valve rod, pushing them into the stuffing boxes. Alternate the splits in the rings so they don't line up with one another. Screw in the glands using finger pressure only. Overtightened glands on overstuffed packings will also kill the performance of any engine.

A high rag content typing paper is a good choice for gasket material. After cutting the gaskets out and punching the holes for the studs, rub light machine oil into the paper.

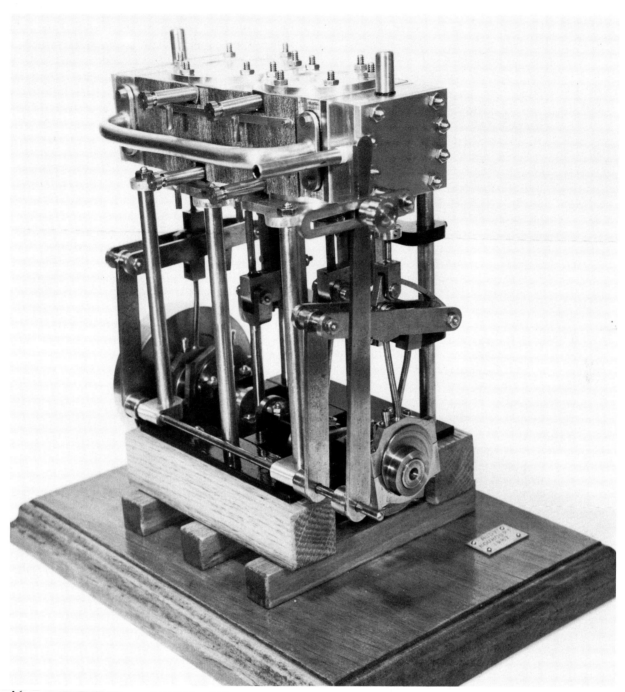

46

You will need gaskets between the cylinder block and each head end and crank end cover. You will also need them between the steam chest covers and steam chests, between the steam chests and port faces, and between the port faces and cylinder block. Make little round gaskets to go between the steam chests and the bearings that support the valve rods. You can adjust the position of the drain valves by varying the thickness of gasket used under them; the side arms from the drain valves should point straight down. Finally, you will need gaskets under the bolting flanges of the exhaust and receiver.

As you put the engine back together with the packings in and the gaskets in place, put a little 20-weight oil on the packings, cylinder walls, and all moving parts where metal could (but should not) touch metal. Follow the general order in which you made the assemblies to put them together. Leave the steam chest covers off until the valve setting is done. Mount the post on a long stud on the HP steam chest so you can use the slide (9.7) in conjunction with the reversing lever while you adjust the valve timing.

When you put the reversing arms on the reversing shaft, position the arms so the trunnions at the upper ends are exactly in line with one another. This is important, because it controls the coordination of the valve movements of the two cylinders. While you are doing this, position the reversing lever on the reversing shaft parallel to the reversing arms. The rectangular cutout in the slide engages the thumbscrew to position the reversing lever. At either end of the slide, it provides a full gear cutoff of 75% with the flywheel rotation clockwise when the reversing lever is *away* from the steam chest and counterclockwise when the reversing lever is *toward* the steam chest. *NOTE:* All rotations are expressed as viewed from the flywheel end of the crankshaft to avoid confusion between the HP and LP ends of the engine.

When you put the eccentrics on the crankshaft, you want them to be back-to-back; that is, with their broad flat sides against one another. Note that the eccentrics, which are adjacent to the bearings (1.2), are the clockwise eccentrics, while the outer eccentrics are the counterclockwise eccentrics. Set the eccentrics in position so the concentric hubs of the clockwise eccentrics act as thrust surfaces against the bearings to keep the crankshaft in its proper end-to-end position. Connect the clevises of the clockwise eccentric rods to the bushings in the expansion link near the trunnion end of the expansion link as shown in the assembly drawing. Connect the counterclockwise eccentric rods to the end of the expansion link away from the trunnion. Check to be sure the expansion links are in a vertical plane and straight across the crankshaft. If things are not straight at this point, you probably have the offset in the eccentric rods out a little and can correct the situation by bending one or the other of them to put things in order. Now you can put the drag links in position on the small shoulders connecting the trunnions in the expansion links with the trunnions in the reversing arms. Cut four lengths of 2-56 threaded rod to pass through the central holes in the trunnions. The drag links are secured by a nut on each end of the 2-56 threaded rods and will move freely on the small shoulders on the trunnions.

There are two adjustments that must be made to time the engine. The first is to equalize or centralize the valve travel. The second is to find the correct positions for the eccentrics. Loosen the setscrew (8.15) in the valve nuts (8.16) to be sure you do not jam the valves while moving things during the early stages of adjusting the valve timing.

Check the motion of the reversing lever at this point. It should move freely from end to end of the slide while shifting the expansion links back and forth. If there are any binds, locate them and get rid of them right away. If you feel satisfied with the freedom of movement, bring the reversing lever to the mid-gear position; that is, exactly at the center of the slot in the slide. Rotate the crankshaft to bring the HP piston to the top dead center position. Loosen both HP eccentrics and move them both around the crankshaft until they are opposite the HP crank. You want the HP crank at its highest point with the HP eccentrics turned to their lowest point. Tighten the eccentric setscrews just enough to hold them in position. Turn the crankshaft to bring the HP piston to mid stroke. Slide the HP valve and valve nut up to about the middle of the HP steam chest and tighten the setscrew (8.15). Now you can rotate the crankshaft to see the valve move up and down. When the valve motion is equalized, or centralized over the ports, you will see the steam ports opening exactly equal amounts at the ends of the valve stroke. If necessary, shift the valve and valve nut up or down on the valve rod to reach the equalized position. When you are sure it is equalized, tighten the setscrew (8.15).

Now you can adjust the angles of the HP eccentrics. With the HP piston at top dead center, move the reversing lever all the way over into the clockwise running position and secure it with the thumbscrew. Loosen the clockwise eccentric (the one adjacent to the bearing) and rotate it slowly around the crankshaft in the clockwise direction for a little over 270°. When you see the top steam port just beginning to crack open, you have the correct angle and can secure the eccentric. Shift the reversing lever all the way over to the counterclockwise running position. Keep the HP piston at the top dead center position. Loosen the counterclockwise eccentric (the outer one) and rotate it around the crankshaft in the counterclockwise direction for a little over 270° until the top steam port is just beginning to crack open. Secure the eccentric at this point. To check it out, rotate the crankshaft counterclockwise until the HP piston is at bottom dead center. At this point, the bottom steam port should be just beginning to crack open. Shift the reversing lever to the clockwise position. With the HP piston at bottom dead center, the bottom steam port should be just beginning to crack open. If the appropriate steam ports are opening just as the HP piston is at either top or bottom dead center

Rudy Kouhoupt is shown here with some of the many miniature engines and other hobby projects he has built over the years. You will no doubt recognize some of them from this book.

in both direction of rotation, it is correct. If necessary, make fine adjustments to get things just right.

Shift your attention now to the LP end of the engine. The procedure for timing the LP valve movement is exactly the same as for timing the HP valve movement. Be careful that the shift from end to end of the engine does not confuse your sense of rotation. When you are satisfied that you have the valves both timed correctly, put the steam chest covers on, but don't forget the gaskets. Your engine is now ready for test running on compressed air or steam. Remember that all compound engines must be off dead center of the HP piston to be self-starting, just like single cylinder engines. It is one of the characteristics of the breed.